THE
FORTY-SIXTH YEARBOOK

OF THE

NATIONAL SOCIETY FOR THE STUDY
OF EDUCATION

PART I

SCIENCE EDUCATION IN
AMERICAN SCHOOLS

Prepared by the Society's Committee

Victor H. Noll (*Chairman*), William A. Brownell, Otis W. Caldwell,
Gerald S. Craig, Francis D. Curtis, and Ellsworth S. Obourn

Edited by

NELSON B. HENRY

Distributed by

THE UNIVERSITY OF CHICAGO PRESS
CHICAGO 37, ILLINOIS

1947

Published by

THE NATIONAL SOCIETY FOR THE STUDY OF EDUCATION

5835 KIMBARK AVENUE, CHICAGO 37, ILLINOIS

*The responsibilities of the Board of Directors of the National
Society for the Study of Education in the case of yearbooks
prepared by the Society's committees are (1) to select the subjects to be investigated, (2) to appoint committees calculated in
their personnel to insure consideration of all significant points
of view, (3) to provide appropriate subsidies for necessary
expenses, (4) to publish and distribute the committees' reports,
and (5) to arrange for their discussion at the annual meetings.*

*The responsibility of the Yearbook Editor is to prepare the
submitted manuscripts for publication in accordance with the
principles and regulations approved by the Board of Directors
in the "Guide for Contributors."*

*Neither the Board of Directors, nor the Yearbook Editor,
nor the Society is responsible for the conclusions reached or the
opinions expressed by the Society's yearbook committees.*

Published 1947
First Printing, 4,000 Copies

Printed in the United States of America

OFFICERS OF THE SOCIETY
1946–1947

Board of Directors
(Term of Office expires March 1 of the year indicated)

WILLIAM A. BROWNELL (1948)
Duke University, Durham, North Carolina

W. W. CHARTERS (1948)
Stephens College, Columbia, Missouri

HARL R. DOUGLASS (1950)*
University of Colorado, Boulder, Colorado

ERNEST HORN (1949)
State University of Iowa, Iowa City, Iowa

T. R. McCONNELL (1949)
University of Minnesota, Minneapolis, Minnesota

ERNEST O. MELBY (1947)
New York University, New York, New York

GEORGE D. STODDARD (1947)
University of Illinois, Urbana, Illinois

RALPH W. TYLER (1950)*
University of Chicago, Chicago, Illinois

NELSON B. HENRY (*Ex-officio*)
University of Chicago, Chicago, Illinois

Secretary-Treasurer
NELSON B. HENRY (1948)
University of Chicago, Chicago, Illinois

* Elected for three years beginning March 1, 1947.

THE SOCIETY'S COMMITTEE ON SCIENCE
EDUCATION IN AMERICAN SCHOOLS

WILLIAM A. BROWNELL, Professor of Educational Psychology, Duke University, Durham, North Carolina

OTIS W. CALDWELL, General Secretary, American Association for the Advancement of Science, Yonkers, New York

GERALD S. CRAIG, Professor of Natural Science, Teachers College, Columbia University, New York, New York

FRANCIS D. CURTIS, Professor of Education and of the Teaching of Science, University of Michigan, Ann Arbor, Michigan

VICTOR H. NOLL (*Chairman*), Professor of Education, Michigan State College, East Lansing, Michigan

ELLSWORTH S. OBOURN, Head, Science Department, John Burroughs School, Clayton, Missouri

ASSOCIATED CONTRIBUTORS

CHARLES K. AREY, Assistant Professor of Education, University of Alabama, University, Alabama

FLORENCE G. BILLIG, Professor of Science Education and Supervisor of Science in Elementary Schools, Wayne University, Detroit, Michigan

FRANKLYN M. BRANLEY, Teacher of Science, Horace Mann School for Boys, New York, New York

H. EMMETT BROWN, Head, Department of Science, New York State College for Teachers, Buffalo, New York

G. P. CAHOON, Professor of Education, Ohio State University, Columbus, Ohio

ROBERT H. CARLETON, Assistant Professor of Chemistry, Newark College of Engineering, Newark, New Jersey

VICTOR L. CROWELL, Professor of Science and Head of Science Department, State Teachers' College, Trenton, New Jersey

W. C. CROXTON, Professor of Biology and Chairman, Division of Mathematics and Science, St. Cloud State Teachers College, St. Cloud, Minnesota

ETHELEEN DANIEL, Supervisor of Elementary Education, Montgomery County, Rockville, Maryland

DAVID J. GOODMAN, Editor-in-Chief, Audio-Visual Division, Popular Science Publishing Company, New York, New York

BENJAMIN C. GRUENBERG, New York, New York

ELWOOD D. HEISS, Professor of Science, New Haven State Teachers College, New Haven, Connecticut

KATHERINE E. HILL, Department of Natural Sciences and Science Education, Wheelock College, Boston, Massachusetts

ALBERT J. HUGGETT, Associate Professor of Education, Michigan State College, East Lansing, Michigan

NELLE LEE JENKINSON, Assistant Director, Division of Audio-Visual Education, St. Louis Public Schools, St. Louis, Missouri

PALMER O. JOHNSON, Professor of Education, University of Minnesota, Minneapolis, Minnesota

J. GORDON MANZER, Head, Science Department, Central High School, Trenton, New Jersey

MORRIS MEISTER, Principal, Bronx High School of Science, New York, New York

MARY W. MOFFITT, Horace Mann-Lincoln School, Teachers College, Columbia University, New York, New York

GAYLORD C. MONTGOMERY, Teacher of Science, John Burroughs School, Clayton, Missouri

NATHAN NEAL, in charge of Radio Education, Board of Education, Cleveland, Ohio

DAISY PARTON, Associate Professor of Education and Director of Verner School, University of Alabama, University, Alabama

S. RALPH POWERS, Professor of Natural Science, Teachers College, Columbia University, New York, New York

RALPH C. PRESTON, Associate Professor of Education, University of Pennsylvania, Philadelphia, Pennsylvania

LEONA M. SUNDQUIST, Chairman, Science Department, Western Washington College of Education, Bellingham, Washington

JOHN URBAN, Professor of Science, New York State College for Teachers, Buffalo, New York

RALPH K. WATKINS, Professor of Education, University of Missouri, Columbia, Missouri

HARRY H. WILLIAMS, Instructor in Chemistry, Horace Mann School for Boys, and Instructor in the Teaching of the Physical Sciences, Teachers College, Columbia University, New York, New York

EDITOR'S PREFACE

The present volume represents this Society's third response to a recognized need for some reorientation of prevailing programs of science education in the elementary and secondary schools. The Third Yearbook, Part II, was designed to redirect the nature-study movement toward a functional relationship with studies in natural science at the high-school level. To this end, the principle of progression in curriculum content in the field of science was strongly emphasized. Part I of the Thirty-first Yearbook undertook the interpretation of the accumulated results of research in the teaching of science and of relevant concepts in the fields of philosophy and psychology with the aim of developing an integrated program of instruction in science from the primary through the high-school years. As formulated by the yearbook committee, this program was directed toward the understanding of the major generalizations of science and the associated scientific attitudes, the graded courses of instruction being organized so as to present "an increasingly enlarged and increasingly mature development of objectives."

Science Education in American Schools, Part I of the Society's yearbook for 1947, is presented in recognition of the progress in science as well as in science education since the publication of the yearbook for 1932. It is imperative that the science curriculum be reviewed in light of the advancement of scientific knowledge in areas directly related to impending problems of readjustment entailed by the social and economic dislocations of modernized warfare. It is important, moreover, that such reorientation of science education take cognizance of the studied experimentation and the validated research in the teaching of science in recent years. These purposes are well served by the present yearbook. The guidance value of the volume is further enhanced by a discussion of the foremost issues in science teaching and the frankly stated consensus of the committee with respect to the alternatives considered.

This publication was initiated by a proposal submitted by Professor Noll and accepted by the Board of Directors at the October meeting in 1945. Because of the urgency of the considerations which prompted the proposal, it was thought desirable to complete the preparation of the volume at the earliest possible time. The committee was organized immediately, Professor Noll being appointed chairman. The co-operative spirit and the enterprise of the several members of the committee and their collaborators have made it possible for the Society to present the science yearbook at this most opportune time.

NELSON B. HENRY

TABLE OF CONTENTS

CHAPTER I

THE PURPOSE AND SCOPE OF THE YEARBOOK

Need for a Yearbook

Several useful reports dealing with instruction in science have appeared during the past two decades. There are, however, a number of considerations justifying the preparation at this time of a yearbook in this area.

First to be mentioned is the scientific progress which has been made during the past decade and more especially during World War II. Advances in transportation have drastically altered our concepts of time and space and consequently of the relationships of peoples and nations to each other. Research in causes and therapy of diseases and improvements in medical and surgical care and techniques have affected both our standards of health and our manner of living. The far-reaching consequences of newly developed methods for releasing atomic energy can as yet be only dimly seen. It is possible that such sources of energy may cause war to be outlawed entirely; certainly they will affect peacetime pursuits in countless and very fundamental ways.

Scientific discoveries and developments affect not only man's material existence but also his thinking. Instruction in science must take cognizance of the social impact of developments produced by science. It is not enough that they be understood in a technical or scientific sense; it is most important that their effects on attitudes and relationships of people be studied and understood. Science instruction has not only a great potential contribution to make but also a responsibility to help develop in our youth the qualities of mind and the attitudes that will be of greatest usefulness to them in meeting the pressing social and economic problems that face the world.

Second, important new movements in science education have appeared which have far-reaching effects. One is the growth of organized science in the elementary grades, which is influencing fundamentally the program through the entire public school. Another movement is the introduction of fused science courses at the upper secondary level. General science at the junior high school level is now well established and is almost universally accepted in this country. The same is true of general biology. However, not many realize that an appreciable proportion of en-

1

rolments in senior high school science is now represented in courses called by such titles as "senior science," "consumer science," "survey science," or "physical science." A similar trend is evident at the junior-college level where survey courses in biological sciences and in the physical sciences are replacing separate courses in the basic sciences for many college students.

Third, the new research literature in science instruction needs to be synthesized, integrated, and implemented. Although the number of research studies produced in this area since 1930 has been smaller than in the two decades just before 1930, it is the opinion of the committee responsible for the present yearbook that the average quality of investigations has improved. It is important that available research be surveyed critically, analyzed, and appraised, and that the findings be related to classroom practice.

PURPOSE OF THE YEARBOOK

The foregoing are some of the most important factors which a yearbook on science instruction should take into account and evaluate. In the light of these needs, the purposes of the present volume may be stated as follows:

A. To present a challenging and workable philosophy which will assist and encourage teachers of science to make the contribution to the welfare of our society which they, through their instruction and professional activities, can make and which society expects them to make. As a means to this end, the committee throughout its work has adhered to the following principles:

1. To make the report as practicable as possible. It has been the aim to present the material from the viewpoint of the classroom teacher and to show how the daily activities of classroom and laboratory can be made to contribute to the ultimate goals of education in a democracy.
2. To review and appraise available research in science teaching and to suggest desirable types of problems for further study. To enhance the usefulness of research data and conclusions, the citations and discussion of research studies have been introduced wherever they seem pertinent rather than in separate chapters or sections.
3. To select and describe the best practices in science teaching that could be found and to show how they can be adapted to daily use by any qualified science teacher.

B. Another important purpose of this report stems from the movements and trends referred to above. New kinds of courses and new methods and devices in science instruction are being developed in many places. It is the purpose here to examine these developments, to appraise them, and to determine, in so far as possible, what their implications for the future seem to be. Time will reveal to what extent the analyses are significant but the attempt to interpret such movements is regarded as one of the important obligations of the yearbook committee.

C. Although not a major purpose of the yearbook, it should be stated that, as a working principle, the committee decided to make a constant effort to attain unity of thought and presentation. This was done with full recognition of the fact that this unity holds chiefly in larger aspects of science instruction, and that such unity does not require, or perhaps even make desirable, unity in detail. To strive toward such unity in larger perspective the committee agreed:

1. To consider in an early chapter perennial issues for which unity in larger aspects offers no single solution, and to make recommendations based on the consensus of the committee.
2. To have all manuscripts read and criticized by each member of the committee, and to approve them in final form only when acceptable to a majority of the committee.
3. To supply specific orientation to all associated contributors as to the point of view to be presented in the yearbook.
4. To share jointly as a committee the responsibility for all chapters in Section I, which is considered basic to the entire report.

Scope of the Yearbook

In its deliberations and in the preparation of the yearbook, the committee considered all elementary and secondary grades, including the junior college, or thirteenth and fourteenth grades. For several reasons it was decided not to go beyond this point. The usual limits of the public school system are from kindergarten to the twelfth grade, inclusive, or, in some situations, through the fourteenth grade. This upper limit is generally regarded as the finishing point of general education; at least general education seldom continues beyond the fourteenth grade. From here on specialization and specialized courses are common, and these were felt to be outside the scope of this yearbook.

Organization of the Yearbook

Following the introductory chapter the report is divided into four sections.

Section I (except for chapter iv) is a general statement of what the committee feels to be the desirable objectives of science instruction, both in the ultimate and in the more immediate sense. The purpose of chapter ii is to orient science as a field of instruction by pointing out the functions science serves in modern society. The expanding limits of science are noted, but the discussion is not completed at this point. It leads, rather, into chapter iii where the objectives of science instruction are presented and discussed more specifically. In chapter iii reference is made to similar and related statements by various other agencies and organizations. Section I is concluded with a chapter on persistent issues in science instruction. Here are identified a number of recurring problems, and the best collective judgment of the committee is presented on each one.

Section II deals with the problems of science teaching in the elementary grades. It includes discussions of expected outcomes as related to the objectives of chapters ii and iii, of methods and materials, including multi-sensory aids, evaluation, training of teachers, and of significant research.

Section III is concerned with the teaching of science in the junior high school grades and in the higher secondary grades. Throughout Section III consideration is given to the same phases of instruction as in Section II.

In Section IV, chapter xvii, the discussion begun in chapter ii is carried to a conclusion, in the attempt to envisage what science teaching in the future may involve and what it may be expected to accomplish.

SECTION I

GENERAL PROBLEMS OF SCIENCE TEACHING

CHAPTER II

SCIENCE AND PEOPLE

IT IS A LONG AND ENDLESS PROCESS THROUGH WHICH THE RACE
LEARNS TO BELIEVE IN AND TO ACT UPON FUNDAMENTAL
TRUTH

Most educated people would agree that there is an age-old tendency
toward fact-mindedness. It is unlikely that anyone would claim to know
when or under what circumstances humans first found that facts and
valid inferences can be depended on. Clearly, the cave man's family had
gone a long way toward deriving conclusions from experiences and toward a measure of guidance in meeting recurrent practical problems.
The fear-filled cave children probably soon learned not to destroy the
family hunting clubs. They probably learned not to be out too late at
night, lest they never come home. Questions of cleanliness and styles in
clothing consumed little if any of their time. No one really knows, but
one may guess how meager and harsh was the youngsters' education. It
may have consisted entirely of observational and practical learning followed by life or death results for successes and failures, respectively.
There is no known record of the beginnings of discrimination between
right and wrong, as derived from observed natural phenomena or from
human practices. There is a record, however, of the existence many
thousands of years ago of such discriminations based upon experiential
thinking, and the translation and interpretation of that old record illustrates the use of modern scientific methods in the study of factual thinking in early human history.

In the British Museum there is a treasured piece of black stone which
was uncovered in the valley of the Nile River in Egypt. On this stone are
organized markings made a very long time ago by one or more persons.
A few thousand years ago some practically minded Egyptians had
found this piece of flat stone and, not noting that it was a record, used
it in the process of grinding their grain. The grinding wore away part of
the stone, but enough of the ancient writing remains to permit its reading by those rare persons who are gifted and trained in studying such

5

things. In his book, *The Dawn of Conscience*,[1] Breasted presents a factually supported account of this ancient black-stone book of records. King Shabaka of ancient Egypt used this stone book in the eighth century B.C. He added to its records and referred to the book as "the work of the ancestors." After long, careful study Breasted concluded the records were mostly written about 3400 B.C.

It is recorded on this stone that the purely arbitrary sun god, Re, had begun to lose some of the previously unquestioned power and authority through which he ruled and controlled all human life. The stone document reports that distinctions were beginning to be made between ideas of right and wrong, and that people were claiming that the truth should be their guide. Breasted says, "The document attempted to account for the origin of moral order in the world," and cited occurrences in early Egyptian life to show consciousness and appreciation of factual evidence as a foundation for decisions. The inscriptions claim that thought and its expression are foundations of all human accomplishment in orderly living. Improved human living, which we now associate with our improved social organizations, came about, as the document says, because "all things came into being through what the heart [mind] thought and the tongue [speech] commanded." These facts are here stated for the first time so far as definite records are available. Breasted comments,

The idea thus took on being in the world of objective existence. That is, thinking and expression were recognized as realities along with other factors of objective existence. Undoubtedly such recognition slowly developed through long preceding ages and did not suddenly spring into existence.

Though in these incipient stages some kinds of thinking, expression, and conduct were approved and some were disapproved, it was clearly recorded that "Pharaoh was still the source of right and wrong" and was the final judge of any person's conduct. It would thus seem that in these very early stages of objectivity, there was abject obeisance to the authority of the rulers, though there existed the elemental phases of the processes of securing evidence and making dependable inferences therefrom. Such primitive thinking, unorganized and with such confusions between natural phenomena, ideas of morals, and conscious efforts to secure orientation in a fearsome natural world, and so dominated by the dictates of all-powerful rulers, seems very far from present-day methods and standards.

We are disappointed when we observe people acting according to wholly imaginative superstitions. Present-day writers continue to use the fig-

---

[1] James H. Breasted, *Dawn of Conscience*. New York: Charles Scribner's Sons, 1933.

ure of an ostrich hiding his head in the sand, whereas no recorded or personal observations have ever established any such act by the ostrich. It is humans, not ostriches, who put away their heads when hard problems come along. The ground-hog story is good for newspaper space when February 2 arrives each year, a fact which should offend intelligent readers. The more important problems of personal affairs, of human relations, and of political organizations and services are in great need of scientific thinking. Indeed, many scientists of today are scientific only within the narrow fields of their specialties, not in their own homes or in their human and political relations. We have made commendable progress in factual thinking and acting. The differences between our day and that of the ancients are in refinements and degree. We are on our way, but have far to go.

MATERIAL BENEFITS FROM SCIENCE ARE VERY GREAT BUT MAY BE EXAGGERATED UNLESS CONSIDERED IN RELATION TO WHAT IS NOT KNOWN

Any bright pupil can prepare an instructive list of the benefits from science which he may encounter within a single day's experience. They may begin with his being wakened upon his "just-right" mattress by a musical alarm clock, within a comfortably heated and properly ventilated room, to go to his automatic-balance-heated bath, thence to breakfast consisting of foods almost too predigested for his best uses, while the radio or morning paper informs him about the near and distant parts of the earth and sky. His grandfather's one weekly newspaper is supplanted by one or more of several daily issues. He talks with his companions about radio waves, which, unseen and unheard except through remarkable, complex machines, he knows to pass beneath, above, and through him, and at speeds which defy his imagination. He discusses the wonder of jet propulsion. He realizes that here is a new application of energy with untold possibilities. Wheels attached to transportation machines have allowed civilization to get where it now is. Jet propulsion does not depend on wheels. The engineers who apply science report that jet-propelled machines rise as high as seventy miles in a few seconds, may travel to a city five hundred miles away in a few more seconds, and may land a load within a fairly restricted prescribed location. Indeed, this pupil, like his elders, wonders but does not yet know how a human heart and breathing apparatus can safely endure the extreme journeys which this new machine of science can make, but he believes that men will soon learn how to do it safely. He turns his attention to the nature and possibilities of energy from broken atoms, and, if he has scientific insight, he reflects upon the unimaginable amount of energy now used in holding together all the atoms of this earth, or the untold work that might be accomplished if even a small portion of this energy could be released in such ways that it could be made to do useful work for the betterment of human society. He senses and trembles at the idea that the uncontrolled release of atomic energy might destroy not only those who release it but no end of others—maybe all within a very large area. And he asks a scientist whether there is danger that atoms, once started to break, might continue in "a way setting one another to breaking." When the scientist says, "Yes, under certain conditions that might happen," he turns pale and thinks, "Who is responsible for new science knowledge?"

As our young friend continues his day's list, he hears of a companion whose appendix became hopelessly clogged. At the hospital an expert surgeon had quickly carved out the offending appendix, had dressed the wound, and had given instructions to the well-trained and highly responsible nurse. As the doctor left, he had remarked, "You've kept your body healthy. You'll be out in a few days. Less than a hundred years ago you would have died with 'inflammation of the bowels,' as they called it, because they didn't then know much about such things." And as our pupil thinks of this account from his friend, he recalls that there are many diseases which formerly killed people but from which no one need die now if only his body is otherwise healthy and he does the things modern science has found good to do. He writes in his notes,

Yes, that is what the literature teacher had in mind when she wrote on the board Shakespeare's statement from *The Merchant of Venice*, "If 'twere as easy to do as to know what were good to do, chapels had been churches and poor men's cottages princes' palaces." Even knowing what is good to do isn't enough. It must be done correctly and at the proper time.

If at dinner that night our young friend were to report on his very incomplete list of his contacts with achievements of science, many important additions would be suggested. The foods served would suggest dozens of achievements of first magnitude. Sunlight, chlorophyll, and plant and animal breeding have been brought into remarkable co-operation. Refrigeration, canning, transportation, and special researches in the chemistry of plant and animal production have made a greatly enlarged and improved food world. Prolonged hunger anywhere in the world is due not to nature and her scientific relations, primarily, but to men's wrong or ineffective political and economic relations. Some men might become scientifically selfish, some men too indolent, some too lacking in foresight, some too dependent upon the kindness of others, no matter how abundant the potential food supply. Science has not remade men but has provided almost unbelievable benefits for men's uses. One noted scientist has said that from the point of view of the achievements and discoveries of modern science, he lives farther away from his grandfather than the grandfather lived from King Tutankhamen.

It would not be appropriate for the purposes of this chapter to list the scientific achievements of any single year. This has been done for 1945.[2] It is a most astonishing list, containing something more than three hundred separate items of accomplishments, each of which adds to what men know, or what they can use in peace and war, or what will improve health, well-being, and future growth in knowledge. Nor is it appropriate to list the still greater unknowns toward which scientists and other people must direct their energies. Nevertheless, a few illustrations will help to remind us of how much we do not know.

We still know almost nothing about some aspects of public health. Our accident toll annually exceeds the lives lost in World War II. Our natural resources—soil, water, timber, minerals, and so forth—on which so much depends, are inadequately known and are controlled by such ignorance, or carelessness, or selfishness, as to constitute a crime against our future peoples.

The fundamental process, second to none, through which all living things are fed, directly or indirectly, still holds its own secrets against tremendous expenditure of funds and the prolonged efforts of the ablest scientists. Green plants are green because of their chlorophyll, by means of which radiant energy is absorbed in such ways that it results in the making of food. All other food processes depend upon this initial process. The mystery of photosynthesis seems even more baffling just because people and all other living things are so completely dependent upon that process. We know about hybridizing corn so that its improved stalks, roots, and leaves will yield more and better food materials, but from the chlorophyll point of view we do not know just what it is that we have done. A recent publication from the research laboratory of the Massachusetts Institute of Technology says:

Photosynthesis by green plants is by far the most important biochemical process on earth. It produces organic matter from stable inorganic materials and thus prevents life from becoming extinct. It is also the most puzzling of all biochemical reactions. Plant physiologists, chemists, and physicists have all attacked the problem. This is evidenced by the tremendous literature which has accumulated since the middle of the last century.[3]

---

[2] Watson Davis, "Science Review: The Important Science Developments of the Year," *Science News Letter*, XLVIII (December 22, 1945), 396.

[3] Eugene I. Rabinowitch, *Photosynthesis and Related Processes*. New York: Interscience Publishers, Inc., 1945.

What an age and what a world in which to live! But that is not the whole story nor the most important part of the story. Any benefit or achievement carries commensurate responsibility to its possessor. What we learn imposes obligations upon us. Possession of knowledge has not necessarily implied its prompt, effective, and proper use. In a true sense one must gain an emotional drive which helps provide effective uses of what he knows. For example, a person who travels much finds the exact time of departure of his train. He plans to go on that train. He fixes the time in his mind. He decides when and how he'll reach the station. He accepts the known facts. As his time approaches, he is "set to go," and goes. He does not wobble and argue with himself, but goes and attends to the affairs of his journey. Using tried and useful science knowledge must come to be like that.

Continuing Scientific Achievements Vitally Influence Social Customs

Science now bears a definite relation to many kinds of social standards, and social standards are influential in people's conduct. Certain practices are acceptable, others are not. Science steadily contributes to those social standards by providing better things to do and showing why they are better. Good illustrations may be taken from the field of individual and public health. It is within the memory of many of us that expectoration in public was regarded as a normal and proper physiological function, but cuspidors are not now acceptable or respectable articles of household equipment in the best families. A cuspidor is an antique novelty to some young people. Laws have been passed and are supposed to be enforced against expectoration in public places. Social standards do put severe criticism on offenders. Scientific knowledge about germs of disease and their spread had much to do in producing present standards.

Time was, and not long ago, when certain skin diseases, due to our being hosts for small animal parasites, were unpleasant misfortunes to an entire community. Sulphur and molasses, properly administered, were bad for the insects which produced "the itch." When some rural children came to school, the odor of sulphur advertised that at least some of the parents proposed to avoid "the itch," for they had learned that no one need have this loathsome disease if the insects were killed and proper cleanliness and care were observed by all. Scientific knowledge and controls have ruled such diseases "out of the best social circles." This unpleasant disease is now "bad form." The pleasures of mildly scratching an itching surface would be permissable and respectable were it not for the social taboo against having a disease which suggests uncleanliness. The unembarrassed offender is uncommon.

Having smallpox now suggests uncleanliness. Typhoid will soon not be respectable. The common cold is still a misfortune which most of us know should have been avoided. Several types of pneumonia are rapidly being headed for the "last round-up." Social diseases, so-called, are abhorrent to nearly everybody. Science knowledge often needs to be emotionally standardized in order to become most effective. Good health reaches beyond freedom from disease. It must become emotionally respectable.

Not only health knowledge but other kinds of science are rapidly becoming elements of social respectability. No vocation and no avocation is devoid of some contact with the achievement or methods of modern science. The entire world of which we are part, its forces, materials, and never-ending changes, the daily press, magazines, common conversation, indeed all our contacts seem shot through with one or more aspects of science. Even those people who incline toward minimizing the contributions of science use them constantly in their own lives.

Discoveries and Information to the Public Are Usually Closely Related

It is not within the nature of new truth for it to be static. Its relations to what was previously known promptly begin to take form. And when new and old knowledge take form together, there usually appear new areas of the unknown which call for further discoveries. These in their turn are incorporated into old knowledge and help to define new unknowns. Though this process may be rapid at times and slow at others, it is constant. The process will be as endless as are human curiosity, planned inquiry, and purposeful experiment. Such constantly growing knowledge finds its way more or less rapidly among people in general, particularly among those who have the fundamental education by means of which to sense the meaning of new knowledge. Without at least a little education regarding fundamentals, any reported discovery may seem little more than scientific gossip. The better the understanding of the basis of what was previously known, the better the resulting understanding of the new. Therefore, two facts must be recognized: (1) that discoveries are constant and develop from what was previously known, and (2) new knowledge cannot be "bottled up" but finds its way to those sufficiently educated that they may understand.

A current illustration will serve to present important considerations. An area in which future research is imperative, almost certain to be made, and almost certain to produce new knowledge of great human benefits, is that of nuclear physics. Thousands of well-trained scientists now plan their next procedures to the end of discovering the truth about problems disclosed through the remarkable advances of recent years. Few

areas have given more potent proof of the fact that major achievements
lead inevitably into demands for researches of equal or still greater import. We may confidently look toward achievements which will take
full rank with those already made.

Few areas of achievement better illustrate the ways through which
new elements of knowledge rapidly spread to those trained to understand. It was German scientists (Hahn and Strassman) who discovered and announced the procedure "for unlocking the storehouse of one
form of atomic energy."[4] Nuclear studies had become dominant in research in physical science and had engaged the active attention of many
men in many countries. Even the details of atomic splitting were known,
were openly discussed, and were used as guides in further research in
Britain, United States, Canada, Germany, Russia, and Japan. The so-
called wartime secrets pertain to securing and applying the energy from
atomic splitting to make destructive weapons. Even the "secrets" seem
very difficult of restraint and have elicited some absurd legislative proposals. The international conferences reported thus far have claimed restraint upon only about 25 per cent of the knowledge underlying atomic
bombs.[5]

Real knowledge is kept secret with great difficulty and not for long.
Fundamental scientific discoveries eventually find their way into the
possession of those persons who are educated, who are interested, and
who take the trouble to find out. The futility of the harangue about keeping science secret is apparent to many persons and will probably be generally recognized by the time this book is in print.

Interesting suggestions for the war-clearing period have been made
about ways for keeping atomic energy from being used harmfully. One
illustration of those suggestions is here included. Dr. Hull urges that
there be organized a world-wide and thoroughly representative and comprehensive group of scientists who are engaged in atomic research. The
members of this organization would commit themselves to respect for
the work of other members regardless of nationality; each member would
pledge not to advise about or assist in making atomic bombs; each would
continue fundamental research and would publish his results; each would
assist as he could in beneficial uses of atomic energy. Dr. Hull says:

This association would be not only international, it would be supernational.
At least its members would not take orders from any government to assist in making atomic bombs. And since its membership would probably include 99 per cent

---

[4] Gordon F. Hull, "A Proposal for the Formation of a World Association of Physicists or Nuclear Scientists," *Science*, CII (December 28, 1945), 672.

[5] *New York Times*, December 30, 1945.

of the physicists of the world, atomic bombs would not be made. For the making of such a bomb requires the ultimate in knowledge concerning radioactive and nuclear physics.[6]

Scientific discovery is certain to continue. While science is making important discoveries, society must simultaneously guide men's knowledge and ideals so that useful results shall follow. Removal of ignorance by clear and effective presentation of knowledge comes slowly for the masses, more rapidly for those committed to careers in science. As educational opportunities for all are used more widely, more effectively, and for longer periods, there is imperative need for increase in education by means of science and for spread of scientific knowledge. But most of all there are needed ideals and practices to help insure that worthy uses may be made of education, of sciences in general, and of the constantly developing special achievements in science. The tragic results of misuse of knowledge are regularly illustrated in the mistakes of human society. Airplanes, automobiles, and electric currents often destroy those who do not or who cannot use adequate knowledge and control. Chemicals that will ease pain may also produce habits of use, or may cause death. Men gain knowledge and learn about applications of it, making possible almost daily additions to human welfare. But the stream of deaths and of injuries gives graphic evidence that so-called civilization lags far behind the progress of knowledge. We must improve our general education by including convincing and effective personal and community controls of knowledge. Merely factual education might have only harmful results for future peoples.

Science Is an Inescapable Factor of Modern Cultures

Important retroactive effects may come to the persons and the society with whom science thrives. Some people, however, escape the cultural aspects of science. Prolonged and thoughtful work affects the worker. Hunting for facts and trying to discover their meaning are processes which exemplify an attitude of investigation and belief in reliable inference. The futility of falseness, both in fact and in inference, is shown when truth and proved inference are established. It is a belief in a tendency which is here emphasized, and no claim is made for universal achievement. But all people who regularly observe and study nature have the opportunity to appreciate her constancy and regularity. Even nature's never-ending variations and newness may be appreciated because of the major constancy and regularity of nature's facts and occurrences. It is noted that "spring came late this year," because ages of observation have

---

[6] Hull, *op. cit.*

established "a usual time." Or, "Here are offspring with different color and quality from their immediate ancestors," so biologists discover the underlying factors of hybrid inheritance. Men are beginning to find that much of what was regarded as irregularity in nature is caused by factors waiting men's further study. Science is the endless frontier.[7] It is not the kind of frontier which opens only to brawny and physically courageous men; but it opens to men who know many of the older and well-traveled intellectual highways, who know and use the fundamental ways of science, and who gladly and with intellectual and moral courage carefully push their way into the areas of new truth.

One of the conspicuous elements of the culture of science is found in the fact that search for truth exemplifies an attitude of expectancy of new truth. The man of true culture has the desire to know, to learn, and he often gladly teaches to others something related to what was known, but which lies a bit beyond. Material needs and uses sometimes set one's problem for study, but a scientist seeks new truth whether or not he expects uses of it. The major function of science is to reveal new truth. There is, however, a cumulative beauty that is revealed when old and new truth steadily fit together to compose a clearer picture of nature's enduring realities. In 1922 Marie Curie, speaking at Vassar College, said: "But we must not forget that when radium was discovered no one knew that it would prove useful in hospitals. The work was one of pure science. And this is a proof that scientific work must not be considered from the point of view of the direct usefulness of it. It must be done for itself, for the beauty of science, and then there is always the chance that a scientific discovery may become, like the radium, a benefit for humanity."[8]

The fascinatingly potent George Washington Carver began an address to teachers about new uses of sweet potatoes by recalling to his audience some of the beauties of the flower of the morning-glory plant. He told them that sweet potatoes and morning glories belong to the same plant family. Then as he launched upon the chemistry, the household and industrial values of sweet potatoes, he said: "First of all, you must never forget that the sweet potato is a morning glory."

SCIENCE AND THE PEOPLE'S GOVERNMENT ARE CLOSELY RELATED

If all citizens are to participate intelligently in affairs of government, all need to know something about government. And if the people's rep-

---

[7] Vannevar Bush, *Science: The Endless Frontier*. Washington: Government Printing Office, 1945.

[8] *The Autobiography of Science*. Edited by F. R. Moulton and Justin J. Schifferes. Garden City, New York: Doubleday, Doran & Co., Inc., 1945.

resentatives, who pass legislation, are to make decisions for an age of science, they need at least a reasonable knowledge of science and her ways of working. The ways of thinking of the politician and of the scientist have differed widely. Each group needs to understand and co-operate with the other. And the common man, if not a scientist, nonetheless needs knowledge of both science and legislation, since both profoundly affect his welfare.

Furthermore, points of view differ widely among government representatives, as they do among scientists. It may surprise some readers to recognize that a considerable group of scientists regard science as existing chiefly for the benefit of people as a whole. As such, they believe that it should be publicly managed and guided in its endeavors. The management and guidance should come primarily from representatives of the people—from the constituted central authorities and not from organized scientists. That is, management of the work of scientists should be a government function. Public welfare is regarded as of more importance than any particular scientific achievements may be. And if science is for public benefit, it is a function of politically elected government. Furthermore, those holding this view believe that scientists themselves, as citizens, and as part of the public which benefits from science, should participate politically in electing the officials who are to manage and guide scientific endeavors. It is further argued that scientists are obligated to the public and have no escape from association with the pressure groups which affect legislation and any subsequent actions of legislators. It has even been argued in England and to some extent in America that organized scientists need to make sure that they are allied with the winning sides in the elections and legislatures, in order that the welfare of science may be cared for. Such arguments appear foreign to the thinking and wishes of most American scientists; but there are eminent scientists who honestly believe in the substantial soundness of arguments for centralized control of scientific research and for publicity regarding discoveries. More will certainly be heard from the advocates of legislation to increase the centralization of authority over the people's welfare, not only as it relates to science but also to other sorts of human affairs.

Thus far in America and in other so-called democratic countries most scientists have sought new truth and its significance as direct results of their work. This has been done without immediate thought of possible human uses or of personal or governmental controls to be made of new truth. Main purposes have been to establish the facts, to learn new truth, and to interpret the meanings and significance of truth. Later, the same workers, but more commonly others, at times have applied the discovered facts and have secured patents upon appliances designed for human uses. Those who secured patents may be truly scientific but also may be merely ingenious. Anyway, the appliances they have developed may be very useful. Then there are the engineers who produce all sorts of services for men, based upon knowledge, inventions, and engineering ingenuity. All these are citizens.

Those who cultivate science, that is, the scientists, are taking note of severe statements now being directed against them. The accusing finger and tongue are translated into vehement print. There are too many accusations printed in pages that are too well known for scientists longer to ignore them. As a sample we quote from a widely known sociologist:

The present prospect is that, no matter what its way of working may be, science may itself be the end of the human enterprise. The belief in social progress, of which science has nearly always been viewed as the efficient cause, has come to a low state in our time. Few people, after beholding the work of the demigod in the laboratory and the practical effects of that work outside, any longer believe that mankind is moving forward in the direction of a desirable goal. Even the hope that this might be so is rapidly waning. People are beginning to doubt the world view of science, and what is more, science itself. . . . . Indeed, security, peace of mind, loyalty, friendship, kindliness, and the general attitudes associated with the brotherhood of man appear to be becoming less as science moves forward.[9]

Most American scientists probably regard it as their main obligation to make substantial contributions to demonstrable knowledge within specialized fields. A secondary duty is to instruct and guide their science students. Usually, if they accept it at all, they regard lightly or intermittently the duty to ally themselves with public affairs in which their scientific attainments and attitudes may help. The world-wide developments of the last decade make it imperative that scientists change this attitude of aloofness from the essential affairs of the common citizen. Scientists may help to guide public thought, action, and legislation. If they do not, thinking, acting, and legislating will proceed anyway. The scientist may have a part in developing the on-coming co-operation on social responsibilities. His absence will not prevent the movement but will deprive it of his valuable help. He should not forget that he, too, is a citizen, expecting and claiming his privileges and benefits as a citizen.

Other countries recognized tendencies toward central control of science and society more clearly than did this country until quite recently. The situation especially as relating to Great Britain has been stated as follows:

[9] Joseph Schneider, "On the Social and Moral Implications of Science," *Scientific Monthly*, LXI (November, 1945), 353–58.

Those who think that science should be centrally planned are undeterred by doubts as to their qualifications to give advice on ethical subjects. They have spread powerful propaganda intended to make scientists believe that they have three social obligations: to devote all their energies to the solution of the problems of man's material wants; to accept central planning in their own subject; and to press for adoption of central planning of society as a whole. This, so far as one can make out, is what is meant by the social responsibilities of scientists, as the term is usually used. Scientists who have other ideas about their social responsibilities have not yet bothered to challenge the propaganda, which is effective because it is not answered.[10]

Obviously, education and politics are the main agencies through which we can engage effectively in social responsibilities. Since American education deals with all the people's children, nearly all their youth, and many of the adults, science in our country has opportunities matching its responsibilities. These unequalled opportunities and unsurpassed obligations must now be accepted. An uninformed, unintelligent, or irresponsible democratic control may be avoided through co-operation in scientific education. No other course appears to be open to science and scientists.

If good scientists enter politics they do not find the going easy. Nor are comfortable paths found by those who oppose good scientists. It is fortunate and hopeful that most intelligent men prefer the guidance of facts and their proved meanings if only they are acquanted with them. There are the dependable attitudes of getting and expressing the facts, of using reason in discovering the course to follow, of learning from others who have experience and knowledge, and above all, of not being too sure until abundant available data are set down. Those attitudes, if displayed by reasonably agreeable personalities, will win support. They must be widely tried. The demands of science for freedom of action, of speech, and of thought carry the obligation to use action, speech, and thought for worthy purposes. Education and politics are indispensible agencies in a democracy through which free action, speech, and thought have their greatest opportunities for worthy services. Both will increase in respectability when they do their jobs better.

SCIENCE EDUCATION IS IMPERATIVE AND UNAVOIDABLE

The alternative to omitting, reducing, or failing to improve and increase science education is to deny the achievements and impact made by science in modern living. He who reads may run, but he who does not read *must* run. Time was when persons, capable but uninterested, could

---

[10] John R. Baker, *Science and the Planned State.* New York: Macmillan Co., 1945.

choose not to be educated. That time has almost passed. Civilization, so-called, requires a modicum of education of all fairly normal persons and provides far-reaching opportunities for those of superior capacities. Civilization cares for, as dependents of one kind or another, those incapable or unwilling to gain and use a self-protecting amount and kind of education. Education is a privilege with a strongly inherent element of social compulsion. Even in a democracy the element of compulsion must increase for common social welfare. The materials for use in education are the accumulated knowledge, the social customs, ambitions, and ideals, the ways of thinking and acting, which have slowly grown up through man's long progress. The mathematical and astronomical sciences allowed men to orient themselves as earth's human inhabitants. The physical sciences allowed men to learn about the materials and processes of the earth and heavens. The biological sciences allowed men to learn of life about them, and particularly of themselves. The psychological sciences allowed men to look into the mirrors provided by all the other sciences and thus to learn more of themselves as self-named wise human beings (Homo sapiens). And now all science is focused upon man in his relations with other men and asks him to learn how to use his accumulated progress and how to educate his own offspring, so that further progress may go on toward ends worthy of all that has gone before. The assignment cannot be avoided if worthy next steps are to be made.

CHAPTER III

THE OBJECTIVES OF SCIENCE INSTRUCTION

It is the purpose in the preceding chapter and in this one to present a statement of the objectives for science instruction at the elementary and secondary levels. As this sentence implies, the two chapters are essentially a unit. Chapter ii sets forth the underlying reasons why a prominent place must be found for the subject in the curriculum. Chapter iii, continuing the same line of thought developed in chapter ii, deals with ways and means. It undertakes to show how the major aims of science education are to be realized by teaching that is directed toward the achievement of more immediate goals, here designated "the objectives of science instruction."

RECENT REPORTS BEARING ON THE OBJECTIVES OF SCIENCE INSTRUCTION

Before the statement is presented, it seems advisable to review briefly some outstanding examples of two types of documents bearing on the problem. The first type includes reports which relate to the purposes of general education. The second type is that which deals exclusively with science instruction in the elementary and secondary schools. Then follows the large section devoted to a presentation and discussion of the statement of objectives as formulated by the present yearbook committee. The chapter closes with a discussion of the objectives in relation to some of the commonly recognized purposes of general education.

Reports on General Education

The first report to be cited is a recent publication (**15**) on the purposes of education for youth in American democracy. Although the report deals primarily with education at the secondary level, it has important implications for all education below the university. In this report, science instruction is assigned some part in contributing to the purposes of general education for American youth, which are designed to:

(1) Equip him to enter an occupation suited to his abilities and offering reasonable opportunity for personal growth and social usefulness; (2) prepare him to assume the full responsibilities of American citizenship; (3) give him a fair chance to exercise his right to the pursuit of happiness; (4) stimulate intellectual curiosity, engender satisfaction in intellectual achievement, and cultivate the

ability to think rationally; and (5) help him develop an appreciation of the ethical values which should undergird all life in a democratic society (**15**:21).

Certainly these purposes are laudable and idealistic enough and there is no doubt that science can contribute something to each one, though more to some than to others. Most science teachers will probably not be satisfied with the kind of science courses which are recommended in this report of the Educational Policies Commission. Some writers have criticized the report severely on the ground of its inadequate recognition of science in education (**5**). The document accords a significant place to science instruction and for that reason science teachers will need to study the report with care and with an open mind.

The second report in this group, typical of several similar reports emanating from higher institutions, is that of the Harvard Committee on General Education (**16**). Its field is education at the college level and it naturally brings into the discussion education at the secondary level. Indeed, the report is primarily concerned with the secondary level, if the latter is taken to include the junior-college years.

The point of view from which this report is written is that education should be general for all persons below the university level:

Science instruction in general education should be characterized mainly by broad integrative elements—the comparison of scientific with other modes of thought, the comparison and contrast of the individual sciences with one another, the relations of science with its own past and with general human history, and of science with problems of human society. These are areas in which science can make a lasting contribution to the general education of all students (**16**:155).

The two reports under review agree remarkably well in major recommendations regarding science instruction. These might be summarized as follows:

a) Science instruction should begin early in the experience of the child.

b) All education in science at the elementary and secondary levels should be general. Even for students going to college, general courses in biological science and in physical science (according to the Harvard Report) "should make a greater contribution to the student's general education and his preparation for future study than separate one-year courses in physics and chemistry" (**16**:160). The document of the Educational Policies Commission goes even further in its recommendations for reorganization of high-school science courses.

c) The development of competence in use of the scientific method of problem-solving and the inculcation of scientific attitudes transcend in importance other objectives in science instruction.

Reports in Science Education

The first comprehensive report dealing exclusively with the teaching of science in our public schools was that of the Science Committee of the Commission on Reorganization of Secondary Education (**10**). Although the committee confined its attention to the secondary grades, sixth through twelfth, its report is significant as a pioneering attempt which undoubtedly had a marked effect on science teaching. In the main, the committee's report aimed to do the following things.

a) To bring some systematic plan of organization to the science offerings in the grades included.

b) To show how science instruction could contribute to the attainment of the seven cardinal principles or objectives of secondary education as formulated by the Commission on the Reorganization of Secondary Education.

c) To present practical suggestions as to aims, content, and method in each of the sciences commonly taught in the secondary schools as an aid to classroom teachers in their daily work.

The report helped to clarify educational thinking concerning trends in the organization of science sequences. It gave support to a then emerging pattern of courses which still predominates in the great majority of secondary schools. Most important, as far as our interest here is concerned, was its attempt, the first in educational literature, to set up, in terms of the seven cardinal principles, large social objectives for science instruction.

In 1927, a special committee of the American Association for the Advancement of Science prepared a report entitled "On the Place of Science in Education" (**1**). As its chief contribution this report emphasized a growing awareness of the importance of scientific method as an objective of instruction. It recommended that studies of science teaching be undertaken on a national scope, that a field secretary be appointed by the American Association for the Advancement of Science to assist teachers of science and others in the study of their problems, and that a national council of science teachers be organized.

The next report comparable in importance to the ones just discussed appeared in 1932, when the Thirty-first Yearbook of the National Society for the Study of Education was published (**22**). This yearbook for the first time offered a comprehensive program and advocated the definite organization of science instruction in all grades from first through twelfth. It proposed that all science instruction, including such specialized areas as chemistry and physics, be organized about certain broad generalizations or principles. It held the purpose of science teaching to be the development of understandings of the major generalizations and of associated scientific attitudes. A quotation from the report will make this clear:

The major generalizations and associated scientific attitudes are seen as of such importance that understandings of them are made the objectives of science teaching. These statements are so far-reaching in their implications that they may be said to encompass the fields of science. They touch life in so many ways that their attainment as educational objectives constitutes a large part of the program of life enrichment. . . . . In the light of the foregoing it is proposed that the curriculum in science for a program of general education be organized about large objectives, that understanding and enlargement of these objectives shall constitute the contribution of science teaching to the ultimate aim of education, and that the course of study be so organized that each succeeding grade level shall present an increasingly enlarged and increasingly mature development of objectives (**22**:44).

The report goes on to analyze typical generalizations, such as "The earth seems very old when its age is measured in the ordinary units of time" and "The sun is the chief source of energy for the earth," and presents a list of thirty-eight major generalizations considered to be basic to all science instruction.

The report stimulated development of science as a subject of instruction in elementary grades; it encouraged the development of content of science courses about large topics, or generalizations, as opposed to an atomistic or artificial organization; and it helped materially to advance a program of science instruction in all grades from the first through the twelfth.

Another comprehensive statement of the purposes of science in general secondary education is the volume (**23**) sponsored by the Progressive Education Association. It is the purpose of this document to orient science teaching to broad areas of living characterized as (1) personal living, (2) immediate personal-social relationships, (3) social-civic relationships, and (4) economic relationships. These categories are adopted from publications of the Educational Policies Commission of the National Education Association, and to them the report adds a fifth, the disposition and ability to use reflective thinking in the solution of problems. Each category is analyzed into so-called major needs of the adolescent which are then thoroughly discussed and explained in relation to science instruction.

The report is challenging, but it is difficult to appraise its effect on practices in science instruction. The report does not, as a rule, develop the discussion of problems from the familiar ground of the present organization of science courses in the schools. Also, it concerns itself to a considerable extent with curriculum organization, which is of direct concern only to a small minority of teachers, and it deals with science instruction in the secondary school only, thus offering little to challenge the interest of the elementary-school teacher. Nevertheless, the report has much value. It sets forth a stimulating viewpoint of interest not only to science teachers but also to teachers of social studies and of physical education and to counselors. It also emphasizes in a very desirable way the importance of scientific method as an objective of instruction in science.

The most recent report of the type under review is a bulletin (3) dealing with a philosophy or point of view for science teaching as formulated by a rather large and representative committee of science teachers. This bulletin reviews previous reports on the subject and presents a point of view for science teaching which is very similar to that of the report of the Progressive Education Association which has just been discussed. It is helpful in that it gives emphasis to the contribution which science teaching should make to the broad areas of living previously referred to in the P.E.A. report as well as to such matters as safety, consumer, and conservation education.

One other type of report on objectives in science instruction should be mentioned. Several investigators have analyzed courses of study or textbooks in science, or have asked science teachers for statements of objectives. Beauchamp (4) checked 58 courses of study in general science, 45 in biology, 27 in physics, and 30 in chemistry "to discover the educational objectives of the course."

Noll (21) analyzed 130 different sources, including textbooks, courses of study, and questionnaire studies of aims of science instruction, and tabulated the aims or objectives as found therein.

The findings of these two investigations are similar enough to permit general summarization. The outstanding fact is the great diversity of aims, both as to nature and as to type. Beauchamp's tabulation shows approximately 75 different objectives ranging from the very specific (such as "to acquire a scientific vocabulary") to the most general (such as those included in the seven cardinal principles). Noll's analysis showed a like diversity of aims.

Hunter and Spore (17) submitted a statement of objectives for evaluation to science teachers in 655 secondary schools in all parts of the country. A list of 30 rather broad objectives formulated by the investigators was checked by the teachers as to the importance of each in terms of what actually happened in the science classes of their respective schools. The data were tabulated separately for junior and senior high schools. The results show that in practice, as reported or judged by these teachers, such objectives as "knowledge, understanding, and appreciation of

the environment" and "understanding of personal health needs" stand
at or near the top of the list in both junior and senior high schools; that
habits and attitudes of the scientist taken collectively rank high in both
lists; and that preparation for college entrance and for a scientific vocation are ranked consistently low. The report is representative of the opinions of a large number of science teachers as they relate to the particular
list of objectives submitted.

One other study (2) of a similar nature is reported by the National
Committee on Science Teaching. An inquiry prepared by a subcommittee
was sent to teachers in many schools and at all levels from kindergarten
to junior college. In it they were asked to list desirable functional outcomes of science related to such personal-social needs of children and
young people as health, safety, consumership, conservation, recreation,
responsible socio-economic action, work, and a maturing philosophy of
life. The subcommittee analyzed the returns, prepared a list of outcomes,
and submitted it to the teachers for refinement and enlargement and for
checking as to the relative importance of the respective outcomes. The
returns were again analyzed, and a new check list was formulated, which
includes many of the functional outcomes toward which science teaching
can contribute. The list is subdivided according to grade level, such as
kindergarten, primary, intermediate, etc. At each level the outcomes
are grouped according to the personal-social needs to which they contribute.

The report has significance because it represents the collective effort
and judgment of many persons in formulating and appraising a list of
outcomes for science teaching. It is valuable to teachers in suggesting
ways in which instruction in science can be related to areas such as health,
safety, recreation, and others already mentioned.

Studies based upon teacher judgment generally result in a large number of different objectives. Committee reports such as these have served
a very useful purpose in narrowing down such lists to a more practical,
functional organization.

CRITERIA FOR SELECTION OF OBJECTIVES

To state objectives for science instruction involves the risk of for-
getting or disregarding the dominant purposes of science education. This
error must be avoided. The objectives listed later in this chapter do not
lessen the emphasis throughout this yearbook on the function of science
in modern education. As stated in chapter ii, "science education is imperative and unavoidable." In science lies man's hope for his continuous
and progressive welfare. It is for this reason, fundamentally, that science
justifies, even demands, a prominent place in the school program.

The committee's objectives for science teaching and the explanatory content are intended to provide a working philosophy to pervade and unify the entire report. An attempt has been made to incorporate the best elements of other statements, particularly those emphasizing a social viewpoint for science teaching. Acknowledgment is due especially to reports of the National Society for the Study of Education (22) and the Progressive Education Association (23) reviewed earlier in this chapter.

The criteria employed in formulating the objectives are briefly these: In the first place, the statement should be *practicable* for the classroom teacher. It must be usable; when properly used, it should lead logically from one step to the next; and, if carefully followed, it should result in progress toward the objectives ultimately sought.

In the second place, the statement of objectives should be *psychologically sound*. It should be based on generally accepted principles of learning and should be as little subject as possible to the conflicting postulates of various theories of the psychology of learning.

In the third place, the objectives should be *possible of attainment* under reasonably favorable circumstances and to a measurable degree. A teacher in an ordinary classroom, with the average group of pupils, should be able to bring about demonstrable progress toward the attainment of all the objectives which are appropriate to the level of development of the learners.

In the fourth place, the selected objectives should be *universal* in a democratic society. Objectives should not be limited by political or geographical considerations; they should not apply to one sect or creed or racial group any more than to any other. They should impinge on man's thinking about himself and the society and the world in which he lives, whoever and wherever he may be.

Finally, the statement of objectives and the explanatory context should indicate, directly or by clear implication, the *relationship of classroom activity to desired changes in human behavior*. Too often objectives are stated either in overly broad, general terms, and hence are vague, or in terms of specific subject-matter content.

In accordance with the criteria listed, the committee proposes the following types of objectives. These are: (A) functional information or facts; (B) functional concepts; (C) functional understanding of principles; (D) instrumental skills; (E) problem-solving skills; (F) attitudes; (G) appreciations; (H) interests. These eight categories represent the major types of learning outcomes; moreover, they are believed to meet the criteria which have been set up. No attempt is made at this point to further define these categories. Rather, the categories will be illustrated with numerous examples, after which comes an analysis and definition of each.

Further Considerations regarding Objectives

Two additional considerations regarding the viewpoint of the committee on the objectives of science instruction will be mentioned. In the first place, it cannot be emphasized too strongly that objectives are here conceived as *directions of growth* and not as final outcomes to be completely and perfectly attained. The learning process is held to be one of *growth toward* the objectives rather than one of sudden and complete attainment of any goal. Also, it would not be expected that all children would progress at the same rate toward any objective or that all would arrive at the same degree of understanding and attainment of it. The ideal is rather that of taking each individual where he is and assisting him to make the maximum progress of which he is capable and at the optimum rate for him.

Every teacher knows that when he first meets a class, let us say in general science, there will be wide variation in the background of science knowledge and experiences of the members of the class. He knows that some of them probably understand more science the first day of the term than others will on the last. Yet, he also knows that every worth-while objective should present a stimulating opportunity for some growth to every member of the group. This is as it should be. The able teacher will accept this situation as a challenge to his best endeavors. He will strive to help each learner make as much progress toward the objectives as he can with a maximum of benefit and satisfaction to himself.

Closely related to the foregoing is the second point. It is expected that learning outcomes in science education, whatever their type, shall *function* in changed behavior. Occasion is taken throughout the yearbook, indeed is repeatedly created, to attack instructional procedures which produce mere verbalizations and mechanical skills. Such learning outcomes cannot function and are not worth the time and effort required to achieve them.

To recognize information as an objective of science instruction, as is here done, is not to indorse the acquisition of a body of isolated facts whose usefulness is limited to the particular science period in which they are learned or recited. On the contrary, the information learned must result in altered thinking and in altered behavior. It must make the pupil (and later, the adult) more intelligent and readier for adequate adjustment whenever that information is relevant to life situations.

Science concepts and principles must also be taught so that they will be *functional*. It is one thing to be able to repeat Boyle's law of gases.

It may be quite another thing to be able to identify the operation of the law under new conditions or to be able to control phenomena through the use of the law. It is one thing to be able to recite a neat statement covering a concept. It may be something else to be able to use the concept correctly in thinking, speaking, or writing about a relatively unfamiliar situation in which the concept properly plays a part.

The critical element in functional concepts and principles, as in functional information, is understanding. Understanding is not quickly achieved. It rarely results in any useful amount from a single experience or from exact duplicates of that experience, however often it is repeated. In either case the resultant understanding is virtually limited to a single given situation. For the kinds of concepts and principles which are properly science objectives there must be many and varied experiences in which the same idea, large or small, occurs in differing situations. Moreover, for the most fruitful learning these experiences must be arranged and graded with respect to complexity and difficulty, so that the pupil may be guided to organize his meanings at higher and higher levels. Meaningful learning is spiral. Each experience adds a new loop in the spiral of meaning (6).

Moreover, once concepts and principles have been meaningfully developed, they should be used, and used over and over, under conditions of sound motivation and in appropriate situations inside and outside of the school. This statement reiterates what was said in the preceding paragraph about the need for varied experience; but the statement bears repetition if for no other reason than to combat the fallacy that concepts and principles, once taught, may be turned over to "memory" for safekeeping. There is no evidence that concepts and principles maintain their vigor in cold storage.

The skills which are set as objectives for science instruction must likewise *function* in the daily activities of young people. The term "instrumental," which describes the first set of skill objectives in the list above, obviously carried this implication.

A second set of skill objectives is those involved in problem-solving (the elements of the scientific method). These skills, too, must be taught so that they will *function* throughout life. It is not enough that an occasional pupil recognize their importance and use them to some extent in the science laboratory. To the limit possible, all pupils must become sensitive to the value of these skills in connection with their affairs—sensitive to their values, disposed to use them as occasion permits, and expert in applying them to their problems.

Appreciations, attitudes, and interests must also be *functional* learning outcomes of science instruction. In each of these types of outcome there are verbal elements which may or may not be accompanied with understanding. Obviously, the pupil must have some information about great scientists in order to have an appreciation of their contributions, and he must know something about ferns in order to make a collection. But in each case the degree of his understanding may be minimal. His "appreciation" of great scientists may amount to no more than an empty statement which he accepts as fact because he obviously is expected to do so. And his "interest" in ferns may be accompanied by insufficient understanding to support an intelligent hobby.

The appreciations, attitudes, and interests selected as science objectives need then to be buttressed by understanding. But they need more than this. If these outcomes are to be *functional*, they must contain strong emotional elements. Because of their emotional elements they dispose the learner favorably or unfavorably with respect to particular aspects of his experiences; and they lead him to react thereto either positively or negatively. The emotional elements in appreciation, attitudes, and interests need to be cultivated just as carefully and just as thoroughly as do the elements relating to understanding.

The Statement of Objectives

It should be emphasized that the statement is not intended to be exhaustive. It aims to show types of objectives and to illustrate, rather than to list in complete detail. As a matter of fact, a complete listing of all possible specific objectives should probably not even be considered. The statement of objectives, like the objectives themselves, is intended in a real sense to indicate directions of growth—perhaps never complete, but always being revised by classroom teachers and others, and thus something never finally and wholly realized.

Types of Objectives for Science Teaching

A. *Functional information* or *facts* about such matters as:
1. Our universe—earth, sun, moon, stars, weather, and climate.
2. Living things—plants and animals.
3. The human body—structure, functions, and care.
4. The nature of matter—elements, compounds, mixtures, chemical change, physical change, solids, liquids, gases.
5. Energy—sources, types of energy, machines.
6. Contributions of science to the life of our times—radio, telephone, telegraph, electric lights, motion picture, household appliances, and airplanes.

B. *Functional concepts*,[1] such as:
1. Space is vast.
2. The earth is very old.

---

[1] Adapted (**22**:53–55).

3. All life has evolved from simpler forms.

4. All matter is probably electrical in structure.

C. *Functional understanding of principles*, such as:

1. All living things reproduce their kind.

2. Changes in the seasons and differences in weather and climate depend largely upon the relation of the earth to the sun.

3. Energy can be changed from one form to another.

4. All matter is composed of single elements or combinations of elements.

5. Living things in a given environment or locality are mutually interdependent.

D. *Instrumental skills*, such as ability to:

1. Read science content with understanding and satisfaction.

2. Perform fundamental operations with reasonable accuracy.

3. Perform simple manipulatory activities with science equipment.

4. Read maps, graphs, charts, and tables and to interpret them.

5. Make accurate measurements, readings, titrations, etc.

E. *Problem-solving skills*,[2] such as ability to:

1. Sense a problem.

2. Define the problem.

3. Study the situation for all facts and clues bearing upon the problem.

4. Make the best tentative explanations or hypotheses.

5. Select the most likely hypothesis.

6. Test the hypothesis by experimental or other means.

7. Accept tentatively, or reject the hypothesis and test other hypotheses.

8. Draw conclusions.

F. *Attitudes*, such as:

1. Open-mindedness—willingness to consider new facts.

2. Intellectual honesty—scientific integrity, unwillingness to compromise with truth as known.

3. Suspended judgment—scientific control, withholding conclusions until all available facts are in, not generalizing from insufficient data.

G. *Appreciations*, such as:

1. Appreciation of the contributions of scientists.

2. Appreciation of basic cause-and-effect relationships.

3. Sensitivity to possible uses and applications of science in personal relationships and disposition to use scientific knowledge and abilities in such relationships (attitude).

H. *Interests*, such as:

1. Interest in some phase of science as a recreational activity or hobby.

2. Interest in science as a field for a vocation.

It will be the purpose in the remainder of this chapter to define and discuss these objectives and to attempt to illustrate how some of them

---

[2] This list is based in large measure on such sources as (**9, 13, 18**) in bibliography.

may function in the process of growth toward the larger goals of education in a democracy.

ANALYSIS OF OBJECTIVES

A. *Functional Information or Facts.* The first division in the statement of objectives is concerned with functional information or facts. Thus the statements that "gold is malleable," or that "air has weight," or that "cows give milk" are facts. Facts may be specific as in the first two illustrations, or general as in the third.

B. *Functional Concepts.* Concepts are syntheses or constellations of ideas or meanings. Thus, a number of facts may be combined to produce a concept. It seems evident that concepts vary greatly in complexity. One may hold a relatively simple concept such as that of a straight line. On the other hand, a concept may be very complex, as for example, the concept of space. In this sense, concepts vary from simple to complex, according to the subject or basis for them.

A child or an uneducated person has a very elementary concept of time. He will perhaps understand that today is later than (follows) yesterday; that it takes time to go somewhere or to perform a task. Gradually he learns that the passage of time is measured by instruments, but to him a day or a week or a year still seem endlessly long. As he grows older he finds that many generations have preceded his and that in the historical sense his lifetime is very short. From this he may eventually progress to a sense of time in the geological and biological sense. During all this learning he is developing a concept which may be expressed in some such general terms as "the earth is very old." This concept takes on greater meaning as his knowledge and understanding grow. It will influence his thinking and modes of reaction in many ways. He will realize that the earth has existed for a long time and that it will probably continue to exist for a long time to come.

Concepts of space, time, and evolution, such as this, are important objectives of science instruction and have relationships to all the other objectives. This point has been clearly enunciated and stressed in the Thirty-first Yearbook (22) where so-called "big ideas" of science were listed as major objectives of science instruction. These "big ideas" are not to be thought of as purely intellectual products, the results, as it were, of emotionless and abstract thinking about the facts of science. Rather, these "big ideas" are fundamentally true, enduring, and essential. They are highly charged with social significance. They carry vital implications for the behavior of the individual. They are drives to action. The "interdependence of man" is one such "big idea." Once the individual comprehends such a big idea his behavior is permanently different. Witness, for example, the effects of the discovery of the atomic bomb on the thinking and behavior, the hopes and fears, of the common man.

C. *Functional Understanding of Principles.* Several investigators (Downing [14], Pruitt [24], Robertson [25]) have arrived at criteria for identifying and selecting scientific principles about which to organize instructional material in science. An analysis of those lists of criteria seems to reveal substantial agreement on the following points: A scientific principle must (*a*) be a statement of a fundamental process, or constant mode of beahvior; (*b*) be true without known exception within the limitations stated; (*c*) be capable of demonstration or illustration; (*d*) *not* be part of a larger principle; (*e*) *not* be a definition; (*f*) *not* deal with specific substances or varieties or with limited groups of substances or varieties

The statement of objectives carries illustrations of scientific principles from several areas or fields of science. Functional understanding of such principles is considered to be an important objective of science teaching. They provide focal points for the organization of instructional material and they constitute the generalizations toward the formulation of which most work in science is directed.

The functional understanding, for example, of such a principle as "energy can be changed from one form to another" is basic to an understanding of physical science and of many human relationships. It has far-reaching social and economic relationships. As the learner's understanding of such a principle grows, he will attain a more intelligent and sympathetic appreciation of many problems of the world in which he lives.

It seems evident that facts, concepts, and principles overlap and interact. To attempt to draw artificial boundaries or distinctions between them would serve no useful purpose. Ideally, perhaps, every bit of functional information would contribute to the increased understanding of a principle or a concept. However, it is obvious that some facts are worth while in themselves; for example, the fact that water will quench fire is worthy of teaching for its own functional value in the life of an individual. Typically, however, a knowledge of facts serves not as an end product of learning, but rather as a means to other ends. Thus, learning should usually be directed toward the acquisition of facts as a means of gaining understanding of concepts and principles, inculcating scientific attitudes, and providing skill in the use of scientific method. For example, a child of preschool age may observe that one kind of bird builds its nest on the ground and another builds its nest in a tree. From these simple facts he may advance to the generalization that *different birds build nests in different places.* Later experiences, in and out of school, may add relevant facts which, by the time he is studying biology in high school, may lead him to the understanding of such a principle as "many animals build shelters in which they live and rear their young."

D. *Instrumental Skills*. The instrumental skills are considered to be basic to successful study of science at all, except perhaps the earliest, levels. Unless the learner can read science material planned and written for his level of development, he will not make much progress. His ability to perform the fundamental operations of arithmetic with a degree of accuracy and sureness appropriate for his level is also essential to getting beyond a mere listing or descriptive phase of the study. Science is quantitative and exact or it is not science. Some of the sciences lend themselves more readily to quantitative techniques than others, but all sciences strive for exact measurement. Counting the number of legs on a housefly is an exact process. The answer is no more to be left to guesswork than the determination of the end-point in a delicate titration or the calculation of the time of beginning of a solar eclipse. All are subject to human error, but all require quantitative measurement of an exact nature. The degree of refinement of measurement is different in each case; a seven-year-old can do the first, a college Senior the second, and a trained astronomer the third.

E. *Problem-solving Skills*. The problem-solving skills are those employed in reflective thinking. A number of lists and descriptions of such skills has been presented, but all of them agree fairly well on the essential elements or steps. Although most science teachers profess great faith in problem-solving skills as objectives of science instruction, no objectives are probably more vaguely thought of or less specifically made the purpose of instruction. In his visitation of science teachers in 1930, Beauchamp (4) asked twenty-six teachers how they trained pupils to do scientific thinking.

[Most of the replies were evasive and] none was sufficiently definite to give the investigator a clear idea of what was being done in this direction. This does not necessarily mean that no training in scientific thinking is being carried on but it does mean that such training is not given in a systematic fashion.

The position of the committee as it relates to this type of objective should be stated clearly and positively:

a) It is possible to train pupils in scientific techniques of problem-solving. That improvement in such skills is attainable through science instruction has been demonstrated in numerous investigations, some of which will be cited later in this volume.

b) The success of such training is increased as the objectives are specifically defined and as they are definitely made purposes in instruction. This means that again, as in the case of transfer of training, gains are increased when the teacher tells the learner what the goals of instruction are, or, perhaps better still, they agree on them together. It is the teacher's responsibility to make certain that the learner identifies the objectives and that opportunity for, and practice in, generalizing or transfer is provided.

c) Problem-solving skills should be developed wherever and whenever the situation seems appropriate. Many ordinary situations in the laboratory and classroom can be utilized by the alert teacher for experience in developing these skills. There can, of course, be separate units to deal with them, but attention to these objectives should not be confined to such units.

It is not the function of this chapter to outline methods and subject matter for the attainment of these higher-order skills. Later chapters will give more specific suggestions as to methods and content to be used to this end.

It may be said here, however, that these so-called higher-order skills are not simple skills in the same sense as threading a needle or bouncing a ball. They are complex behavior patterns involving not only the elements commonly characteristic of a skill but also ideational content and attitudes. For example, "sensing and defining a problem" may involve all the things just mentioned. One learner may sense a problem where all seems well to another. Two farmers owning adjoining farms may react quite differently to the problem of soil conservation. One may sense that expenditure of time, energy, and money now may pay large dividends later while the other may be unable to see this at all. Sensing such a problem involves knowledge and attitudes, as does defining the problem and going on to do something to meet it. The ideational components include knowledge of the effects of temperature, wind, and weather on soil and of successful practices to counteract these effects; just as important are the attitudes which determine whether or not the farmer will use his knowledge and skills in solving his problem. The story of the potato grower who refused assistance from his local county agent because, as he said, "he already knew how to grow better potatoes than he was producing" is a case in point.

F. *Attitudes;* G. *Appreciations;* H. *Interests.* These objectives include those which have sometimes been referred to as the "intangibles." But attitudes, appreciations, and interests are, in all probability, no less tangible than are other types of objectives. Moreover, once we accept them as objectives and once we really look for them, they reveal themselves no less clearly in behavior. The pupil or adult who is open-minded, for example, gives plenty of evidence that he possesses the attitude; and the pupil or adult who does not possess the attitude shows his lack just as unmistakably.

Attitudes, interests, and appreciations are not separate and distinct from the other types of objectives listed. For example, they overlap the first category in that they are usually based on information, or misinformation. Such studies as those of Caldwell and Lundeen (**8**) on unfounded beliefs show clearly that such beliefs are based on misinformation or misunderstanding and that when correct information is supplied many such superstitions disappear. Likewise, the scientific attitudes are held to be concomitants of the scientific method. Suspended judgment and openmindedness go hand in hand with scientific techniques of problem-solving. Formulation and acceptance of new hypotheses is aided by an attitude of willingness to consider additional facts; suspended judgment will certainly help to prevent formulation of erroneous conclusions.

As has already been pointed out, the task in engendering desirable science attitudes, interests, and appreciations is twofold. It consists in part in building a sound foundation in accurate information, concepts, and principles. And it consists in part in emotionalizing this knowledge content to the point that it will carry over into action.

To attach an emotional response (attitude, interest, or appreciation) to any phase of science the pupil must have experience in reacting emotionally. There is no sense in barring emotion from classroom or laboratory. On the contrary, the pupil very much needs to feel the "thrill" of discovery (even if it can be only rediscovery). He needs to be "startled" by the consequences of superstitions which should be replaced by scientific fact, and he should really "care" whether his own actions are dictated by truth or by fallacy. He should actually be "curious" about the scientific problems with which he is faced, and be "concerned" in their solution. He should be "moved" by the drama of scientific progress. He should "feel humble" and at the same time "be proud" of the achievement of men of science as they have conquered ignorance; and he should be "confident" that man through science can achieve his lasting welfare. He should "dread" the possibilities that men of evil intent may gain control of scientific processes; he should "want" such processes to be turned only to good ends and should actively seek to accomplish this purpose. Such emotional experiences are entirely practicable as parts of science learning. They are more than practicable; they are essential, if attitudes, interests, and appreciations of functional power are to be developed at all.

Attitudes, interests, and appreciations which are grounded in understanding and supported by emotional drives do influence conduct in the direction of the ultimate purposes of science. To give but a single illustration: The attitude of tolerance or open-mindedness contributes to our sympathetic comprehension of the people and problems of other cultures. The same attitude on the part of backward or less favored peoples would counteract prejudice against new ideas and contribute to their more rapid development and advancement. It should be emphasized that by "tolerance" the committee does not have in mind an insipid or vacillating attitude. Open-mindedness does not mean lack of conviction, nor is it a basis for determining values. The things we believe in and for which we are willing to make any sacrifice are not things about which we are tolerant. However, our ideology does embody tolerance for other ideologies and points of view, so long as they extend to ours the same tolerance and do not deny anyone the right to think as he believes to be right. The concept of open-mindedness also implies no compromise with scientific fact, nor does it condone adherence to outworn theories or superstitious and unfounded beliefs.

It should also be clear that the acceptance of attitudes as objectives by science teachers does not imply any encroachment upon the social studies. Science instruction has its own contribution to make in this area. Where the science and the social studies both work toward the same or similar objectives, greater progress will surely result than where one or the other operates alone. It is not a matter of "either . . . . or" but one of "both . . . . and." Knowledge of science, because of its insistence upon fact and objectivity and upon rational bases for belief, serves a unique function in guiding sound emotional development.

The Relation of Science Objectives to General Education

Having now discussed and illustrated each of the categories in our statement of objectives, it remains to relate the objectives of science instruction to the larger goals of education.

The process of interaction between science and society, between science teaching and the larger goals of education in a democracy, is one that is constantly going on. It is also reciprocal in that it operates in both directions. Growth toward the objectives of science instruction affects the learner's behavior in other situations, both in and out of school. At the same time his experiences and observations outside the science class have a real bearing and effect on his comprehension of, attitudes toward, and his interest in, science.

Probably no child will study science without having his ideas and attitudes on such matters as health, citizenship, or conservation modified. Conversely, his growing understanding of their significance to him will help to motivate his study of science and to make it more meaningful. In the discussion which follows, this process of interaction will be analyzed and illustrated more fully.

A number of excellent descriptions of the larger goals or areas of education are available, including those of the Commission on Reorganization of Secondary Education (**10**), the Educational Policies Commission (**15**), and the Progressive Education Association (**23**). A discussion of more than one of them is not possible here because of limitations of space. It is also made unnecessary because in chapter ii considerable material has already been presented that relates to the problem. The discussion here will, therefore, be limited to one area, namely, conservation. This was selected because of its obvious relationships to science instruction, its important social implications, and its timeliness.

Conservation

In the early years of the history of this country national resources were so vast that they seemed inexhaustible. No attempt was made to conserve them and some, such as forests and wild life, were often considered a hindrance to settling new lands. As a result, precious and irreplaceable resources were wasted and plundered.

The importance of natural resources is recognized in the Atlantic Charter, which emphasizes the need for access to raw materials on equal terms for all states. In the United States we have recognized for a number of years the need for conservation and replacement of forests, soil, and wild life.

The wise use of the nation's natural resources is not only recognized as one of the important goals of education in a democracy, but it also has significant implications for other areas such as health, citizenship, worthy use of leisure time, and consumer education. How can instruction in science contribute to growth in the direction of effective conservation education? An illustration or two may help to answer this question.

Burnett (**7**) describes how a high-school class in biology studied the problem of good land use. Following preliminary discussion of the problem, films such as "The River" and "The Plow That Broke the Plains" were used and discussed. Field observations and studies were made with the help of the local county agent of the Soil Conservation Service. Evidences of erosion were sought, and samples of soil were examined and tested. Through such preliminary work the problem was defined, and then additional information was sought. A plot of ground in the schoolyard was set aside for experimental study. The relation of plants to the general problem was discussed and pertinent reading material was found.

These and similar activities prepared the way for consideration of remedial and preventive work. In this connection a further field study was made of a soil-conservation district and demonstration station. The experimental plot in the schoolyard was cultivated and used for illustrating contour plowing. An exhibit of materials related to the problem was prepared for the school and plans were made for an article in the local newspaper to provide the community with the benefits of the investigation.

Although the above account of the work of this class is necessarily condensed to a bare outline, it will probably suffice to show how such activities in biology may contribute to the goal of conservation education, not only as regards the pupils in the class itself but also to the benefit of the parents and the community. At the same time such a project provides a realistic and practical exercise in use of the scientific method of problem-solving. It also serves to motivate the study of science, to develop interest in it, and to inculcate scientific attitudes. Thus, the project illustrates the process of interaction referred to earlier and shows how it can actually take place and be encouraged.

Although biology may lend itself more directly to teaching conservation than other sciences, geology, chemistry, and physics have an important contribution to make also. The testing of soil is a chemical process; study of mineral resources must draw heavily on earth science; and physics enters into many phases of conservation in such projects as the T.V.A., Boulder Dam, and the engineering aspects of any conservation program.

Likewise, at the elementary level there are many activities which can be oriented in the direction of conservation. Excellent suggestions are given in such articles as those of Croxton (**12**) and McAtee (**19**). Children in elementary science can help to make community surveys of conservation practices and to put on campaigns to protect wild life; they can study the nests, colors, food, habits, etc., of birds which may in turn lead to consideration of their economic importance and to the study of conservation of wild life in general.

An article by Shoemaker (**26**) suggests sources of valuable printed material on conservation available to teachers and which can be adapted for use in classes in elementary science. The article also describes numerous activities that are suitable for such classes in teaching conservation of plants and animals.

A bulletin on wild-life conservation by Mentzer (**20**) describes how a class in general science may study a unit on wild-life conservation which might include observation and survey of a wild-life community. This would involve observation of animal life in its natural habitat, food, cover, environmental conditions, interdependence, diseases, and the like. Such a survey might naturally lead into a study of game laws, economic importance of wild life, methods of protection, and restoration, and perhaps actual participation in the work of conservation.

One of the best discussions of the wise use of natural resources is that by Craig (**11**:55–86). Various resources, including soil, grasslands, forests, water, wild life, mineral deposits, and man himself, are treated from the standpoint of their importance to the welfare of the human race, both present and future. Many practicable activities are suggested which teachers may engage in with their pupils in learning about natural resources of the community and of the world. Emphasis is laid on study of effective procedures which may be employed to insure wise utilization of natural resources. Teachers of science in secondary schools as well as elementary teachers will find the report rich in suggestions for teaching conservation.

Through such units and activities as have been described, contributions to the functional understanding of biological principles would be realized; growth would be made in habits of careful observation and scientific method; and desirable attitudes, interests, and appreciations would be encouraged and developed. At the same time, growth toward the larger goals of education may take place in proportion to the abilities and interests of each learner.

But we must be sure about this; and we must strive to go beyond these attainments. The pupil may stop his learning with an awareness of the problem of conservation and with some comprehension of the factors involved and still fall short of achieving the ultimate purposes of science education. He may not, for example, orient his knowledge in the world scene. His ideas about conservation may be restricted to the situation studied or to the immediate locale. His knowledge must transcend such limits; it should influence his behavior in concrete ways. It should, for example, enter into his decisions in voting for political candidates or for bond issues. It should make him interested in the activities and actions of international bodies organized to further the wise utilization of natural resources. When scientific knowledge carries with it drives of these kinds, then science education is truly attaining its purposes.

It seems unnecessary to illustrate further the application of the objectives of science instruction to general education. Enough has been presented to make clear that these objectives are not conceived in any narrow sense. They do not envisage science instruction as a restricted, compartmentalized discipline confined to any classroom or laboratory. The science teacher who wishes to do so can take the material and point of view set forth in this and the preceding chapter and make broad applications to significant areas of human experience. Succeeding chapters will develop the point of view presented here in relation to different levels and aspects of science teaching.

SUMMARY

A social philosophy and a set of practical objectives for science instruction have been developed and discussed. Due regard is evidenced for existing statements of this nature and no claims are made that the statement presented here is the final word on the subject. The purpose has been primarily to take the best thoughts available at present and to integrate them into a practicable, forward-looking statement which will be acceptable and helpful to science teachers in contributing to the attainment of the larger goals of education in a democracy. An attempt has been made to formulate objectives that will bridge the gap between classroom activities and socially desirable types of human behavior. The objectives have been discussed in relation to an illustrative area of human experience in order to show how they may be related and may contribute to growth in such areas and how growth therein may in turn help to bring about increased achievement of the objectives of science instruction.

If the import of chapters ii and iii could be epitomized in a few words, they might go something like this:

Science is today on a plane of high significance and importance. It is no longer, if indeed it ever was, a mysterious and occult hocus pocus to be known only to a select few. It touches, influences, and molds the lives of every living thing. Science teachers have a great opportunity and responsibility to make a large contribution to the welfare and advancement of humanity. The intellectual aspects of this responsibility are at least coequal in importance with the material. Science is a great social force as well as a method of investigation. The understanding and acceptance of these facts and this point of view and their implementation in practice will, more than anything else, make science teaching what it can and should be.

References

1. AMERICAN ASSOCIATION FOR THE ADVANCEMENT OF SCIENCE. "Committee Report on the Place of Science in Education," *School Science and Mathematics*, XXVIII (June, 1928).
2. AMERICAN COUNCIL OF SCIENCE TEACHERS, NATIONAL COMMITTEE ON SCIENCE TEACHING. *Redirecting Science Teaching in the Light of Personal-Social Needs.* Washington: National Education Association, 1942.
3. AMERICAN COUNCIL OF SCIENCE TEACHERS, NATIONAL COMMITTEE ON SCIENCE TEACHING. *Science Teaching for Better Living.* Washington: National Education Association, 1942.
4. BEAUCHAMP, WILBUR L. *Instruction in Science.* U.S. Office of Education Bulletin, 1932, No. 17, Monograph No. 22. Washington: Government Printing Office, 1933.
5. BOBBITT, FRANKLIN. "The EPC Banishes Science," *Scientific Monthly*, LXIII (August, 1946), 117–24.
6. BROWNELL, WILLIAM A., and SIMS, VERNER M. "The Nature of Understanding," *The Measurement of Understanding*, chap. iii. Forty-fifth Yearbook of the National Society for the Study of Education, Part I. Chicago: University of Chicago Press, 1946.
7. BURNETT, R. WILL. "Conservation: Focus or Incident in Science Education," *Science Education*, XXVIII (March, 1944), 82–87.

8. CALDWELL, OTIS W., and LUNDEEN, GERHARD E. *Do You Believe It?* Garden City, New York: Doubleday Doran & Co., 1934.
9. COHEN, M. R., and NAGEL, E. *An Introduction to Logic and Scientific Method.* New York: Harcourt, Brace & Co., 1934.
10. COMMISSION ON REORGANIZATION OF SECONDARY EDUCATION. *Report of Subcommittee on the Teaching of Science.* U.S. Bureau of Education Bulletin, No. 36. Washington: Government Printing Office, 1920.
11. CRAIG, GERALD S. *Science in Childhood Education.* New York: Bureau of Publications, Teachers College, Columbia University, 1944.
12. CROXTON, W. C. "Functional Outcomes and Purposeful Activities in Elementary Science," *School Science and Mathematics,* XXXIX (April, 1939), 309–15.
13. DEWEY, JOHN. *How We Think.* Boston: D. C. Heath & Co., 1933 (Revised).
14. DOWNING, ELLIOTT R. "An Analysis of Textbooks in General Science," *General Science Quarterly,* XII (May, 1928), 509–16.
15. EDUCATIONAL POLICIES COMMISSION. *Education for All American Youth.* Washington: National Education Association, 1944.
16. HARVARD UNIVERSITY. *General Education in a Free Society.* Cambridge: Harvard University Press, 1945.
17. HUNTER, G. W., and SPORE, LeROY. "The Objectives of Science in the Secondary Schools of the United States," *School Science and Mathematics,* XLIII (October, 1943), 633–47.
18. KEESLAR, OREON. "The Elements of Scientific Method," *Science Education,* XXVIII (December, 1945), 273–78.
19. McATEE, VEVA. "Materials and Equipment for the Teaching of Elementary Science," *School Science and Mathematics,* XXXIX (January, 1939), 15–28.
20. MENTZER, LOREN W. *Wild-life Conservation.* Kansas State Teachers College of Emporia Bulletin, Vol. 21, No. 6. Topeka: Kansas State Printer, 1941.
21. NOLL, VICTOR H. *The Teaching of Science in Elementary and Secondary Schools.* New York: Longmans, Green & Co., 1939.
22. *Program for Teaching Science.* Thirty-first Yearbook of the National Society for the Study of Education, Part I. Chicago: Distributed by the University of Chicago Press, 1932.
23. PROGRESSIVE EDUCATION ASSOCIATION. *Science in General Education.* New York: D. Appleton–Century Co., 1938.
24. PRUITT, CLARENCE M. *An Analysis, Evaluation and Synthesis of Subject-Matter Concepts and Generalizations in Chemistry.* Privately printed and distributed by the author. Doctor's dissertation, Teachers College, Columbia University, 1935.
25. ROBERTSON, MARTIN L. "A Basis for the Selection of Course Content in Elementary Science." Unpublished Doctor's dissertation, University of Michigan, 1934; also in *Science Education,* XIX (February, 1935), 1–4; (April, 1935), 65–70.
26. SHOEMAKER, LOIS MEIER. "Conservation Study," *Science Education,* XXIV (March, 1940), 126–33.

CHAPTER IV

ISSUES IN THE TEACHING OF SCIENCE

Of the issues in the teaching of science that are important today, few are new. At least one, the individual versus the demonstration method of performing experiments, was of major significance before World War I and will probably not be settled beyond question for years to come. In contrast, other issues that were of primary importance a decade ago have been resolved or have ceased to be significant.

In discussing the present important issues in the teaching of science, the committee has carefully considered the reports of research investigations. The findings and conclusions of a considerable number of such studies, however, cannot be accepted at all because of the crudity of techniques employed and the sketchiness and inadequacy of the reporting. The results of many others can be accepted only in part or with respect to certain aspects because of the narrowness of scope of the problems investigated. A relatively limited number are of major significance.

With these considerations in mind, the committee has deemed it desirable to assume the responsibility of judging which of the available research findings are significant and to supplement the available reports with its unanimous opinion whenever the investigational evidence relating to the various issues seems adequate to warrant positive pronouncements. In so doing, it has been guided by its conception of the objectives of science teaching stated in chapter iii.

The order in which the issues are here discussed bears no relation to their relative importance.

1. *What should constitute the science sequence?*

No definite answer regarding any but the elementary level is justified at present, because the science curriculum above the sixth grade is in a state of flux. Instruction in science should begin as early as children enter school; activities involving science should be provided even in the pre-school and the kindergarten. Through the sixth grade the work in elementary science should consist of a continuous integrated program of the sort advocated by the Thirty-first Yearbook.[1] Such a program should

---

[1] *A Program for Teaching Science.* Thirty-first Yearbook of the National Society for the Study of Education, Part I. Chicago: Distributed by University of Chicago Press, 1932.

provide an expanding, spiral development of understandings, attitudes, and skills, as prescribed in chapter iii. This committee further indorses the recommendation of the Thirty-first Yearbook committee, that a three-year integrated course of general science be offered, wherever practicable, through Grades VII, VIII, and IX.

All the work in science through the ninth grade should be planned for general education.

In the senior high school, integrated courses such as general biology and physical science may be offered along with or in place of specialized courses such as physics and chemistry. All courses at this level should be organized so as to provide both general and propaedeutic education.

In one or both of the junior-college years, survey courses in both the physical and biological sciences should be offered for general education along with pretechnical courses planned for those who will need specialized training in science.

It is strongly recommended that the program of studies of every school system provide regular work in science during every grade. It is also strongly recommended that abundant opportunities to study science for both its practical and/or its cultural values be made available as adult education to all who are not attending the regular schools.

2. *What are the relations of nature study and elementary science?*

The term, *nature study,* commonly bears the connotation of elementary botany and zoology, since the traditional nature-study program dealt almost wholly with such materials. *Nature study,* however, was never a unified concept with generally accepted objectives and basic content; nor did it ever have an established place in a unified program of science instruction, as does elementary science in programs advocated by the Thirty-first Yearbook committee and by this committee.

There were a number of divergent basic philosophies which guided the selection and presentation of content in traditional nature-study programs. These were exemplified by natural history through the study of plants and animals in their native habitats; by object teaching; by the opposite of nature history, namely, the practically exclusive use of exotic materials; by anthropomorphism, chiefly through nature fables; by teleology; and by moral and religious interpretations of biological phenomena. Many leaders of the nature-study movement, however, condemned the last four of these approaches as vigorously and as unqualifiedly as do leaders in the elementary-science movement today.

Much that early proponents of nature study advocated is accepted for, and incorporated into, the modern program of elementary science. Thus, recognition and observation of plants and animals as they normally live are essential parts of such instruction. The direct study of objects and the introduction of exotic materials also find some use in the modern program but merely as means of providing breadth and of stimulating interest—not as basic guides to content selection and presentation.

Traditional nature study now possesses chiefly historical interest since it is being replaced at an accelerating pace by the broader, more functional, and coherent program of elementary science. Nevertheless, leaders in elementary science acknowledge a debt for materials and method to the earlier leaders of the nature-study movement from which elementary science has evolved.

3. *Should general science be a required course?*

Yes. There are many situations in which a three-year sequence of general science is impracticable. Some schools can accommodate in their crowded programs only a single year; others can provide only a two-year sequence of science for Grades VII and VIII or Grades VIII and IX. While a two-year integrated course of general science is preferable in the latter schools, a promising alternative is a two-year sequence for these grades consisting of one semester's work of earth science and another of health and physiology, to be followed by a year of general science.

4. *In what grades should the one-year courses of general science and biology, respectively, be offered?*

Throughout the country as a whole, in the schools in which general science is presented as a one-year course, it is much more often scheduled for the ninth grade than for any other. Also, throughout the country as a whole, general biology is most frequently offered in the tenth grade, though usually the pupils in the tenth, eleventh, and twelfth grades are privileged to elect it.

The committee indorses these placements.

5. *How many periods per week should be devoted to general science?*

Science in Grades VII, VIII, and IX should be scheduled for at least three periods per week, and preferably more, wherever the course is offered through two or three years. It should be scheduled for five periods per week where it is given as a one-year course. No course in general science can be adequate which continues through less than a full year.

6. *How many periods per week should be devoted to courses of science in Grades X, XI, and XII?*

This issue has important implications for both administration and instruction. The traditional seven-period plan provides three "recitation" periods and two double laboratory periods per week. Wherever, as is most frequently the case, the double periods must be scheduled for certain days and in a room separate from the one in which the classwork is conducted, such a plan entails great difficulties of administration. Moreover, the necessity for having the laboratory work scheduled for certain days imposes a serious handicap upon effective learning, since it prevents many of the experiments from being introduced at the precise times when they will most favorably articulate with the class discussions. Hence, the work carried on during a double laboratory period frequently deals with a unit different from the one discussed in the classroom on the preceding and the following days. In other words, the result, in many cases, is not an integrated offering of science but instead is essentially two contemporary, related, but separate courses, namely, a textbook-discussion or "recitation" course and a laboratory course.

All the research investigations of the relative values of single and double laboratory periods thus far reported indicate that the learning values derived from double periods are not sufficiently greater (if indeed they are any greater) than those derived from single periods to justify the extra time. More research, however, is needed before positive conclusions concerning this point can be drawn. An unquestionable advantage in the double laboratory period, but one which is infrequently sought and which is not directly related to laboratory work in the generally accepted sense, is that it makes possible some field trips which could not be completed in the limited time of a single period.

A trend is unmistakably developing throughout the country toward eliminating the double laboratory period in senior high school science courses. In the light of the considerations already discussed, this trend is on the whole defensible and seems in most respects desirable. Teachers of such courses must plan to accomplish their objectives in five single periods per week. This has frequently been demonstrated to be readily practicable, provided these periods are one hour long. Research is needed to determine how an acceptable course can be devised for five single periods if these periods provide less than fifty-five minutes class time each.

Shifting from seven to five periods per week neither necessitates nor justifies the elimination of all individual pupil experimentation, as has sometimes been contended. To substitute demonstrations, discussions, or other activities for such experimentation, with the excuse that single periods provide insufficient time for individual laboratory work, is indefensible. How to provide in the five-period plan all the kinds of experiences desired is a challenging and urgently important problem.

7. *What should be the nature and function of the physical-science course?*

Many "fused" courses of physical science have been introduced into the senior high school during the last decade. Moreover, the number of such courses seems certain to increase. It is quite as logical to develop such a course at the present time as it was to begin the development of general biology about thirty-five years ago. The formulation of a satisfactory course in physical science, however, has been retarded by a variety of different approaches to the problem, reflecting nebulousness and confusion of ideas with respect to the nature and functions of such a course. The following considerations, therefore, are deemed to be fundamental to a satisfactory solution of the problem of providing a satisfactory course in physical science.

a) The content should be planned so as to develop concepts and principles important not only in physics and chemistry but also in other branches of physical science, namely, geology, astronomy, and meteorology. For example, an understanding of the principle of gravitation may appropriately be developed by presenting applications dealing with falling bodies, decantation and precipitation, air currents, erosion, tides, and movements of heavenly bodies.

b) Practical considerations dictate that the course should be planned for one year and not for two. There is, of course, more than enough material of unquestioned worth to justify a two-year course, but such a course would not have extensive election because too few pupils would find time in their crowded programs to take both years of the work. The failure of the promising two-year program of physical science prepared for use throughout one of the middle-western states about twenty years ago reveals the difficulties encountered in carrying on such a two-year course. In the typical situation many pupils in the last two years of the high school would be able to take only one more year of work in science and hence must take either the first or the second half of a two-year course. Relatively few, and these chiefly the ones corresponding to those who now elect both physics and chemistry, would be able to take the entire two years' work. Consequently, the numbers of pupils who would secure special training in physical science would be even smaller than where the one-year course is offered, because a large proportion of those who might elect a year of physics or of chemistry would be unlikely to elect one-half of a two-year physical-science course.

c) The values of a course of physical science are likely to be largely sacrificed if attempts are made to simplify it too greatly. Deeply concerned over the decreasing elections of physics and chemistry resulting from the formidable reputations of these subjects, some pioneers in the physical-science movement sought to assemble, under a variety of course and book titles designed to camouflage the nature of the course and thus to allay pupil prejudices against it, materials which would be easy enough for the ready comprehension of any of the pupils. These efforts in some cases resulted in courses that were practically on the level of effortless entertainment. They were less demanding of pupil effort and thought and, on the whole, provided a less valuable orientation in physical science than does a good course in general science intended for the junior high school. The worth of many of these early physical-science courses was further lessened by the omission of laboratory work.

There are obviously grave difficulties in the way of organizing a course in physical science which will prove simple enough for ready comprehension by pupils of limited abilities and still retain the unique, intrinsic values attainable within this area. There seems no doubt, however, that a course of this nature can be evolved which can achieve its desired objectives through a much less technical and mathematical approach and with many more contacts with the daily lives of boys and girls than do the conventional present-day courses in physics and chemistry. If, however, physical science is to realize its full potentialities, it must be made to serve both as a "college-preparatory" and as a terminal course.

The devising of satisfactory courses in physical science is one of the greatest challenges in the field of secondary-school science. Their development is especially important for the smaller schools in which the equipping and scheduling of separate courses in physics and chemistry is often a serious problem.

8. *What is the place in the science curriculum of consumer education, conservation, aeronautics, physiology, and health education?*

During the past two decades a considerable number of separate courses in these fields have been taught, chiefly in the senior high school. World War II gave an added importance to such offerings, especially to aeronautics, in which highly technical and specialized courses were constructed and widely taught.

The materials of these areas are of value chiefly for general education. Except, perhaps, for an eighth-grade one-semester course in health and physiology, as suggested earlier, it is probably not desirable to offer separate courses in any of these subjects. Their materials can be more effectively integrated with those of the regular courses of the science sequence and with other courses in the program of studies.

9, *What difficulties are involved in presenting an adequate program of science in a core curriculum?*

The committee strongly approves all opportunities to experiment with new ideas and new procedures. The core curriculum provides salutary opportunities for such experimenting. In a large majority of schools in which the core curriculum is found, however, the major emphasis of this curriculum is upon the social studies. Furthermore, the teacher or teachers having major responsibility for constructing units of instruction are commonly teachers of social science and English. These teachers are not fitted by training, experience, and general outlook to recognize the opportunities certain to arise in any "real-life" units for introducing important materials from the fields of biological and physical science. Even where the program provides for enlisting the help of the science teachers in unit planning and in instruction, the optimal integration of science materials with those of English and social studies is rarely achieved. For these reasons the statement seems justified that in a majority of situations science is introduced into the core curriculum only incidentally or not at all.

It is platitudinous to state that science can be taught effectively only by teachers adequately trained to teach it and by means of units of work whose primary emphasis is scientific. One important means, therefore, of improving the situation described in the preceding paragraph is to introduce into the core curriculum certain units that are fundamentally scientific in concept and content. Examples of such units are "How has science progressed in the conquest of disease?" "How may one's physical and mental health be improved?" and "How are machines used in the work of the home?"

The primary responsibility for directing the planning of such units would necessarily rest with the science teachers. The major emphasis would be directed toward employing the elements of scientific method, inculcating scientific attitudes, and arriving at functional understandings of scientific concepts and principles (chap. iii). The science teachers would welcome the co-operation of the other teachers to insure the inclusion of important social implications and applications. But these would appropriately be developed after the foundations of science had been laid. They would be more meaningful and impressive and potentially more functional through being based upon a sound foundation of science.

10. *To what extent should science instruction be community centered?*

Every good science teacher ties in the community resources with the science activities for purposes of reification, supplementation, and enrichment, wherever such correlation can practically and profitably be made. The extent to which out-of-school materials should be employed needs to be determined in every case by their potential contributions to the achievement of the major aims of science teaching as presented in chapter iii.

11. *What is the function of the textbook?*

Confusion usually results when the pupils turn to an assortment of textbooks for materials on given topics because one author may treat a certain topic near the beginning and another near the end of his book. Each assumes, however, that the pupils will possess the background supplied by the portions of his text preceding the discussion of that topic. In general, what seems likely to prove most satisfactory is to select a basic textbook that provides a good general outline of the course and the primary text materials which all the class may be expected to study and then to supplement this foundational material with a variety of materials from other textbooks, periodicals, and reference works.

The desirable procedure, therefore, is not to "get rid of the textbook" (because any textbook is likely to provide better materials than the average teacher can improvise or assemble in the time and with the facilities available) but to avoid restricting the study to the contents of a single textbook and, instead, to supplement it as abundantly as may be necessary. Such a procedure can, as effectively as any other, provide for the individual differences of the pupils. Also, it possesses the important advantages of providing not only a foundation of minimal essentials common to all the class but also a definiteness of sequence and of continuity which a course based on miscellaneous reference materials rarely possesses.

The practice of supplying the pupils with school-owned textbooks imposes a handicap upon effective teaching and learning. It prevents the teacher from giving instruction in various study techniques, such as those which require the underlining of words, phrases, and sentences, and from writing in the book margins summary sentences, additional subject matter, and critical comments.

12. *Should teachers try to teach all the materials provided in a textbook?*

No. In order to compete successfully for adoptions, a textbook of science must include the areas and topics which the great majority of the teachers of that subject deem important. As a result, authors and publishers have been influenced to provide textbooks of voluminous content. It is probably true that every modern textbook of science contains more material than can be effectively taught to any class within the time and with the facilities available. Such being the case, no teacher should attempt to "teach the whole book." Such an effort can result only in the stressing of factual material to the neglect of the important objectives of the course. The teacher should feel free to teach less material in order to teach it better. The less capable the class, moreover, the more limited should be the amount of materials planned for study. Unfortunately, however, what to retain and what to omit constitutes a difficult problem, because there is no correlation between the importance of a topic and its difficulty.

The teacher should plan in advance at least the general compass of each course and should make a tentative time budget for it. He should then check progress as the work proceeds in order to insure that the pupils get some acquaintance with all the desirable major areas; otherwise, so much time may be expended upon the earlier units that later ones may be scamped or omitted.

13. *What is the place of inductive and deductive teaching in science courses?*

By inductive teaching is meant progressing from the particular to the general, or more specifically, from facts to concepts and principles. By deductive teaching is meant progressing from the general to the particular, or more specifically, from a concept or a principle to an application of it in a specific situation. Inductive teaching is illustrated by having the pupils experiment with simple levers until they are able to arrive at the principle, "In moving an object with a lever, the farther away from the fulcrum the force is exerted, the less the force needs to be." Deductive teaching is illustrated by stating this principle and then by having the pupils apply it in prying up a heavy stone or in explaining how a lever might be used in moving a heavy stone.

Regrettably, in a large majority of science classes, the primary, if not the sole emphasis, is upon the deductive method. Principles and major concepts are presented to the pupils to be memorized and then to be illustrated and exemplified. Thus, in physics the pupils memorize Boyle's law and then seek applications of it. In biology the pupils first learn the principle of phototropism and then seek, by experimenting or observing, to find examples of it.

The inductive and the deductive methods are equally important and both are essential in every science class. The inductive method should, in most cases, be used first in order to develop an understanding of a principle or a concept. The deductive method, with its applications of these principles and concepts, should then follow. Teaching by the inductive method consumes much time, but the potential outcomes abundantly justify the time investment.

14. *What are some effective practices in the use of motion pictures?*

The extensive and effective use of motion pictures in the training programs of the armed forces has provided a strong stimulus to the use of motion pictures in the schools. The mere employment of sound or silent motion pictures in the classroom procedures does not, however, insure desirable outcomes; on the contrary, under frequently existing conditions, the use of films may serve chiefly as effortless entertainment for the children and as a respite from instructional activities for the teacher.

The following suggestions are deemed important in the use of films:

a) Each film should be carefully selected for the specific purposes to be served. Thus, certain ones are excellent for orientation; others provide valuable supplementary materials; some aid in clarifying concepts and principles; and still others offer valuable summarizations of topics and units.

b) The film should be selected for its appropriateness to the grade level in which it is to be used. The advertising prospectus cannot always be relied upon to furnish dependable guidance in this respect.

c) The film should be introduced only at the time when it actually integrates with the materials that are being studied. In some cases it may prove more of a handicap than an aid, if introduced too early or too late.

d) The teacher should have the film long enough in advance of its showing before the class so that he can plan the specific uses he will make of its content and also so that he can provide both guide questions for its study and a test to be used as a follow-up of the presentation.

e) The teacher should discuss these guide questions with the class in advance of the showing so that the pupils will understand what they are expected to learn from the presentation.

f) The film should be shown once and then discussed, so as to enable the teacher to discover to what degree and in what respects the important materials it provides have functioned effectively in achieving their desired purposes. The film should then be shown a second time with attention focused where it has been revealed to be needed.

g) After the second showing, the test should be administered, checked, and discussed.

h) In some cases a film or parts of it may profitably be shown more than twice.

Such a program is manifestly impossible if the films must be scheduled long in advance of presentation. For this and other reasons such a use of motion pictures as that here advocated is usually impracticable in any but a large school or school system which owns its own film library and has special facilities for administering its film program. The smaller schools which must secure their films from more or less distant central agencies find the extensive use of films impracticable if the optimal values from their use are to be gained. A practical solution of the problem for such schools is for groups of them, located within relatively small areas, to establish independent co-operative film bureaus.

15. *What are the relative values of silent and sound motion pictures and of film strips?*

The values of these visual aids are not absolute; they depend on the purposes to be served. The results of many investigations present no convincing evidence of the superiority of either silent or sound motion films over the other type, except that the sound films are superior whenever one of the aims in showing the films is to establish a clear conception of certain sounds, as, for example, bird calls. There is some research evidence which indicates that the unique values of film strips render them superior to motion pictures for some purposes. Each type of film, however, will be found most valuable when it is used not as a substitute for another type but as supplementary to it.

16. *What are the purposes of laboratory work?*

It is regrettable that, in a majority of science classes in which demonstrations and individual pupil experiments are performed, the chief, if not the sole function served by these activities is to verify facts and principles already learned. The experimentation is commonly postponed until the pupils have found out from consulting the text or from the classroom discussion what the experimental results should be. Then the experiments are performed so that the pupils may verify what they already know. As a result, it is common for the pupils to engage in such undesirable practices as "making the answer come out right," and telling "what ought to have happened" instead of what actually did happen.

Performing demonstrations or individual experiments merely for the purpose of verifying facts or principles already known is rarely, if ever, justified. The primary purpose of experimenting is to secure evidence which may reveal answers to problems. In order to effect this purpose the inductive method should in nearly all cases be used; that is, the laboratory work should precede, not follow, the classroom discussion of a topic or a principle.

Under this plan the pupil needs the same careful directions for experimenting that he would require in any other case; he needs to be given, or to work out for himself with the teacher's help, the procedures to follow in securing an answer to a problem. But everything possible should be done to encourage him not to ascertain by other means what that answer should be. If he already knows it, his time can usually be better spent in performing some other experiment or in engaging in some other activity.

Each pupil should be encouraged to record exactly what he observes and, if his efforts have been conscientious and careful, he should not be penalized for failure to secure more accurate results than the limitations of the available apparatus and of his own manipulatory skills make possible. After he has arrived at the best answer to his problem that he can reasonably be expected to obtain, it is proper for him to consult the textbook and references to find out what are the correct results, as obtained by skilled scientists working under ideal conditions.

Such practice is ideal for the teaching of scientific method and for developing scientific attitudes. The practice of carrying on experiments for the mere purpose of verification often emphasizes the antithesis of scientific method.

17. *What place has the workbook in science courses for the high school?*

There is much confusion with respect to what a workbook should be. Some teachers and authors make a distinction between a workbook and a laboratory manual, asserting that the former should provide guides to activities other than demonstrating and experimenting by pupil or teacher and that the latter should furnish merely the directions for laboratory work. Such a distinction causes confusion. The well-constructed workbook should include both directions for experimenting and guides for carrying on and recording other activities inside and outside the classroom.

Some authors of workbooks, in their efforts to reduce the labor of the teacher in checking the pupil reports, have made almost exclusive use of the device of having the pupils record their observations and inferences by merely filling blanks with single words or phrases. This practice has met with vigorous and merited criticism. It is desirable, of course, to lighten the teacher's burden of examining laboratory and other reports, but providing blanks for pupils' recordings is only one means by which this goal may be accomplished. Other devices by which pupils may record the results of activities so that teachers may readily examine such records include reporting by means of sketches and diagrams, completing and/or labeling diagrams provided in incomplete form, and indicating observations, conclusions, and other reactions by responding to various types of short-answer tests, of which the completion type (filling blanks) is only one.

A well-constructed workbook, properly used, can be a valuable teaching and learning aid and can effect substantial saving of the teacher's time and energy. It can, moreover, provide types of learning activities not provided by a textbook. The workbook should, however, be so organized as to make the work of the teacher more efficient. A poor workbook in the hands of a poor teacher may result in less effective work than would be done without it.

18. *Is the observation of a demonstration experiment as effective and valuable to a pupil as his performance of that experiment?*

This issue has persisted through several decades. In the earlier stages of educational research a great number of investigations were reported which were interpreted by the investigators as indicating that the demonstration method was at least as effective as the individual method, if not actually superior to it. These early studies, however, were crude as judged by present-day standards and were confined chiefly to measuring the acquisition and retention of factual information. Later, several investigations were conducted in which more refined and elaborate techniques were employed and in which other outcomes were measured, including ability to manipulate apparatus, to solve problems, and to plan and carry out investigations. These researches indicated that in certain important respects the individual method is superior to the demonstration method (2).

Since experimentation involves "learning by doing," there can be no substitute for it. Pupil experimentation is an essential part of good science education. In every course of science offered at any level, therefore, opportunities should be provided for the pupils to perform experiments. The number of laboratory exercises performed by the pupils will vary with the course and should vary also with the individuals. On the whole, moreover, it will probably be smaller in general science than in biology, physics, and chemistry.

The discussion of the individual and the demonstration methods in the Thirty-first Yearbook is believed by this committee still to be sound and practicable. The summary of it is, therefore, included here with only minor modifications:

a) Each method possesses certain unique values. Hence, both are necessary, each to supplement the other, in every science course at every level.

b) In the interests of economy both of time and of money, it is desirable to perform more laboratory exercises by the demonstration than by the individual method.

c) At the start of every laboratory course there should be a sufficient use of the demonstration method to acquaint the pupils with apparatus and with accepted methods of experimentation. Following this period of orientation, the pupil should be allowed to perform some exercises individually in order to acquire, early in the course, desirable manipulatory skills and laboratory techniques and habits.

d) The time saved in each course by the use of the demonstration method should be used for other types of learning activities, which may include additional laboratory exercises, reading projects, individual investigations, observations, and drill upon essentials. The money saved by purchasing single sets of apparatus for demonstrating certain experiments, instead of multiple sets for individual performance, should be expended for books, visual aids, additional laboratory equipment, and other means of enriching and improving science instruction.

There is widespread confusion among teachers with respect to what constitutes individual pupil experimentation. Many confuse group experimentation with individual experimentation. For example, one chemistry teacher designated as "individual pupil experimentation" laboratory exercises in which as many as twelve pupils "worked together" with a single set of apparatus. In this case the teacher considered it individual work because the pupils, and not the teacher, performed the experiments. Individual laboratory work can mean only experiments performed by a single pupil.

Research evidence indicates that pupils working in pairs derive less benefit from an experiment than do pupils working individually. The difference, however, is not great enough to justify the added expense of providing individual sets of equipment for all experiments. A few experiments, namely, those requiring two people to carry on the manipulation or one to observe while the other manipulates, will need to be performed by pairs. When, however, more than two pupils attempt to perform an experiment with one set of apparatus, the benefits derived by all but one or perhaps two members of the group will almost inevitably be small.

19. *Should demonstration experiments be performed by the teacher or by pupils?*

The primary purpose of a demonstration is to provide vicarious experience; it is not intended to provide a means by which pupils secure firsthand experience in manipulating apparatus and in conducting experiments. It is impossible, with any but small classes, to provide opportunities for all the pupils to demonstrate experiments before the class; and there is no justification for bestowing the privileges and the advantages of performing them upon a favored one or a few of the more capable ones. Furthermore, pupils, especially those of limited abilities, cannot perform demonstrations satisfactorily before a group without having first been carefully coached and rehearsed by the teacher. Such training requires a substantial, if not a prohibitive, expenditure of the teacher's time and energy. Since, moreover, the success of a demonstration must depend chiefly upon the skill with which it is performed, the teacher should be able to perform it more skilfully than any of the pupils.

From all these considerations it seems logical to conclude that demonstrations should in most cases be performed by the teacher and not by the pupils. It is good practice, however, to have the pupils assist the teacher during demonstrations, but such participation should be distributed as widely as possible throughout the class so that all may profit by whatever values such participation provides. It is also good practice to encourage pupils to demonstrate, before the class, models and experiments which they have themselves prepared as projects outside of class.

20. *Should pupils be required to make a record of every experiment performed?*

If an exercise is worth performing it is worth recording. Unless the pupil knows that he is expected to make a recording of his observations and manipulations, he is almost certain not to observe with sufficient care and to forget much that he will later need to remember. In every case the kind of record required should be determined from answers to such questions as these: "Exactly what is the purpose of this experiment? Exactly what is the pupil expected to experience and to remember from it?"

Usually the experiment may be satisfactorily and effectively reported in a brief time by such means as these: making and labeling a diagram, completing and/or labeling a diagram supplied by the teacher, writing one or a few sentences which summarize the results of the experiment, or responding to a few short-answer test items supplied by the teacher to cover the essential features of the experiment. Rarely is the reporting of an experiment in complete "story" (expositional) form justified, because of the great amount of time required for the pupil to write it and for the teacher to give the report the careful and detailed reading it should have.

21. *Should pupils be required to make representative drawings of apparatus setups and biological specimens?*

The research on various aspects of this issue has been relatively extensive. It indicates unmistakably that there is an inverse relation between the degree of attention focused upon artistic and exact representation and the achievement of accepted goals of science teaching. Investigational evidence indicates, moreover, that even at the junior-college level the traditional practice of having the students make representative drawings of biological specimens is not justified in terms of the learning values derived from the activity. Research evidence further indicates that the inking or coloring of laboratory drawings is likewise not justified from the standpoint of realizing the major objectives of a science course.

The almost universal practice in high-school and first-year college biology classes of requiring the students to make representative drawings of laboratory specimens should be replaced by one of having them make diagrams and sketches and use, in various ways, ready-prepared outline drawings. Training in making representative drawings should be postponed until the advanced courses above the college Freshman level.

In order to give the pupils the necessary training in making suitable diagrams and sketches, the teacher must first perfect his own skill in making them.

The not-infrequent practice, observed especially in high-school biology classes, of requiring pupils to trace drawings from textbooks is without justification and can only be condemned.

22. *What is the best time for pupils to record their experiments and for teachers to check pupils' laboratory reports?*

It is common practice in high schools for pupils to "write up" their reports of laboratory experiments out of class and for the teacher to examine and return the reports later. Such practices are likely to prove ineffective for several reasons:

a) Too much time elapses between the experimenting and the reporting. The best time for reporting the results of an experiment, either one which the pupil performs individually or one which he observes as a demonstration, is immediately upon the completion of it. The data should be recorded as they are collected. When the reporting is delayed, the pupil is likely to forget important phases. Postponed reporting, moreover, encourages the pupil to copy the reports of other students, especially if he has "gotten behind in his laboratory work."

b) It is rarely, if ever, possible for a teacher with several laboratory courses to read carefully every report handed in. Inevitably student reports accumulate more rapidly than the teacher can make detailed examination of them. The class soon becomes cognizant of this fact with the result that some pupils are likely to write up their experiments sketchily, superficially, and inaccurately, with the well-founded hope of "getting by" with at least some substandard reporting.

c) There is too much delay, after the pupil hands in his report, before it is returned by the teacher. As a result, such criticisms and suggestions as the teacher may have found time and opportunity to make lose much of their value because the pupil has forgotten the details of the experiment.

From the standpoint of value to the pupil and from the equally important standpoint of optimal use of the teacher's time and energy, it is best
for the pupils to record their experimental and observational work as it
proceeds and for the teacher to supervise these records as they are being
made and, to the maximum extent possible, to check them before the
close of the laboratory period. Suggestions, help, and criticisms are most
effective when given while the pupils are experimenting and are recording their results. The teacher, in passing from desk to desk while the
work is progressing, has a far better chance than by any other procedure
to give needed assistance, to note omissions and errors at the moment
they occur, and to give constructive criticism as needed. Also, the teacher
is able to make a better evaluation of the quality of a pupil's work by observing him while he works than by subsequently scrutinizing his laboratory report.

23. *Should a special laboratory, separate from the classroom, be provided
for biology, physics, and chemistry?*

No. The administrative disadvantages of having the classwork and the
laboratory work conducted in different rooms has already been indicated.
The disadvantages from the instructional standpoint are even more important.

Ideally, every science class should be conducted in a room which is a
combination classroom and laboratory. In such a room, discussion, demonstration, pupil experimentation, and other activities can be introduced
at the most suitable times. There are likely to be occasions when it is desirable to have the laboratory work continue during several consecutive
days, or to introduce it at some point during a class discussion when it is
needed for answering a question or clarifying a concept. By so doing, a
better use of time is assured than is possible under conditions in which
laboratory work and classroom activities must be carried on in different
rooms and on different days.

It is practicable to design complete and satisfactory combination
classrooms and laboratories which occupy considerably less space than
would be occupied by both separately.

24. *Should a science room be designed to serve for more than one branch of
high-school science?*

In the large high schools it is usually preferable to provide separate
rooms for biology, physics, and chemistry. In the small high schools,
however, it is preferable to equip one room adequately for the work in
all these courses and for general science in addition. A difficulty often
arises whenever laboratory experiments in chemistry are performed in

the same room in which brass pieces of equipment and apparatus (especially numerous for physics) are being used or are stored, because some of the chemical fumes attack brass.

25. *Should recognition be given to college-entrance board, regents', statewide, or similar examinations in science instruction?*

Wherever such examinations are strongly stressed, there is inevitably a considerable expenditure of time and energy by teachers and pupils in specific preparation for them. In varying degrees, depending on how seriously the school authorities emphasize the need for high achievement in these tests, the classroom activities degenerate into sessions in which the answers to questions in previously administered examinations are learned and the attention is focused upon "cramming" for similar questions which seem likely to constitute the next set of such examinations. Such misdirection of instruction militates against developing scientific attitudes, skills in reflective thinking and in the use of elements of scientific method, and functional understandings of concepts and principles. Instead, it places a premium upon memorization of factual material.

The influence of such testing programs not only affects classroom instruction unfavorably but also lowers the standards of some textbooks. In certain cases these are little more than "keys" or "answer books" in which the factual materials most often covered in the tests are presented in concise form for ready memorization.

26. *Can a teacher with inadequate preparation in a branch of science successfully teach it?*

No. Instances are often found in which teachers are assigned to teach courses of junior or senior high school science without adequate subject-matter training and, occasionally, to teach general science or biology with no subject-matter training whatever. The administrative assumption justifying such assignments is that the teacher can "keep ahead of the class," that he "can learn what he needs to know along with the class," or (still more to be condemned) that he will be stimulated to put forth greater effort and will thus insure his doing more dynamic teaching.

Such practice cannot be condoned. The primary requisite for teaching any course is a sound subject-matter background for that course. Teachers who lack such a foundation and the perspective that can be gained only from adequate subject-matter training must inevitably fail to achieve the accepted major objectives of science teaching.

The only available investigational evidence bearing upon this issue clearly indicates a high correlation between the subject-matter competence of the teacher and achievement of the pupils.

The effects of the war in taking from the schools appallingly large numbers of qualified instructors and replacing them to a considerable extent with inadequately qualified emergency teachers constitute a serious menace to American education as a whole and especially to the teaching of science. In spite of legal provisions designed to terminate the contracts of such incumbents with the end of the war, the continued shortage of thoroughly qualified teachers is likely to enable emergency teachers to remain in the schools of some parts of the country for years. Continuous and unrelaxing efforts should be made to eliminate every inadequately qualified teacher from the classroom at the earliest possible opportunity.

REFERENCES

1. BLICK, DAVID J. *Digest of Investigations in the Teaching of Science, 1937-1943.* University of Connecticut (mimeographed). Pp. 105.
2. CUNNINGHAM, HARRY A. "Lecture Demonstration versus Individual Laboratory Method in Science Teaching: A Summary," *Science Education*, XXX (March, 1946), 70–82.
3. CURTIS, FRANCIS D. *A Digest of Investigations in the Teaching of Science in the Elementary and Secondary Schools.* Philadelphia: P. Blakiston's Son & Co., 1926.
4. ———. *Second Digest of Investigations in the Teaching of Science.* Philadelphia: P. Blakiston's Son & Co., 1931.
5. ———. *Third Digest of Investigations in the Teaching of Science.* Philadelphia: P. Blakiston's Son & Co., 1939.
6. KEESLAR, OREON. "A Survey of Research Studies Dealing with the Elements of Scientific Method as Objectives of Instruction in Science," *Science Education*, XXIX (October, 1945), 212–16.
7. MARTIN, W. EDGAR. "A Chronological Survey of Research Studies on Principles as Objectives of Instruction in Science," *Science Education*, XXIX (February, 1945), 45–52.
8. NOLL, VICTOR H. *The Teaching of Science in Elementary and Secondary Schools.* New York: Longmans, Green & Co., 1939.
9. *Review of Educational Research*, XII (October, 1942), 369–85, 412–24, 435–42, 443–50; XV (October, 1945), 272–75, 289–97, 301–9, 321–30.

CHAPTER V

BACKGROUND OF THE CURRICULUM IN SCIENCE

THE PLACE OF SCIENCE IN THE EDUCATION OF CHILDREN

One aim of education is the development of the abilities of children as individuals to the end that they will be able to secure the maximum of good for themselves. Another major aim is the development of the individual for social responsibility. There is no dichotomy in the content and procedures of these aims. Children can be in the process of growth toward science objectives if they respond to the challenges and problems with which the environments are filled. Children may seek explanations of many of the events they encounter. In turn, the explanations they understand and accept as children have much to do with the kind of individuals they will be when they become adults.

In considering these aims in the elementary school, it is necessary to take into account the potentialities of science as a factor in the successful adjustment of children to the world which surrounds them. The meanings which man attaches to the things that happen in his environment greatly affect his social adjustment. These meanings involve interpretations. If the individual interprets his environment in terms of unfounded opinions, his mental development is likely to be stunted. If, on the other hand, the individual sees his environment as something that can be studied and utilized, he will have a more constructive outlook upon life.

A fundamental purpose, then, in the education of children must be to give the kind of guidance which leads them to make adjustments to the world about them through interpretations that are consistent with the best statements of truth available. Hence, in determining the background for the curriculum of the elementary school, the content and method of science must be considered for its contribution to successful adjustment and the development of desirable social behavior. It should be noted that the aims of elementary education are in effect the aims of society. Science is, therefore, not to be developed in the elementary school for its own vested interest but rather for its contribution to the needs of children and to the welfare of society.

Science Education for All of the Nation's Children

Teachers and administrators in the elementary school must be concerned with providing education for all the children since the elementary school is the school of all the people. The task of science instruction is, then, a much larger one than discovering children of exceptional ability in science and starting them on their way to becoming scientists, for in a democratic form of government public education involves consideration of the potential contributions of science to all people. The task involves primarily education for all pupils for their own and society's benefits and only incidentally involves concern for the welfare or future of science.

Recent discoveries demonstrate that, unless man is intelligent about science, he can reap disaster on a scale so great as to wipe out whole civilizations. But it is also apparent that he may, through intelligent action, establish a higher standard of living on a world-wide basis. The solution of social problems in which science is involved cannot be accomplished through the work of experts alone. The experts in the various specialized fields have their functions to perform, but citizens can either assist or retard the work of the experts through their votes and conduct. In a democracy all citizens have a responsibility in determining how science shall be utilized in society. This responsibility calls for a curriculum in the elementary school which is designed to develop intelligence with reference to the place of science in personal and social life.

Objectives of Science in the Elementary School

Functional understanding of information, concepts, and principles. Science contains much useful information for children. There is a wide range of facts from the various fields of science which children need in pursuance of their own activities. These facts may be useful in that they play an important part in giving children the kind of explanations they need in their normal living, such as the cause of day and night, the nature of lightning, etc. There are also facts that are needed because they directly affect the welfare of the child and have value in changing his behavior in such matters as health and safety. There are meanings which contribute to an understanding of large ideas of science, such as those of space, time, change, adaptations, interrelationships, and evolution. It should be noted that the large ideas involve meanings for all levels of educational advancement, from childhood through the period of adult education. They may have great significance in the development of a constructive outlook on life.

Instrumental skills. There are a number of instrumental skills which are necessary as means of achieving the aims of education discussed earlier in this chapter and which must have consideration in the teaching of science in the elementary school. These include the ability to (1) read science content with understanding; (2) make observations of events; and (3) perform the various science activities.

Elements of the scientific method. There have been few points in educational discussions on which there has been greater agreement than that of the desirability of teaching the scientific method (17:226). In recent studies (8) of children's responses it has been found that the scientific method can have its beginnings in the education of children at an early age. However, in the elementary school there are relatively few times when it is appropriate to solve problems through use of all the elements of the scientific method listed in chapter iii. Such a procedure is too difficult for the maturity level of the majority of the children. The teacher can focus the attention of the children on those elements which seem most appropriate to the problem and to the intellectual development of the children involved.

The elements of the scientific method should contribute to intelligent planning. Science has a great contribution to make to individual and to group planning in a democracy. Children should be given an opportunity to participate in planning to the extent that they are aware of the elements of the scientific method in good planning. The elements of the scientific method should lead to action in life and to scientific appreciations and attitudes. Children should be so well educated in the use and implications of these elements that they can participate as individuals and in groups in the advancement of the human race.

Scientific attitudes. It is a difficult matter to disassociate attitudes from the other objectives of science. Attitudes are not secured in a vacuum of verbalizations, but rather are derived out of experiences which have meaning. Characteristic attitudes that may be acquired by children through meaningful content are the following: questioning magic as an explanation of events; searching for an explanation of things which happen; realizing that some natural phenomena have not yet been explained satisfactorily by scientists; rejecting personification, mysticism, animism, anthropomorphism, or gossip in making explanations; realizing that interpretations advanced by scientists today may be corrected and improved by scientists tomorrow; changing one's ideas as the result of new evidence; rejecting guessing and faulty thinking as a means of ascertaining truth; being willing to check conclusions; questioning the accuracy of sources of information; questioning the acceptance of the opinions of those who are not qualified in the field in which the opinions are given; questioning superstition, prejudice, astrology, fortunetelling; placing confidence in the methods and conclusions of scientists.

The use of the elements of the scientific method should result in the attitude of critical-mindedness. At the same time there should be growth in such traits as willingness to consider new information, avoidance of dogmatic attitudes, avoidance of gullibility, willingness to change attitudes, ability to make distinctions between fact and fiction, and willingness to seek and to act upon reliable information.

DEFINING THE PURPOSES OF SCIENCE EDUCATION IN LIGHT OF THE NATURE OF THE CHILD[1]

As knowledge of the elementary-school child accumulates, it becomes increasingly clear that science education is peculiarly adapted to some of childhood's most conspicuous and universal characteristics. An attempt will be made in this section to describe those traits which may be utilized and guided in a striking manner by a faithful pursuit of the aims of science education.

The Child Is an Investigator

The child of elementary-school age is characterized by searching, questioning proclivities. He explores freely his physical environment and, as he matures, he explores the realm of ideas. Mitchell writes:

> The evidence is overwhelming that the essay in discovery is a native drive of children from kindergarten through high school. If children of these ages do not show this drive, I think we can hold adults responsible—not the children themselves. . . . . Curiosity about how things work is one of the strongest drives of young children (**12**:111–19).

The spontaneous drive and curiosity of children in exploring their environment are not dissimilar to the drive and curiosity of scientists. The persistent inquisitiveness of children in exploring their world, in discovering facts, and in finding how things work can be readily utilized through science education.

It has often been noted that maturing children seem to lose some of their zest for inquiry. Environmental factors undoubtedly play the major role in this loss. One factor is the lack of a scientific outlook among many teachers and parents. The absence of open-minded inquiry and the reluctance to suspend final judgment create a fertile field for the habit of accepting ready-made ideas whether they be explanations, superstitions, prejudices, or taboos. Another factor is the school's tendency to assume an authoritarian view of knowledge with emphasis upon the assimilation of predigested information. Needless to say, there is a place for giving information to children, but making this the entire instructional program

---

[1] The Committee has benefited from the collaboration of Ralph C. Preston, University of Pennsylvania, in the following section of this chapter.

has the effect of discouraging children from investigation. Prescott notes that:

There is a real possibility that it [loss of questioning spirit] appears because schools check the normal maturing of concepts, which come as experiences accumulate. Indeed, affective factors may play a large role due to the unpleasant feelings aroused by so many interests and by the frustration of so much natural inquisitiveness during the early years of school (**14**:236-37).

In introducing children to science, teachers have a special responsibility to offset the operation of these factors and likewise have a much greater opportunity than in other fields of instruction for channeling interest and curiosity.

The Child Reacts to All Aspects of His Environment

Teachers are familiar with the great diversity of children's interests. While a particular child may exhibit a specialized interest and seem to concentrate his attention upon airplanes, stamps, baseball, or some other single aspect of his environment, a close analysis will almost invariably reveal a host of subsidiary interests. Witty and Kopel, in reporting the results of the use of their interest inventory, show how widely scattered are children's interests in reading, library use, recreation, ambitions, and wishes (**20**: chap. ii).

Studies of children's questions similarly testify to the variegation of interests. Craig analyzed 6,806 questions from children and found them to be well distributed among more than one hundred categories of objectives, covering the fields of astronomy, biology, chemistry, geology, and physics (**2**). Williams found that children's choices of science books were distributed among all subjects. While topics dealing with certain subjects (such as aviation) appeared more popular than those dealing with certain other subjects (such as plants), the choices were diverse. No subject classification lacked enthusiastic readers (**19**). Teachers need, therefore, to stimulate and to pay close attention to children's interests as displayed through persistent questioning and related behavior. In this way their interests may be harnessed to the science program.

Experience has demonstrated that science may be organized in the elementary school so that a wide range of subject matter may be pursued in a given year of school without sacrificing any of the objectives of science education. Such an organization makes it unnecessary to defer children's questions to another year—a procedure which is too likely to drain curiosity of its imperative quality, with the result that a strategic opportunity for learning is lost. Curriculum balance is attained by providing experiences in each of the broad scientific areas at each successive level rather than through fixed grade-placement of topics.

The Child's Imaginative Activities Contribute to His Growth

The imaginative nature of children's behavior is well known to teachers. In the report of an intensive study of fifty children, Griffiths vividly described the significant role that imagination assumes in childhood. She concludes that, far from being an escape, fantasy represents a normal stage of development, enabling children to deal on their own respective levels with problems encountered in everyday life and to discharge inward tensions that might, unreleased, make a happy adjustment to life very difficult. Her evidence makes it clear that the imagination of children, structurally unscientific and emotional though it is, represents an essential ingredient in human development, contributing to increased adjustment to reality (6). Issacs has pointed out: "We may look upon the inability to join with other children in imaginative and creative play as one of the surest signs of grave inner difficulties that will sooner or later seriously disturb the mental life" (9).

There are few problems that present a greater challenge to imagination than those of science. Contrary to a popular misconception, imagination and scientific thought are not unrelated. It was through imaginative thinking that Franklin, Faraday, and Marconi, for example, advanced far enough beyond existing knowledge to contribute new and useful products like the lightning rod, the electromagnetic generator, and the wireless. In facing their own questions in science it is eminently appropriate that children should be encouraged to employ their imaginative impulses in formulating hypotheses as a first step, to be followed by observation, experimentation, reading, and discussion.

The Child Seeks To Participate in Planning and Carrying Out His Activities

No artifice is needed to enlist the participation of children in planning their learning. It is characteristic of growth for them to desire to do this. Where children have opportunity for sharing, they show gradual and unforced recognition of the need for pooling their thinking and dividing their labor. When we provide for participation, therefore, we are working along with intuitive inclinations of childhood.

This knowledge has been established by research and observation on the part of teachers and students of child development. West investigated the behavior of children engaged in science activities. He found that, in so far as opportunity was provided, children readily assumed obligation for group work, undertook voluntarily to perform out-of-school experimenting and reading, suggested new ways of doing things, and participated in numerous other ways (18). In analyzing his data pertaining to observations of a fifth-grade class, he writes: "One hundred and twenty-six reactions, or 13.87 per cent of the total number of observed reactions, were of a voluntary nature, which is greater than the number of responses to any other single code-item category" (**18:** 45). Lewin and his associates have furnished striking evidence that from almost any angle, including that of sheer learning efficiency, democratic pupil participation is more productive than teacher-dominated situations (**11**).

Above all in importance, participation establishes an atmosphere that facilitates mental health. The reason is not obscure. As Heffernan explains:

> The whole direction of the life of an individual is determined by his ability to make wise choices. The school, therefore, which provides many opportunities in which children make choices is contributing greatly to personal development and social integration (**7:**60).

Thus, when we recognize the child's eagerness to take an active part in his learning we are not doing so out of sentimentality but because of the discovery that, typical of many spontaneous urges, participating, as contrasted with mere assimilating, makes for better learning and better attitudes.

The study of science in the elementary school emphasizes phenomena which are prominent in the child's environment. His wonder at their nature, their causes, and their effects is so insistent that questions scarcely need be formally solicited. The questions and activities suggested by a class, plus those planned by its teacher, may be improved and organized in joint session and may well form the substance of the outline of a unit in science. This is one way in which children may help direct the content and emphasis of their science education. The many-sidedness of the subject matter of science permits wide latitude in selection, without necessarily circumventing any of the objectives of science education. Participation is also easily provided in sharing responsibility for obtaining materials for experiments, in performing demonstrations, and in caring for pets, terrariums, plants, and other adjuncts of science experiences.

Extensive pupil participation, of course, takes time. The closely packed curriculum with the rapid tempo of life in many schools will need modification. One short period following upon the heels of another, one topic rapidly disposed of after another, establishes an atmosphere not conducive to the leisurely pursuit of democratic learning. It is, therefore, gratifying to note the trend toward unhurried introductory sessions during which children and teachers co-operatively plan instruction and share responsibility in science experiences ranging from play and informal experimentation to controlled observation.

The Child Follows His Own Individual Pattern in Developing Concepts

Research in every branch of education supplies overwhelming support to the expectation that children of a given age and grade classification will differ tremendously in terms of rate of growth and concepts already achieved. A number of experimenters have found that the quality of children's reactions to scientific phenomena does not follow a uniform progress from grade to grade and that overlapping of abilities in any one grade is the normal situation. Croxton reported that the ability to apply generalizations, possessed by most ninth-grade pupils, is something which even a few kindergarten children have attained (3). In summarizing her research on children's explanations of natural phenomena, Deutsche stated:

The outstanding finding was the great amount of overlapping [among age groups]. No kind or type of answer was found at a single age [except where the frequency was a fraction of one per cent] nor were the answers of children of a given age classifiable into a single type (4:93).

Hill analyzed statements made during science discussions and found that while, in general, sixth-grade reactions appeared better than first-grade reactions, statements made by individual first-grade children were judged superior to those made by individual sixth-grade children (8).

Does this mean that science instruction must be individualized or that classes in science must be organized in graded groups such as is customary in the teaching of reading? There is nothing in the subject matter of science that would seem to require either. Science has sufficient breadth so that any area may be explored by a heterogeneous group with profit to all. The outcomes may not be uniform from child to child, but, as Hill's study convincingly shows, the general objectives may appropriately be the same for all members of a class and achieved by each child at his own level of comprehension. The search for data and concomitant activities can be shared by all. Children at various stages of maturity can weigh evidence, form conclusions, distinguish between fact and opinion, suggest and try new ways of doing things, and construct apparatus, as West's investigation, already cited, suggests, and thereby experience the method of science. This in no way calls for abandonment of efforts to systematize instruction to the end that scientific concepts are actually advanced.

The Child Learns through Doing

Overt "doing" is an essential element in the child's learning. In a special illustration of this principle, Greene showed the value of providing dramatics in connection with science instruction in the fifth grade. He found a considerable gain in the measurable factual learnings as a result of marionette plays and plays partly written by children themselves. The expenditure of time, of course, was very great. He found, further, that attitudes and traits, such as co-operation, responsibility, and leadership, were improved more through the use of dramatics than without it (**5**). Many teachers have demonstrated the value of having children impersonate the sun and earth in working out the relationship of these two bodies. While dramatics is only one form of "doing," it is emphasized because dramatic play reaches its peak of spontaneity during the elementary-school years and is a strikingly successful vehicle of learning. However, manipulative experiences are equally beneficial.

This kind of doing, of course, should not constitute the entire educational program. So-called passive learning is a natural and enjoyable process. This has been shown by Williams (**19**), who, as previously mentioned, illustrated the varied and spontaneous use children make of science books. Bergen reported that children commonly and spontaneously employ books and other authoritarian sources, in contrast to empirical sources. He also pointed out that children seem to recognize the appropriateness of observation and experimentation and probably get too little practice in using them (**1**).

Activity is the only known antidote for verbalism. Glibness is a poor substitute for true meaning; yet misconceptions are revealed in many studies of children's concepts. Scott and Myers reported that children "have woefully vague and incorrect notions of terms which they use rather glibly in their routine school work" (**16**). Piaget found children's ideas replete with animism, magical causality, "juxtaposition," and "syncretism" (an uncritical acceptance at one and the same time of opposing elements) (**13**).

How are such findings to be interpreted? Do they indicate that children do not possess readiness for study involving these concepts? Experience would seem to deny the validity of such a conclusion. We must provide ample opportunity for the child to gain understanding of the principles and conceptions of science and elements of the scientific method through a process of growth. Children do not come to a full understanding of the scientific concepts of time, space, adaptation, and energy in one month or even one year. It is only natural that the child should reveal elements of misconception or inaccuracy in his concept of the profound ideas of science, particularly since the child is surrounded in many cases by adults who rely upon unscientific attitudes and unfounded opinions.

It would appear in many cases that these misconceptions occur as the result of introducing children to the use of terms and symbols before they have had sufficient firsthand experience, which is the raw material of conceptual knowledge. Such primary experiences as manipulating objects, collecting and constructing simple apparatus, firsthand acquaintance with living things, dramatizing, questioning, designing, experimenting, and planning are ways of acquiring concepts and avoiding mere verbalism. Bergen provides evidence that the teacher may influence the children's choice of sources of information by his own remarks and by arranging apparatus, books, and other materials in the classroom (1). The subject matter and the method of science lend themselves well to meeting children's need for learning actively.

The Child Learns through Seeking To Achieve Purposes

Behavior progresses from crudity to refinement through the pursuit of purposes. Lewin has shown that the experiences through which a child learns are not neutral to him; they are, in fact, almost compulsive determiners of the direction of his behavior (10). Every teacher knows that mere exposure to an experience does not guarantee learning. A child may be present during the discussion and activities that take place in a classroom and yet learn nothing of positive or permanent value that the teacher intends he should learn.

Children have unusual assortments of purposes in the field of science, a fact which has been documented earlier in this chapter. These they bring with them to school. If they appear narrow or trivial, the teacher has the task of broadening them and of stimulating worthier ones. It should scarcely be necessary to resort to artificial incentives in the field of elementary-school science, since its purposes correspond to such an imposing array of children's aims. The success encountered in seeking answers to his multitudinous questions will be adequate encouragement to a child to continue the quest.

THE SETTING OF SCIENCE IN THE ELEMENTARY-SCHOOL CURRICULUM[2]
Trends in Curriculum Development

Growing out of a better understanding of the growth and development of children, and of the importance of science in their social education, certain trends in curriculum development are discernible.

Meaningful and socially significant problems. The content of the science program in many elementary schools is now being organized around problems which have social value and which are significant in the lives of the children. These problems arise from children's interest in the world around them and from their need to meet intelligently their problems of

---

[2] The committee has benefited from the collaboration of Daisy Parton, University of Alabama, in the following section of this chapter.

living in areas such as health, conservation, and safety. They are solved not through the mere accumulation of facts but in such a way as to help children (1) develop meanings which are essential to social understanding, and (2) put into practice desirable social behavior. Problems involve meanings in their solution, and meanings are learned through experiences.

A flexible curriculum suited to the needs of the children and of the community. In order for problems to be meaningful and socially significant to children, they should be selected in terms of interests, background, and needs of the particular group. A rigidly planned science program which sets up specific content and achievement goals cannot provide adequately for varying needs of children in different communities. Neither can it meet needs of individual children within a class. A number of school systems are, therefore, giving individual schools and teachers opportunity within a broad framework to develop science programs suited to the needs of their particular children and communities. When this is done teachers must make intensive studies of their children and their communities. They must set up environments which will stimulate and develop interests on the part of the boys and girls and must utilize the various environmental resources. They must look at the background and needs of the children in relation to well-rounded living and well-rounded growth. They must guide children's planning in such a way that there is growth in ability to make intelligent choices.

An integral relation to other phases of the program. Instruction in science contributes in a large measure to the attainment of the basic purposes of the elementary school as a whole. Since other phases of the elementary-school program contribute also to the attainment of the same purposes, a functional relationship between the phases often exists. This occurs when the satisfactory solution of problems calls for content from different fields, as social studies, science, health education, and mathematics. It occurs also when children, in solving problems, utilize the arts and the language arts as the means of securing information and expressing their ideas.

In many schools and school systems, programs called by such terms as "basic education," "basic social program," and "core program" are being developed. These programs are designed to provide a more adequate social education for children. They deal with personal and social problems of living which are significant in the lives of the children and draw content from any field. A large block of time each day usually is devoted to activities which arise out of the solution of the problems.

Whatever the plan of program organization used in the elementary school, the science in the curriculum should have a close relationship to the other phases of the school program. Regardless of whether the program is organized in terms of subjects or in terms of an integrated curriculum, it is important in solving problems to use content from any field which is needed.

Too frequently in relating science to the other subjects of the curriculum, as in merging the science instruction in an integrated program, the values are lost through a kind of instruction which could be described as a "mere talking about science" with little or no real study of science. This should not be the case. In any type of program there should be an adequate provision for utilizing the tremendous potentialities of science instruction for human welfare in the modern age. It is inconceivable that these potentialities can be realized in childhood education without an actual working with and a study of science.

Continuity in the Program

Instruction in science during the year should provide a continuity of experience which will help children through the extension of their environment to grow continuously (1) in the development of wider and deeper meanings, (2) in the ability to do broader and more critical planning in solving their problems of living, and (3) in the acquisition of desired scientific attitudes, appreciations, and interests. Continuity of experience implies that the science program should be developed in terms of the meanings and understandings which the children have and that it should lead on to the building of larger and fuller meanings. Such meanings are developed as children solve problems of social value which are significant and challenging to them.

The difficult job of the teacher, however, is so to guide children in the selection and solution of problems that continuity of learning results. To accomplish this most effectively, the teacher should:

1. Know children—their growth sequences, their characteristics and differences at the age-level, and how they learn.
2. Know the background, interests, and needs of the particular group of children, both as individuals and as a group.
3. Plan ahead so that he has clearly in mind the needs of the children in relation to the needs of society, the directions in which he expects growth to take place, and the varied types of problems and experiences which may be utilized to bring this growth.
4. Work with the children in the intelligent selection of challenging problems.
5. Guide the solution of the problems in such a way that a variety and balance of learning materials and activities are utilized, that individual and group differences are provided for, and that democratic and scientific methods of work are utilized.

The teacher who works in these ways will utilize the child's past experiences and the resources and problems of the environment in such a way that a readiness for new problems and new meanings is developed.

Balance in the Program

If science instruction is to contribute effectively to the children's understanding of their environment, the program should give them well-rounded experiences. A number of factors need to be taken into account in providing children with a well-balanced content in science.

Balance in terms of areas of environment. A well-balanced science program will provide experiences which help children extend and deepen their understanding in the major areas of their environments. (See chap. vi.)

Balance in terms of areas of living. A well-balanced science program also will provide opportunities for children to understand and meet more intelligently their problems in the various areas of living. Boys and girls need help with problems of home, school, and community living in such areas as health, safety, conservation, consumption, and production. The field of science has valuable content to contribute to the understanding and solution of problems in these phases. Elementary-school teachers should make use of the areas of living as a check list for looking at balance.

Balance in terms of time and space. Another factor which is important to consider in a well-rounded science program is the proper balance between the "near" and the "far," on the one hand, and the "long ago" and "now," on the other. At every grade level children need experiences which help them deepen their understanding of their immediate environment. At the same time they should have experiences in harmony with their maturity level, which will extend their environment in both time and space.

Number and length of problems. Not only does the nature of the content influence balance in the science program but so also does the number and length of the problems studied. Children need a proper balance between short and long problems, and usually both types may go on at the same time. Many problems which arise out of the daily living experiences of the children may be solved satisfactorily within a short span of time. On the other hand, boys and girls need to solve problems which call for more extended planning and working on their part. The scope of long problems should be suited to the maturity level of the children and to their needs and interests at the time. Such considerations will prevent the dragging out of the longer problems and thus will give time for children to explore more aspects of their environment during the year.

Balance throughout elementary-school period. Balance in the science curriculum should be considered in relation to the entire elementary-school period as well as in terms of the yearly program. In order to secure a well-rounded program throughout the child's elementary-school experience there should be co-operative planning on the part of the school staff. Such planning should result in the development of a flexible science curriculum. This should help teachers to have clearly in mind the common purposes toward which they are working. It should suggest also a broad framework within which teachers may develop a program suited to the needs of their children and the community. Such a framework should be revised continuously in the light of the teachers' experiences as they build the curriculum with the children and evaluate their growth.

SUMMARY

The basic purpose of the elementary school is the development of desirable social behavior. Science, with its dynamic aspects, its insistence upon critical-mindedness and better understanding of the world, and its demand for intelligent planning, has a large contribution to make to the content and method of elementary education.

To accomplish this basic purpose a continuous program of science instruction should be developed throughout public school education, based upon a recognition of the large ideas and basic principles of science and the elements of the scientific method. Children must be given opportunity to gain the knowledge necessary for intelligent and co-operative experience with the world of matter, energy, and living things and to develop constructive appreciations, attitudes, and interests. This demands that the individuals in our society become intelligent with reference to the place of science in individual and social life.

When the content and method of science are examined, it is found that the child's normal activities have much in common with the purposes of science in modern society and that the teacher can view the teaching of science as utilizing the natural dynamic drives and potentialities of children.

REFERENCES

1. BERGEN, C. *Some Sources of Children's Science Information.* Teachers College Contributions to Education, No. 881. New York: Teachers College, Columbia University, 1943.
2. CRAIG, GERALD S. *Certain Techniques Used in Developing a Course of Study in Science for the Horace Mann Elementary School.* New York: Bureau of Publications, Teachers College, Columbia University, 1927.
3. CROXTON, W. C. "Pupil's Ability To Generalize," *School Science and Mathematics,* XXXVI (June, 1936), 627–34.
4. DEUTSCHE, J. M. *The Development of Children's Concepts of Causal Relations.* Minneapolis: University of Minnesota Press, 1937.

5. GREENE, R. A. *A Comparative Study of the Efficiency of Dramatic Methods in Teaching Science to Fifth-Grade Children.* Ithaca, New York: Cornell University, 1937.

6. GRIFFITHS, R. *A Study of Imagination in Early Childhood.* London: Kegan, Paul, Trench, Trubner & Co., 1935.

7. HEFFERNAN, H. "An Experiencing Curriculum in the Social Studies," *The Social Studies in the Elementary School.* Twelfth Yearbook of the National Council for the Social Studies, 1941. Washington: National Education Assn., 1941.

8. HILL, KATHERINE E. *Children's Contributions in Science Discussions.* New York: Teachers College, Columbia University, 1946.

9. ISAACS, S. *The Nursery Years.* New York: Vanguard Press, 1929.

10. LEWIN, K. A. "Environmental Forces," *A Handbook of Child Psychology.* Worcester, Massachusetts: Clark University Press, 1933 (second revised edition).

11. LEWIN, K.; LIPPITT, R.; and WHITE, R. W. "Patterns of Aggressive Behavior in Experimentally Created 'Social Climates,'" *Journal of Social Psychology*, X (May, 1939), 271–99.

12. MITCHELL, L. S. "Research on the Child's Level: Possibilities, Limitations, and Techniques," *Educational Planning for Peace.* Proceedings of the Thirty-first Annual Schoolmen's Week. Philadelphia: University of Pennsylvania, 1944.

13. PIAGET, J. *Language and Thought of the Child.* New York: Harcourt, Brace & Co., 1926; *Judgment and Reasoning in the Child.* New York: Harcourt, Brace & Co., 1928; *The Child's Conception of the World.* New York: Harcourt, Brace & Co., 1929; *The Child's Conception of Physical Causality.* New York: Harcourt, Brace & Co., 1930.

14. PRESCOTT, D. A. *Emotion and the Educative Process.* Washington: American Council on Education, 1938.

15. ROBINSON, M. L. *A Basis for the Selection of Course Content in Elementary Science.* Ann Arbor, Michigan: University of Michigan, 1934.

16. SCOTT, F.; and MYERS, G. C. "Children's Empty and Erroneous Concepts of the Commonplace," *Journal of Educational Research*, VIII (November, 1923), 327–34.

17. UNDERHILL, ORRA E. *The Origins and Development of Elementary-School Science.* Chicago: Scott Foresman & Co., 1941.

18. WEST, J. Y. *A Technique for Appraising Certain Observable Behavior of Children in Elementary Schools.* Teachers College Contributions to Education, No. 728. New York: Teachers College, Columbia University, 1937.

19. WILLIAMS, A. M. *Children's Choices in Science Books.* Child Development Monograph No. 27. New York: Teachers College, Columbia University, 1939.

20. WITTY, P., and KOPEL, D. *Reading: The Educative Process.* New York: Ginn & Co., 1939.

CHAPTER VI

ORGANIZATION OF THE CURRICULUM IN SCIENCE

THE BASIC AREAS OF ELEMENTARY-SCHOOL SCIENCE[1]

Areas of the Physical and Biological Environment

When the objectives of science education have been decided, attention then turns to the determination of the basic areas of science from which experiences and content are to be selected. It is important to realize that, from the point of view of children, science has few artificial boundaries. In observing and interpreting the phenomena of the environment, children are not likely to categorize these happenings in terms of the special fields such as astronomy, botany, or chemistry. It seems logical, therefore, to select curriculum materials on the basis of the environment.

The term "environment" should not be construed as necessarily limited to the locality of the school. The environment is considered as including everything to which an individual reacts. An earthquake in the West Indies, the interior of the earth, the "dust bowl," a new invention, the operation at "Crossroads X," and a variable star may be aspects of an individual's environment.

If it were possible to plot for a given period of time the profile of growth of an individual child in his understanding of the environment, the teacher would find that the pupil had not grown equally with respect to all aspects of his environment. Because of interest, attitude, individual enterprise, accessibility of material, special aptitude or some other factor, he would be found to have pursued certain aspects (such as weather, electricity, or stars) more than he had others.

It has already been indicated that there is a need for a broad, well-balanced instruction in science (chap. v). By the end of each year the children should have experienced some growth in the broader areas of the physical and biological environment, such as the following:

The universe. Here provision is made for the study of the stars, the sun, the moon, the planets, and their interrelationships. Pertinent materials would include those essential to an understanding of the causes of day and night, seasonal changes, tides, eclipses, and (less completely) of the vastness of the Milky Way galaxy and galactic systems beyond our own.

---

[1] The committee has profited from the collaboration of John Urban, State Teachers College, Buffalo, New York, in the following section of this chapter.

The earth. Among the pertinent topics in this phase of the environment are such problems as the origin of the earth, the formation of mountains, weathering of rock into soil, erosion, volcanism, prehistoric life, and the forces which have changed and are still changing the surface of the earth.

Conditions necessary to life. What living things need in order to exist, how they are affected by changes in the environment, and the struggle for the conditions necessary to life are suggested materials in the development of this aspect of the environment.

Living things. Suitable materials include the variety of living things, the social life of animals, adaptations for protection, life cycles of plants and animals, how living things obtain their food, the economic importance of living things, and man's influence upon nature.

Physical and chemical phenomena. Such chemical phenomena as rusting are considered in this phase of the environment. Physical phenomena which may be appropriate include: light, sound, gravity, magnetism and electricity, changes in state of matter, and the phenomena associated with radiant energy and atmospheric changes.

Man's attempt to control his environment. In this aspect of science the child may study man's control in gardens, on farms, in orchards; his inventions and discoveries; his use of power, of minerals; his control over living things; his study of places he cannot reach directly; and other such topics.

Areas of Social Needs

In addition to the areas of the physical and biological environment, the curriculum-maker and the teacher should consider the areas growing out of living and social needs, such as health, safety, conservation, economics. It is evident that these areas of living will utilize content described in the areas of the physical and biological environment and will form a basis for the development of desirable knowledges, attitudes and appreciations.[2]

A program in science should develop a large background for the teaching of health. Many schools are now integrating health entirely with science and the social studies. Science provides much of the necessary background for the teaching of health facts and the development of good health habits. Moreover, in their study of science, pupils should gain a vision of the potentialities of science in the improvement of the health of the nation and of the world.

The relation between science and economics has too long been neglected. Because of his own ignorance of the operation of biological and physical principles, man is at present beset by a host of problems concern-

---

[2] National Committee on Science Teaching, *Redirecting Science Teaching in the Light of Personal-Social Needs.* Washington: American Council of Science Teachers, National Education Association, 1942.

ing national and international economy. The place of science in bringing about the wise utilization of natural resources to the welfare of mankind is an important aspect of the science areas related to the social needs.

Likewise, science is involved in accident prevention and safety instruction. We cannot fully anticipate the environment of the future. New inventions may eliminate present hazards and create new ones, making it impossible to develop a code of conduct in safety instruction which will be functional for an entire life span. It may be well, then, in safety instruction to place more emphasis upon the scientific principles which are basic to safe conduct.

Analysis of the Areas into Learning Elements

The basic areas lend themselves to an analysis in terms of the objectives of science education. Such analysis results in a number of meanings, skills, attitudes, appreciations, and interests which may be classified in sequence from simple to complex. The curriculum-maker then has a body of source material of value in constructing syllabi for teachers and for the consideration of problems of scope and sequence of learning in science. In all cases, however, the sequence should be revised as seems necessary after a study of the needs of the children in a classroom.

For instance, the fact that, when it is day on one half of the earth, it is night on the other half is relatively simple in meaning and would come earlier in the sequence than a more complicated concept, such as the explanation for the cause of change of seasons.

Another illustration can be taken from the area of living things. A relatively simple concept in this area is that plants need water. A more complicated idea is the dependence of all animal life upon green plants for food. Even more complicated would be the idea that energy for plant and animal life is secured from the sun. Haupt has made an extensive study of the factors that enter into the development of sequence of learning.[3] In his study of the statements made by children of their learning in science, he found certain differences which may be defined as follows:

1. The concepts needed for the associations made on lower grade levels depend upon few experiences which are easily given or acquired.

2. The concepts needed for the associations made on the higher grade levels depend upon series of experiences which must be selected and held. These experiences are not so easily acquired or presented.

3. More concepts are associated in the statements made on the higher grade levels.

---

[3] George W. Haupt, *A Philosophy of Science Teaching in an Elementary School*, pp. 42–51. New York: Bureau of Publications, Teachers College, Columbia University, 1935.

Associated with the understandings of ideas there can be the development of attitudes. For instance, early in the development of attitudes may be the questioning of accuracy of a given story through such questions as: Is it so? Much later in the sequence is the ability to distinguish between accurate and inaccurate source material and the ability to recognize and reject prejudice. So in the scientific attitudes a sequence can be developed from the simple to the more complicated.

Related to the development of meanings and attitudes is the growth of appreciations. An illustration may be secured from the area of conservation. Early in a child's experience may come the meaning that what he and his friends sometimes call "dirt" is "soil." Later he may develop an appreciation of the relation of soil and other resources to the welfare of his country and to international relations. He may then feel a sense of "hurt" when he sees these resources wasted.

The Preschool Child and Sciences[4]

The young child (two, three, four, and five years of age) is vitally interested in and concerned about his environment. Persons who work with a little child are amazed at the resourcefulness, the persistence, and the variety of devices he uses to find out about the forces about him. The urge to be successful in an environment results in self-knowledge. The thrill of discovery, the joy of power, the delight in sensation is constantly activating him and stimulating him, mentally and emotionally.

How the Child Learns about His Environment

The child is forced by the nature of events to orient himself to the universe that surrounds him; this orientation continues throughout life. There is a constant need for interaction between the child and his environment for adequate existence as well as for creative expression.

Physically, the child is equipped to learn about his world. The whole nervous system is so organized that satisfaction results when the needs of the organism are met.

Children have a high degree of tactile sensitivity. "This greater sensitivity in childhood is due to a great number of tactile corpuscles per unit area of skin and to a more delicate and thinner skin."[5] These corpuscles are especially numerous in the hands. It is largely through this sensitivity that the child learns about things by handling them. Skin and muscle co-

---

[4] The committee has profited from the collaboration of Mary W. Moffitt, Teachers College, Columbia University, New York, New York, in the following section of this chapter.

[5] J. F. Williams, *Anatomy and Physiology*, p. 231. Philadelphia: W. B. Saunders Co., 1943.

operate to give impressions of the characteristics of objects. Thus size, shape, weight, as well as impressions of such qualities as hot, cold, smooth, rough, hard, etc., are experienced. Through manipulation, the possibilities and the limitations of objects are perceived. Present experiences are oriented with past experiences and simple relationships are seen. This knowledge, when translated into dramatic play, becomes functional and serves to clarify many concepts. However, lack of enough varied experiences often leads to errors in concepts; hence, a great many opportunities are needed to relive experiences through other sensory and motor expressions, such as seeing pictures, hearing stories, and taking excursions. Correct terminology should be given during these experiences in order that children may express ideas more adequately and have a basis for future thinking.

Much of the conditioning in attitudes toward environment occurs in this period of early childhood. The experiences of a little child in modern society are often very frustrating. He frequently lives too much in an adult world which gives him little opportunity for freedom to experiment at his level of understanding or for firsthand experiences. Too often there is condemnation for breaking things or for being "messy," when the action occurs in the investigation of some interesting object. Restraint is placed upon firsthand experiences by such commands as, "Don't touch!" Lack of adequate or accurate information and certain adult attitudes concerning experiences and questions may cause fear and inhibitions. Fear, anger, and frustration appear when situations arise that cannot be dealt with. The conditioning of emotional responses affects the child's learning at the time and also affects his approach to future situations.

The Role of the Adult

During the early childhood period there is a wonderful opportunity to help develop desirable attitudes in relation to experiences. Adults need to use ingenuity in providing play materials and adapting them to the child's level of understanding. It is important, too, that these play materials should be on hand in the nursery school and kindergarten so the teacher can seize opportunities quickly when an interest is shown or expressed by children in play situations.

Adults should be thoroughly familiar with the developmental levels of the child. Knowledge of the growth characteristics should serve as a guide to good planning. There is a wide range of skill and there are many levels of comprehension between the ages of three to five years which determine the type of experience to be provided. It is necessary for the adult to select materials which are sturdy, relatively simple to operate, and large enough to handle easily. Many values are lost if there are too many limitations imposed in the use of play materials or if close supervision is exercised. The reaction to fragile or complicated objects may result in destructiveness, in appeals for help, or in complete rejection. The attention span of the young child is very short, and his orientation to time is not well developed. Therefore, it is important that results from use of materials should be noted quickly and clearly before there is a shift in his interest.

Adults should set the stage for varied experiences. When adults set the stage, the range of experiences should be related to as many environmental situations as possible.

Play objects should be included which will provide for experiences with light, sound, heat, matter, time, space, measurement, simple functional electricity, action of the wind, earth, plant life, animal life, etc. Out of these experiences and activities, certain initial learnings evolve which help the child to understand his world. The following illustration is used to clarify the way in which certain materials and activities serve to provide the child with some fundamental learnings.

Some Experiences with Water

Some Materials Used	Some Activities	Some Initial Learnings
Water tank, doll and doll clothing, soap, sponge, brushes, egg beater, funnel, containers of different kinds, rubber hose, also plastic balls, corks, sprinkler, water wheel, boats, oil can, etc.	Washing and wringing doll clothes. Playing with soap bubbles. Pouring from one container to another. Playing with boats, etc. Seeing water operate water wheel. Emptying with siphon. Seeing ice and snow melt and water freeze. Watering of plants, calling attention to sun drying walks, etc. Painting with water on dry surfaces.	Concepts about the properties of water. Wetness and dryness, weight, buoyancy, volume, suspension, and absorption of materials. Water performing work. Substances dissolved in water, etc.

Adults should help the child interpret his experiences. Besides setting the stage and providing for firsthand experiences with many kinds of materials, adults should help interpret and integrate the child's knowledge and experience. More knowledge is of little value if the information cannot be used effectively. The child's ability to comprehend is governed somewhat by the adult's ability to bring certain aspects into focus within the child's level of comprehension. This means that the teacher or parent should have a wide range of information and should use correct names when talking about objects or functions. Questions should be answered simply and directly, and ideas should be clearly stated. In this way the child gains verbal formulations for the concepts he is forming. However, certain precautions must be mentioned. Often there is such eagerness to dispense information that the child is confused with multiple details, or the fun of discovery is taken away by explanations given before the child has a chance to find out for himself. "Here let me show you" is another way by which a child is robbed of many worth-while experiences. Each child will approach an object or happening differently, and he should have plenty of time to explore in his own way. Many times a quiet observer contributes more to a learning situation than a distracting conversationalist. An interest shared or the fun of doing things together will be more effective than the mere acquiring of knowledge.

THE PRIMARY-SCHOOL CHILD AND SCIENCE[6]
How the Child Extends His Environment

The teacher can encourage young children to widen their educational environment and to extend it from home and neighborhood into the larger community. The pupil has developed some sensitivity to time and space. Concepts of space, such as *near* and *far*, *here* and *there*, *indoors* and *outdoors*, have meaning before the child enters the first grade. Likewise, concepts of time, such as *now* and *soon*, *today*, *yesterday*, and *tomorrow*, may have emerged by the age of four or five. At about six years, time words like *morning*, *afternoon*, *Monday*, or *three o'clock* may be understood. Thus, the child's language development reveals the stage of development of his science concepts of time and space. Only with continued use of time concepts in experiences, such as observation, discussion, and reading, will the concept of years and seasons have meaning.

Similarly, as the young child's language and physical structures develop, his space concepts increase. Meanings will be limited or broad to the degree that he has moved about, observed, or possibly understood what others have told or read to him. The young child's concept of space may be that of his own backyard, a near-by park or forest, or the next town. He certainly knows there is a sun, a moon, and clouds. In other words, the young child is forming a basis for the study of science although he may hold misconceptions. On the other hand, the child in the primary school can be helped to learn about such concepts as "the earth moves," "the earth is round," "it moves all the time," "the sun is very, very hot," "it is very large but far, far away."

Again, primary children may have experience with a wide range of natural phenomena, such as friction, inertia, momentum, magnetism, static electricity, simple electrical circuits, snow, ice, water, steam, melt-

---

[6] The committee has profited from the collaboration of Etheleen Daniel, Montgomery County, Maryland, Public Schools, in the following section of this chapter.

ing, boiling, freezing, evaporation, and condensation. They have a natural tendency to explore conditions necessary to certain living things, to care for animals, and to become aware of the effect of seasonal change. They may use simple equipment such as mirrors, magnifying glasses, magnets, and simple tools and machines. For example, play and work with building blocks and wagons can develop an awareness of balance.

Work in the primary grades should not be exhaustive. Rather, the child should feel that there is more to learn about everything that he does. A developmental point of view demands that a well-balanced program provide contacts with realities. It cannot allow omissions in the development of the concepts, principles, attitudes, appreciations, and interests derived from the field of science.

The child's mental powers are such that satisfaction and security, under appropriate conditions, can be gained when his needs are met. However, if interpretations and explanations are partial or restricted at any age, attitudes are likely to be biased or prejudiced. Accordingly, growth may be retarded or delayed. Sometimes children's conversations are based on prejudices, opinions, gossip, superstitions, and other unscientific influences secured largely from adults. Comments, as "Kill the snake," "The sun is small," "It is true because father (or teacher) said so," and "Can the Runaway Bunny really fly like the book said?" reveal the necessity of helping children to interpret accurately.

How the Adult Contributes to the Adjustment of the Child of the Primary School

The child at the primary levels has gained considerable power in language usage, ability to work and think with others, and to generalize. If he is to continue growing, he must improve in his ability to use elements of the scientific method. His adjustments demand also that he become open-minded and critical-minded. The six- to eight-year-old may learn to listen to the comments of others, to their proposals or objections, if his own ideas are given sufficient attention. The adult may help the child to state two or three facts leading to a conclusion. A simple experiment may give children new facts or provide an opportunity to check their facts or to suggest an experiment under different conditions. Thus, if children are led to check their thinking by experimenting, making observations, or using science books written to their level, they may listen to the ideas of others, become willing to have their ideas challenged, or accept the explanations of others. An attitude of open-mindedness on the part of children does not necessarily signify that they are inactive and passively tolerant; it may show a willingness to find the best solution to a situation.

Children in the primary grades are likely to confuse everyday fantasy with realities. Especially in reading many stories, they are confused by fantasy and personification. When facts learned from fiction, coupled with gossip, prejudices, and superstitions of others, are used as their sources of information, children should be helped to secure reliable information. When they ask, "Is it true?" or show signs of irritation, they may be ready for help in becoming more critical-minded. If such is not the case, the adult might challenge a child with "Do you know that is true?" "How can you show it to be true?"

The child in the primary school can plan a little more for himself each year. It has taken time through the preschool years for him to mature as an individual, to sense the individuality of other persons, to grow from individual play to play and work with others. Where the three-year-old concentrated in a smaller degree and for a shorter time, the four- and five-year-old can study a larger area for a longer time. The five-year-old will plan "to feed the animals," "to gather different kinds of seeds," or "to build a house." Children in the primary school can participate more in planning if such inquiries are given as "How may we find out?" "What is the next step?" "What do you suggest?" Thus, a beginning in co-operative action is made. Such an instructional program creates a democratic atmosphere in keeping with the natural developmental needs of children.

The Primary School Should Provide Balanced Instruction

The opinion prevalent in some quarters that content and experiences of the physical sciences are inappropriate in the primary grades is not substantiated by research studies. Haupt found that:

> When the objective type of aim is used, the criterion of grade placement is complexity of learning experiences irrespective of the fields of science from which these experiences are taken. There is no experimental evidence that content from the biological science is less difficult for children than the content from the physical sciences and, therefore, better adapted to the lower grades of the elementary school.[7]

Craig discovered that the inquiries of children involved content from all of the major sciences; that is, astronomy, biology, chemistry, geology, and physics. Children's interests in the primary grades involve the physical sciences as well as the biological.[8] From the physical sciences, simple but basic meanings can be secured about rocks, soil, sun, moon, stars,

---

[7] Haupt, *op. cit.*, p.104.

[8] G. S. Craig, *Certain Techniques Used in Developing a Course of Study for the Horace Mann Elementary School*, pp. 33–40. New York: Bureau of Publications, Teachers College, Columbia University, 1927.

magnetism, static and current electricity, weather, air, water, light, sound, and simple machines. From the biological sciences, there are meanings to be secured from such phenomena as the effect of seasonal change upon living things, animal care of the young, conditions necessary to living things, and the economic value of plants and animals.

It is most important that the material selected for each grade of the primary school be balanced to include the elements of learning which represent a rich experience with science. Each level should give the child some opportunity for exploration with content derived from the five great major fields of science: astronomy, biology, chemistry, geology, and physics. This cannot be accomplished by studying only plants and animals.

There should also be balanced instruction as to the types of activities employed. Children should have rich opportunity to develop their abilities in discussion, in experimentation, in observing in the out of doors, and in reading for information and motivation. A complete program of instruction in primary science can be maintained only by the full utilization of all of these activities, for each plays its part in the development of the purposes of science education.

THE INTERMEDIATE-SCHOOL CHILD AND SCIENCE[9]

Intermediate-grade children have many of the characteristics of primary children in that they like to explore, manipulate materials, discuss, read, and write, but they have a great enough command of these skills so that they are not so much concerned with learning the skill as in making use of the skill.

Basic Values for Science in Relation to the Abilities of Intermediate-Grade Children

Some of the elementary scientific abilities of intermediate-grade children are fairly well developed and opportunities should be provided to help the children retain these worth-while abilities. Other desirable abilities just beginning to appear should be fostered.

Developing further understanding concerning the environment. Since curiosity is the basis of much constructive thinking, opportunity should be provided for exploration which may stimulate, direct, and use curiosity. These experiences may take the form of a trip to a stream, a walk in the park, the observation of an animal, a visit to a powerhouse, or the opening of a dry cell. On the other hand, explorations may involve mental processes primarily. There is little physical exploration involved in a

---

[9] The committee has profited from the collaboration of Katherine E. Hill, Wheelock College, Boston, Massachusetts, in the following section of this chapter.

discussion of the questions "How did the earth come to be?" "Do people live on Mars?" and "What happened to the dinosaurs?"

Explorations at the intermediate-age level differ from those at the primary-age level in that they are more often undertaken for an expressed reason. Science experiences for children from eight to twelve may be play, and some of this is good. Teachers may have many opportunities for suggesting experiences which will help children to answer their questions.

Exploratory experiences of any type are likely to be valuable. They help children to feel at home in their environment, an environment which includes events of the past as well as of the present and the future. Some understanding of the total environment may play an important part in human relationships. Much of the foundation for future social responsibilities is laid at this time. A broad understanding of the environment is a goal for science in the intermediate grades.

Developing ability to solve problems. Solving problems is another ability which is important at all levels of development. Intermediate-grade teachers may begin to place special emphasis on problem-solving since intermediate-grade children have begun to master certain skills which are useful in problem-solving.

Science offers exceptional opportunities for problem-solving. This is because many problems in this area may be solved, at least in part, by experimentation with concrete materials or by observations of real things. "Will a magnet pick up copper, iron, and silver?" "Is granite harder than sandstone?" "Will an onion plant grow from an onion bulb?" These are problems which may be solved by eight- and nine-year-olds. These and similar questions could be answered by the teacher, but such questions also offer opportunity for problem-solving by the children.

The choice of a specific problem for investigation may be the result of the co-operative effort of the entire group, including the teacher. However, in some instances it is well for the teacher to choose the problem for investigation and to present this problem to the group in such a manner that the children will be eager to work toward the solution. This latter procedure is often necessary if children are to become familiar with much of their total environment. Some interesting problems could not be proposed by intermediate-grade children with their limited background of experience.

The major goal in a problem-solving situation, so far as the teacher is concerned, is for individuals to improve their ability to solve a problem. With this major goal in mind, teachers will need to help children state their problem clearly, gather data necessary for the solution of the problem, and reach a satisfactory solution of the problem.

The first of these three steps is often carried out in group discussions.

Each child is given a chance to contribute. The questions formulated during discussion may be arranged, with the help of the teacher, so that fundamental questions will be considered first. The teacher has a significant role in this planning since he is able to offer further questions for study as well as to help with the general organization. It is important to remember that intermediate-grade children can help in planning and in evaluation. They express ideas with ease and are able to organize ideas. Some intermediate-grade children are able to begin to evaluate the methods they are using in problem-solving.

The study of a problem may be pursued by the group as a whole. An experiment may be presented to the group by two or three children or by the teacher, and opportunity may be given for the experiment to be repeated. But it is very important that there be time for individual experimentation. Individual experimentation is an important means of gathering data.

As children work they become acquainted with many methods of gathering information. Careful observations may be made during trips outside the classroom and in connection with experiments within the classroom. Books may be used for securing facts. Also, children obtain facts from informed adults. They should be encouraged to experiment for themselves and to check their experimentation by consulting authority. They should be helped to observe with as much accuracy as possible.

Such a period of gathering information should terminate in the drawing of a satisfactory conclusion. In many cases, children will be able to find a positive factual answer for their problem. In answering other problems, such as "Do people live on Mars?" the answer will be "We can't really tell, but we don't think so." Whatever the answer, the teacher has helped children to have a meaningful experience in problem-solving.

Further development of scientific attitudes. As is true of problem-solving, science situations offer unusual potentialities for the building of scientific attitudes. Because children work with concrete materials, there is opportunity for the development of individual responsibility in the use of these materials. Co-operation is necessary if a group of children are to use concrete materials successfully. Children are able to grow in responsibility and co-operation only if they are led into situations where they can be responsible and co-operative. These attitudes are active, not passive.

Co-operation is also necessary in the development of such attitudes as "critical-mindedness" and "open-mindedness." Children have a better chance to develop these attitudes if they are allowed to participate in discussions. One of the responsibilities of teachers as leaders of discussions is to guide children in questioning their own ideas as well as the ideas of others. At the same time, however, teachers must help children to keep their minds open to the opinions of others.

Such a goal as the development of attitudes may seem somewhat elusive. But, as we consider the future responsibilities of citizens, we will probably agree that helping children to become more co-operative, more responsible, more "open-minded," and, at the same time, more "critical-minded" is certainly worth the effort.

The Study of the Environment for the Development of Understandings, Attitudes, and Appreciations[10]

The ever changing environment furnishes situations and materials for science education. The teacher provides opportunities for exploring the environment and, also, for the children's discovery of themselves as an integral part of the world about them. From such an exploration may be developed desirable understandings, attitudes, appreciations, and interests.

Educational Resources of the Local Community

If his pupils are to study the environment, the teacher should himself explore the materials and situations in the local community. Such a study will reveal richer resources than one usually is aware of. Even in regions which often seem entirely barren, it is surprising what materials and relationships are revealed when one turns over stones, boards, or logs, examines the surfaces of apparently bare rocks or cliffs, digs up roots of plants in waste places, probes decaying logs, examines compost piles, and hoes in the family garden. Fence corners, roadsides, and waste places are equally as rich in science materials as are the forest, the field, the pond, or the seashore.

A teacher's exploration of community resources for study should involve contacts with such agencies as the County Agricultural Extension Service, the U.S. Soil Conservation Service, the U.S. Forestry Service, the Fish and Wild-Life Service, the local weather bureau, the health department, and the water department. Through these agencies teachers may secure opportunities for trips which will provide definite illustrations of factors involved in man's dealing with his environment. Bulletins, charts, pictures, and publications of various kinds may be secured through them. Some are of great value to the teacher in his preparation for instruction; others are useful in working with children.

---

[10] The committee has profited from the collaboration of Leona Sundquist, Western Washington College of Education, Bellingham, Washington, in the following section of this chapter.

In one's local community there are always persons and enterprises which present special interests or hobbies. These are often rich sources of ideas and provide suggestions for trips to take, things to see, and things to do. For example, there may be a dairy farm, an apiary, a sawmill, a stone quarry, a forest, a grain field, etc.

Basic Facts To Consider in Using the Environment

How can methods of instruction in the elementary school be managed so as to help children understand that man is an integral part of nature? Situations and experiences should be so ordered that the following facts become a part of the framework of the children's social outlook. Man, as well as other organisms, is dependent upon his environment for adequate living. All life, including man, is interdependent. Change is a fundamental characteristic of the environment to which man, as well as other organisms, must be able to adjust in order to survive and to live comfortably. The interaction of physical forces and living things, including man, maintains constant conditions of change in the framework of living. The individual organism or group which does not have capacity to adjust successfully to continually changing demands is doomed to extinction. The best adapted are most successful in the game of life. It should follow that man, being a rational creature, should, through his knowledge of natural processes, intelligently use the environment for his survival and ultimate welfare.

Man is an integral part of the environment. Man's attitude toward himself and his environment determines many of his actions which affect his ultimate success or failure as an individual or a species. The attitude that man is a being set apart from the rest of living organisms accounts for many of his personal and social problems. In order to live successfully and abundantly man must recognize that he is part of the environment, influencing it and being affected by it. The sooner man recognizes the fact that he is a part of nature and is subject to the operation of the same forces and processes as other creatures, the sooner he will come to satisfactory solutions for many of his social ills.

The teacher should not consider environment as merely another tool in education, for such an attitude sets the child apart from and above the environment. Rather, the environment and man should be thought of as organically interrelated aspects of the general phenomenon of living. The extent to which man lives successfully is measured by the degree to which he uses the natural processes and resources of his environment in maintaining a high standard of living without hazarding the welfare of future generations. The teacher should consider this relationship of man and environment in arranging materials and situations for instruction.

Opportunities must be provided through field trips for children to begin to understand their environment, to become aware of the forces operating in it, and to recognize the interrelationships existing in it. Children should begin to realize that man, through knowledge, can live in such a manner that the forces and processes of the environment may function to his benefit.

All living organisms, including man, are dependent upon the environment. The dependence of man and animals upon each other and the dependence of both upon plants, and likewise the dependence of plants upon certain physical conditions of the environment may be observed in their changes in seasonal activities. Many birds migrate. Certain animals hibernate; others store food. Some die but leave eggs in appropriate places. Man harvests and conserves food products for himself and his domesticated animals. Changes in the type of foods in markets reveal seasonal changes. An analysis made of the types and sources of food would indicate that when light, heat, and physical conditions of soil are adequate, the normal population of a locality may amply support itself. In winter, man, as well as other animals, lives upon the food manufactured by plants in previous growing seasons or upon food transported from regions where growing conditions are favorable.

Exploration and analysis of the structures of plants reveal that plants, too, survive unfavorable periods through food stored in adequate quantities and in appropriate places and that they resume growth when conditions become favorable. Collection and analysis of seeds and other fruiting structures, explorations by digging for roots, bulbs, tubers, and underground rootstalks of plants will reveal the ways in which food is stored.

Observations supplemented by simple experimentation should indicate that plants are dependent upon light, heat, water, and certain conditions of soil in order to manufacture food. Discussions of observed facts in the field and in experimental demonstrations in the classroom provide opportunities for growth in understanding that plants are at the base of the feeding pattern of all life.

Changes in plant and animal activities conform to the physical changes in the environment as the seasons pass. Life is tied up with relationships existing between the earth and the sun. Awareness of factors involved can be attained by observing the changes in the relative length of day and night, the position of the sun in the sky at noon, the lengths of shadows, the temperature readings, and the weather conditions. Further observations and records of the time and position of the rising and setting of the sun will reveal a relationship existing between the position of the earth and the sun. This relationship determines the recurring changes in the environment to which living organisms must adjust. These observations are effective in developing an understanding of the dependence of living things on the sun as a great source of energy.

Resources other than food may be explored by children in developing an understanding of man's dependence. Examine the local community for answers to the following types of questions: What materials are used in the building of homes, in the making of clothes, in providing for heat, light, and transportation, and in running the local industries? Where are these materials found? How are they obtained? How is the local community dependent upon neighboring communities, other regions, and other countries for the material needs of life?

It is well to encourage children to inquire how each one of us is dependent upon the knowledge and technology possessed by others. This involves the science underlying such phases of living as medical care, health, sanitation, fire protection, and communication. Suitable experiences can be provided by well-organized trips to hospitals, garbage and sewage disposal centers, and water-purification establishments. It must be stressed, however, that these trips should provide experiments to accompany, elaborate, and demonstrate the work done in the classroom.

Man must recognize sequence of events. The sequence of events is usually described as the cause-and-effect relationship; any change in one or more significant factors in one place may produce consequent changes in another. As discussed above, plant growth is dependent upon certain factors of the physical environment, such as temperature, moisture, fertility, and soil conditions. A change in any one or a number of these may produce changes in plant growth. Changes in plant growth determine the character of the year's crop, which in turn may modify price. Income influences the life of the family and the community. Pests, drought, excess rainfall, and extremes in temperature are factors which influence directly or indirectly the activities of the community. Innumerable situations in a home, on a farm, or in a community will reveal these relationships.

The experiences of farmers and gardeners may be explored as to the causes of successes and failures. Neighboring lawns, fields, and gardens reveal spots where drought, pests, and lack of care and cultivation have played havoc. The county agent and leaders of the 4-H and garden clubs can suggest places to visit and experiences to be had.

Towns and cities are not immune from the operation of forces that affect life in rural areas. One is apt to consider city and country as separate, independent entities when actually they are bound together by a devious network of cause and effect. Children should come to an understanding of interrelationships in the activities of people of town and city, in different sections of the nation and regions of the world. The underlying conditions of physical forces, plant growth, natural resources, and technology which generate these interrelationships may be studied. It can be shown that droughts, pests, or floods occurring in one area upset the economy in another. The need for man to recognize this sequence of events in the operation of forces and to act accordingly, so that he may live more abundantly, should be indicated.

Man is a factor in changing his environment. That man is a factor in changing his environment and upsetting an existing balance in nature has been forced to the attention of all by such tragedies as the dust storms of the Great Plains and the floods of the Mississippi Valley. Conservation becomes a supremely important watchword. Teachers are encouraged to introduce elements of conservation education at all levels.

Teachers may help in developing the understanding that soil is a constantly changing substance resulting from the interaction of physical forces and living things by providing for such activities as the following: Rocks may be examined for evidences of decay and gradual conversion into soil. Exposed surfaces of rocks, such as bluffs, cliffs, road cuts, or even stone and cement sidewalks, stone steps, and rocks used in buildings, may be observed for results of the action of the agencies of weathering. The succession in the types of plant growth that occur as soil accumulates may be found. The condition of soil as to texture and content where it is shallow, sandy, and rocky may be compared with good garden loam. The action of fungus plants may be noted on fallen leaves, dead logs, twigs, and sticks in the field, roadside, and forest. Many observations may be made to show the place of decay in the formation of soil.

Such activities are indicative of the type of experiences which have possibilities for promoting understanding that soil is usually slow in formation, that many forces and organisms take part in its formation, that its condition is constantly changing, that decay and decomposition are necessary, that man is dependent upon the action of such lowly organisms as bacteria, fungi, and lichens, that man must care for soil in order to have an ever productive source of food and the other necessities of life, and that man has become a determining factor in the supply of good soil for the world. This kind of work can be started in the primary grades. Appropriate elements may be selected at different stages of the child's growth to aid him in continually enlarging his concepts of soil formation and care.

Similarly, forest growth and change may be studied to indicate the many interrelationships of physical factors and plant growth, the resulting responses in animal life, the influences upon lumber products, and the effects upon water sheds and floods. Every opportunity should be utilized to develop the idea of the necessity for man to recognize that he is a part of nature, influencing it, and being affected by it.

Summary

The new program of science, which emphasizes the development of desirable social behavior, is organized around problems that have social value and are challenging and worth while to children. The teacher must, therefore, look back of the objects of the universe to the problems which involve meanings that children will need to understand in order to participate intelligently in life. This means that, in science, opportunities must be provided for the development of understandings in all the areas of the environment and at all levels of social needs.

The classroom teacher in the elementary school should consider himself an agent of both education and science in the community and be willing to co-operate with reliable health, welfare, recreational, and scientific agencies, local and national, which serve his community. His teaching should lead the children to an understanding and appreciation of how, through their own activity, they may participate intelligently in the work of the present and the future. It is essential that he have a realization of the potentialities of science in society.

CHAPTER VII

MATERIALS AND METHODS OF TEACHING SCIENCE IN THE ELEMENTARY SCHOOL

The Teaching Procedures

The Utilization of the Scientific Method in Developing Procedures for Instruction

Of all the methods that have been proposed for use in the elementary school, one method must have first consideration in the teaching of science, namely, the scientific method. Within the comprehension of children, the application of the scientific method is a matter of securing the correct explanation, or, if that is not definitely known, of finding the best explanation. It is evident that children do not discover new facts for mankind; but they do discover new facts for themselves and they must do that day by day if they are to become fully equipped for the age in which they will live. Fortunately, they have the assistance of the rich scientific heritage provided for them by the scientists of the past and the present.

If the teacher will keep in mind the kinds of questions asked by children on many occasions, he will have a natural approach to the scientific method. For instance, such challenges as: How do we find out? How do we know this is true? Are you sure of your facts? Is that a guess or can you prove it? The elements of the scientific method (see chap. iii) can be adapted to the level of the children in such a way that they will know what they are doing and why they are doing it and will have some control over the process.

Children can orient themselves to problems. Children at all grade levels orient themselves to problems or questions. This orientation may come through short or long intervals of manipulation (including play), observation, and use of appropriate reading material and visual aids. The teacher can use discussion to give point to these activities and to cause the problem to emerge more clearly for the children.

Children can define problems. In the elementary school the problem (what is to be discovered) may need to be stated and restated. This is true even though the problem has been well stated on a printed page. The teacher should find out what the children have in mind when they use the words in the statement of the problem. Perhaps the children have a different meaning or concept of the problem from the teacher's or from that stated in a book. A discussion which provides for children an opportunity to state ideas freely assists in making relatively certain that the teacher and the children have the same problem in mind.

Children can suggest and test hypotheses. Such a question as "How may we find the explanation to this phenomenon?" may cause children to propose a hypothesis. In fact, teachers should condition the learning situation in a classroom in such a way that children naturally propose hypotheses.

There should be the kind of discussion which allows children to give expression to speculation, to suggest methods of solution, to deliberate in planning, and to evaluate the whole process at many points in instruction. In other words, if the elements of the scientific method are to be utilized, there should be provision for initiative on the part of both the teacher and the children.

Children can draw conclusions. Children can draw conclusions when the problem and the method of solving the problem are sufficiently within their grasp. The traditional concept that children cannot generalize is false. There are many problems in science which are sufficiently within the comprehension of children to provide them with ample opportunity for generalization and for drawing conclusions.

Children can check conclusions with authentic material. Children must learn the value of depending upon the information provided by scientists. They must learn that they cannot gain truth through discussion alone; nor can they be certain that the conclusions they themselves draw from experiments or observations are infallible. They must be willing to check conclusions against the contributions of men who have spent their lives studying and investigating in the fields involved. Since in most cases children cannot consult scientific authorities, they must turn to authentic material developed for them at their own level of comprehension, such as books or visual aids, but with the recognition that such material needs frequent revision.

Children can focus attention upon the elements of the scientific method. Too often one sees in the elementary school a type of instruction which varies but little from a ferreting of answers from the children. In this procedure the teacher asks a question, expecting the children to give a correct response. This response is followed by another question from the teacher to which another correct response is sought. Such teaching gives little opportunity for the children to participate in the guidance of their learning. It also provides little opportunity for the teacher to learn about the children's experiences, their ideas, their questions, or their planning for the solution of problems. Such a procedure makes little use of the elements of the scientific method.

There is more to instruction in science than eliciting pat answers to questions and problems. Attention should be focused upon the elements of scientific method and the attitudes of children. This statement does not imply that the teacher will assume an arbitrary position as a judge to call forth decisions as to whether a given child has exhibited a right or wrong attitude. Rather, the attention is upon the procedure of how we secure truth. Good teaching involves evaluation on the part of teachers and children of the procedures which they employ.

This discussion of scientific method should not be interpreted to indicate that the elements of scientific method should monopolize instruction. It might be uninteresting if children were forced to utilize in all their work in science the procedures involved in scientific method. Children should be led to the realization many different times in the elementary school that statements in an accurate source of science material are reliable and that they can begin their study on many subjects with such sources.

The attitude of the teacher. An important aspect in the teaching of scientific attitudes is the attitude of the teacher himself. In his behavior, the teacher must display the elements of scientific method. He must indicate his willingness to solve problems. There must be willingness to have statements challenged and investigated by the group. The teacher must display critical-mindedness and willingness to participate in intelligent planning.

For the teacher to assume a learning attitude need not be hypocritical. Even though the teacher has taught the same material many times, it may present novel elements when he is approaching the material with a new group of children.

Vitalization of Instruction in Science

It should be recognized that science is a dynamic subject for children because it relates to their understanding of the universe of energy, matter, and life. The teaching of science to children can be a dynamic process filled with interest for both teachers and children.

Instruction should begin with children where they are. Regardless of how the instruction is initiated, vital teaching recognizes the concepts children may have on the subject or problem. For instance, children may be studying about the sky. They may think of the night sky as a hard-shelled dome with holes in it for the stars. Or again they may account for the evaporation of water in a dish by saying the dish leaked. It is well for the teacher to provide opportunity for children to express their ideas, however incomplete or inaccurate, in order that misconceptions may be brought into the open. In the study of science they should be allowed to express themselves without the fear of censure or ridicule.

Very frequently children's concepts have originality and imagination. Their concepts also provide opportunities for evaluation of preceding work and reveal the kind of instruction needed for clarification of ideas, such as that of studying material in books and visual aids or performing experiments or making observations.

There is vitalization within the content of science. Teachers giving instruction in science learn that there is a natural motivation to be secured from the content of science if it is approached from the children's own level of understanding. Questions relating to the age of the earth, the formation of mountains, causes of weather, the adaptations of plants and animals, and many other subjects have natural challenges. Hence, the teacher looking for the development of readiness for instruction in science will do well to have confidence in the appeal that is found in the content of science for children. He will also do well to provide opportunity for children to react naturally and to toss ideas about. Syllabuses and professional material prepared for teachers, and books carefully designed for children at various levels of advancement in school work, can be of assistance to the teachers in selecting appropriate problems, meanings, and experiences for children in their classrooms.

Identification and observation should be viewed as means to interpretation. The identification or proper naming of an object should not be considered the final objective of instruction. Identification and observation should be viewed as means to interpretation. The centrally important implication is that the teacher need have no feeling of responsibility for identifying all the plants, animals, and rocks in a community. His task is that of teaching children, and identification of objects should be done in a manner appropriate for children. For instance, for young children it may be sufficient identification of a rock to say that this is a hard rock from John's yard. Later in the elementary school it might be identified as granite. Elementary-school workers should recognize that there are few scientists or naturalists who are able to identify objects accurately in a large number of fields in science. Furthermore, it should be recognized that identification has little meaning to children unless they can assist in the process of identification. There is no great value in a teacher's labeling things for children.

Problems and topics should not be pursued beyond the level of the children's span of interest or their level of ability. Instruction in many subjects of the elementary school has been characterized by exhaustive teaching units which give children the impression that they have learned all there is to know about the topic. This approach is not in keeping with the nature of science, for no subject or topic in this field can be exhausted or completely mastered. After a study of the air by pupils of any grade, there is much more still to be learned. As a matter of fact, the specialists in meteorology have not yet learned all there is to know about the atmosphere. Indeed, what is learned at one level is the beginning of learning at a subsequent level.

Children should be given opportunity to participate in planning. Children should be given an opportunity to participate in the planning of their learning activities. The teacher's objectives determine the direction of instruction, and the instruction takes its form largely in terms of the children's conceptions or misconceptions and experiences regarding the large values of science (see chaps. ii, iii, and v). Much of the instruction in the elementary school is characterized by haste, which inhibits critical thinking.

The utilization of children's participation in the guidance of instruction does not free the teacher from constant planning. Flexible planning demands adaptation of the plans to the children's needs. It calls for the kinds of plans that can be modified, that can be stepped up or stepped down in difficulty as the situation may require for the utilization of experiences.

Children need rich experiences with experimentation. Children should have a rich experience in experimentation. Work space should be provided in every classroom where children can perform experiments and exhibit materials of interest. This working section of a classroom can be made attractive and orderly. The tables and cabinets in the work space should be utilized for active experimentation and study, rather than as museums.

Too frequently experiments, as they are employed in classrooms, degenerate into a series of stunts, tricks, or demonstrations. Experiments should be utilized for instruction rather than as a display of magic. Children should become aware of the meaning of experimentation. This applies not only to simple experiments in science as a school subject but also to planning related to their own affairs and on their own level of understanding, whether pertaining to experiences in the school, in the home, on the school grounds, or in the community.

Children need rich experiences with science books. Frequently children's books are not utilized as well as they should be. Most basic textbooks in science are designed with the thought that the teacher will work with the children while they are using the books, reading with them while they read, discussing matters with them when they engage in discussion. In other words, the teacher should be a member of the group, learning with the children in a natural situation, rather than watching their activities as a by-stander or observer. Used in this manner, the basic book in science can lead to dynamic motivation and vitality of instruction.

In using books the children should be given an opportunity to express their own ideas and to develop lines of interest. Reading in science should lead to other types of activities such as discussion, performing an experiment, or planning a science excursion. These activities will, in turn, cause the children and teacher to turn to the books for information and for new interests and subjects.

Provision should be made for the development of special interests. Through the provision made for work space in a classroom, consideration can be given to individual differences, including the development of hobbies and special interests. Experiments performed in the class can be repeated by individuals at work tables during free periods. Children wishing to express a science idea through the fine or industrial arts may do so by utilizing work space in the classroom.

In any group there will be some that will learn the necessary skills and information more quickly than others. Work space can be utilized by the slower pupils for the development of skills through additional practice in free periods. An example of this might be in the wiring of a simple circuit. In free periods some of the children that are more skilful with wiring circuits can assist those that are less successful.

Equipment for Science in the Elementary School[1]

Materials from the Environment

If the viewpoint is taken that many everyday experiences of children have important implications for science, then it becomes clear that science should be taught to a large extent with materials which are found in the children's own environment. For example, the expansion of air when heated may be taught by heating air in a chemical flask over a Bunsen burner or by holding a partially inflated balloon over the radiator. The choice should be for the latter, for the balloon is a thing familiar to children, whereas the flask and burner may not be.

Use of the General Equipment of School

Much of the general equipment of modern schools has use in science. For example, dark window shades are necessary in a program of visual education, but they are equally valuable as a part of the equipment for showing the causes of seasonal change or of day and night or of the operation of mirrors and lenses, for some of the best ways of showing these

---

[1] The committee has profited from the collaboration of Charles K. Arey, University of Alabama, University, Alabama, in the following section of this chapter.

things involve the use of a darkened room. In the absence of built-in devices, an ingenious teacher can find ways of darkening a room.

Globes and maps are equipment for science as well as for other parts of the school program. A globe can be used for showing seasonal change, day and night, and the location of wind belts. Maps are useful in studying climates and the location of natural resources.

In science teaching there is often need of a strong beam of light. This may be supplied by a lantern slide projector, an item of equipment found in many school systems. On the other hand, a "gooseneck" desk lamp or a strong flashlight will serve as the "sun" in demonstrating the causes of seasonal change, day and night, eclipses, and phases of the moon. For such demonstrations an old tennis ball makes a good "moon."

Construction of Simple Equipment

A desirable form of learning goes on when children, working alone or with the teacher, construct their own simple apparatus. They are more apt to understand the basic working principles of things they have built themselves. Furthermore, a child has the added gain of a feeling of creativeness about something he himself has constructed. For these reasons tools and materials should be provided so that children may construct such equipment as animal cages, boxes for growing seeds, model water wheels, shelves, and storage cabinets. Among the simple tools needed may be listed saws, hammers, planes, pliers, tinner's shears, and screw drivers. A variety of construction materials should be at hand, for example, wood (preferably soft pine lumber in various sizes, when available), nails and screws, paint, cardboard or Bristol board, construction paper in assorted colors, water colors, and brushes.

Making Use of Materials That Are Readily Available

So far as it is practical to do so, science materials ought to be kept on hand to use as the need arises. There are many occasions to use such materials as bottles, jars, jugs, and flowerpots, a collection of which in various sizes will be found useful. Tin cans with their lids cleanly removed will be valuable not only as containers but also as sources of easily worked sheet metal. A collection of stoppers in various sizes should also be available.

Hand lenses or reading glasses are frequently needed for examining small objects such as flowers, insects, and rocks.

Certain simple materials should be available for the study of electricity and magnetism. A single collection of these materials can usually be made to serve several classrooms. Half a dozen dry cells bought at the beginning of the year will probably serve throughout the year as sources of power for electrical experiments. One or two electric doorbells, some miniature lamp sockets secured by cutting up an old Christmas-tree lighting outfit, some flashlight bulbs, and some copper bell wire will find many uses. Much of this material may be brought in by the children; the rest may be purchased at hardware and "Five-and-Ten" stores. Powerful permanent magnets may be secured from junked "Model-T" Ford cars, old radio loudspeakers, discarded hand-cranked telephones, or old truck magnetos. Bar magnets must usually be purchased in pairs from scientific supply houses. Two pairs are recommended. Darning needles and steel knitting needles are useful as objects to be magnetized. A magnetized darning needle suspended by a silk thread is useful in a study of the compass.

The small amounts of rubber tubing and glass tubing needed in elementary-school science may be secured through local sources. The glass and rubber tubing should be of sizes which will fit together.

It is often desirable to heat water or other materials in glass so that the class can see what is going on. Pyrex nursing bottles and dishes make good equipment for this purpose.

For semipermanent schoolroom aquariums, the five-gallon size is recommended. It is desirable to have a number of small aquariums for specimens which, for one reason or another, the class does not wish to place in the large aquarium, such as specimens which are to be kept for only a short time. Aquariums for such purposes may be set up in large glass jars. Such containers are also useful for terrariums.

Equipment for Study in the Field

Field trips are often scheduled for children in a modern school, and some field-collecting equipment is desirable. A basket or other container for plants, a large tin can or two, a trowel, nets for fish and insects, field glasses, and a magnifying glass are useful equipment. If collecting is done with conservation in mind, only a few specimens will be taken in any case. A mason's hammer is useful for breaking off rock specimens.

Sources of Heat

So many uses for heat are found in science that some means of heating needs to be provided. For many experiments candles are useful. "Canned heat" (solidified alcohol) is an extremely useful source of heat, as are the "Heat-Tabs" on sale in many drug stores. An alcohol lamp may be made by punching a hole through the metal cap of an ink bottle and inserting a piece of lamp wicking. An electric hot plate can be used for many purposes, and it presents little danger of setting fires. Sometimes science experiments involving heat may be done in the kitchen, if the school has one. Many experiments with air may be done over a stove or radiator.

Storage Space for Equipment in the Classroom

Schoolrooms should have ample closet space for storage of materials. It is recommended that this need be kept in mind in planning new school construction. Where space permits, counters constructed along one side of the room, with storage closets underneath, are suggested. If built to suitable dimensions, such counters are useful as places for children to work, and the closets will hold a great deal of equipment.

Material which is used frequently in a classroom should be stored in the classroom, whereas the material which is used only occasionally can be stored in a central storage space where it is available for use by all groups.

There is some material which could have permanent display. For example, a school weather station can be established in a school corridor where weather maps, barometers, and thermometers can be exhibited. Information about the local community, such as altitude, latitude, and longitude, can likewise be displayed. In other words, a partial solution to storage is the more effective utilization of material.

The Role of Equipment in Instruction

Equipment in science should be viewed by the teacher in the perspective of the total pattern of teaching and learning. In this discussion the emphasis has been placed upon the selection and utilization of equipment that has meaning for children.

VISUAL AND AUDITORY INSTRUCTIONAL MATERIAL[2]

Use of Motion Pictures and Slidefilms in Teaching Science

Motion pictures and slidefilms may be used to achieve many of the objectives of science teaching. Motion pictures and slidefilms are in most cases the next best thing to direct experience when such experience is impossible. In addition, they have two special values. They may depict excellent instruction, thus serving as a sample for the effective use of equipment and materials in teaching science, as well as illustrating good method and content. Also, they may, by virtue of their unique characteristics, illustrate scientific phenomena which cannot be seen by the naked eye, such as the solar system, bacteria, and the structure of the atom. The inherent characteristics of the motion picture, including animation, microphotography, time-lapse photography, and slow motion, make possible a realistic understanding of abstract subjects and events of scientific interest.

---

[2] The committee has profited from the collaboration of David J. Goodman, *Popular Science Publishing Co.*, New York, N.Y., in the following section of this chapter.

Characteristics of a Desirable Motion Picture or Slidefilm

There is a paucity of motion pictures and slidefilms that are well adapted for use in elementary-school science, although indications are that this is one of the most fertile fields for future development. The following set of criteria relating to the planning and development of motion pictures and slidefilms may govern science educators in helping to develop the right kind of materials and to select the best teaching aids from available sources.

a. The motion picture or slidefilm should be conceived in idea and vocabulary for a particular grade span, such as primary grades, intermediate grades, junior high school, or senior high school.

b. The educational objectives of the motion picture or slidefilm should be clearly defined. There may be two types of films produced in terms of their utilization in the classroom. One type of film may depict a broad overview of the subject and the second type may make clear some particular idea or fact.

c. The motion picture or slidefilm should not be overcrowded with factual information which is difficult for pupils to comprehend after one or two showings. Only those facts which are absolutely basic to the content of a topic should be depicted. A major criticism of science motion pictures and slidefilms heretofore produced is the attempt to encompass too much content and information.

d. The motion picture or slidefilm should be planned the way children learn, not necessarily the way the subject is traditionally taught or the way it is known after it is learned.

e. The subject should not be presented so as to appear too easy. Stumbling blocks and mistakes may be deliberately incorporated.

f. In certain situations the motion picture or slidefilm may be developed as a self-contained unit, embodying motivation, concept teaching, review and summarization, activities, and follow-up work.

g. Almost any film will strike the children in a group at different points in their learning. For some, the film can do little more than motivate; for others it will clinch a point; for others it will show a new application, and so on. This is not to say that films are, therefore, worthless, but that no film can be constructed to meet some absolute and uniform need on the part of all learners.

Respective Advantages of Motion Pictures and Slidefilms

The teacher should understand the true distinction between the motion picture and the slidefilm. There are important differences between the two which should govern their selection and use. The slidefilm is not a feeble substitute for a motion picture. Aside from the fact that each consists of photographs projected on a screen, the two aids have little in common. Each has a different purpose; each calls on the teacher to participate in a different way; each has advantages and limitations not possessed by the other.

Motion pictures are especially valuable where motion is involved, where continuity of action is important, and where it is necessary to point out a number of relationships at one time.

On the other hand, the motion picture has some very definite limitations as a visual aid. It is inflexible in that the teacher cannot alter the time allotted to any one scene in the motion picture. In contrast, the film strip is highly flexible in that the teacher can spend one minute or ten on each frame, according to her conception of its relative importance. In addition, she can, if she wishes, turn back the strip to any frame to which she desires to make additional reference. Also, the slidefilm has obvious possibilities as a teaching medium, since it allows for active participation and discussion on the part of both children and teachers, whereas the motion picture limits such active participation since the presentation of the subject matter is fixed and beyond the control of the teacher.

The Audio-visual Department in Science[3]

Purpose of Centralized Department

The quality of the teaching of science may be improved by the maintenance of a centralized department, sometimes in smaller schools called a "materials bureau," which provides a wide variety of audio-visual instructional aids not now available in the majority of elementary schools. This wider choice of materials aids in developing important concepts by providing a teacher with more opportunities to follow the needs and interests of his group. In the average elementary school, the materials needed to make the teaching and the learning of science basic and exciting are often lacking. Major contributing factors to this condition are the individual school's restricted budget for this purpose, limited information as to the selection and the sources of needed materials, and the lack of proper storage space.

The practice of concentrating at a centralized bureau those materials not considered necessary as permanent equipment in the science classroom has definite advantages. It makes for economy in time, space, and effort. Also, the placing of definite responsibility to secure and maintain high-caliber materials in first-class order results in the availability of a wider choice of equipment. The easy accessibility of this equipment, selected by committees of teachers, results in an increased use of these visual aids, which play a vital role in developing a child's growth in science education. (For discussion of the use of such materials in the rural school, see chap. ix.)

---

[3] The committee has profited from the collaboration of Nelle Lee Jenkinson, St. Louis Public Schools, St. Louis, Missouri, in the following section of this chapter.

Circulation of Materials

Delivery service of materials distributed from a central bureau should be provided to the individual schools on a definite schedule each week. These materials may remain in schools the length of time desired. In order to capitalize interests, it is desirable that teachers' requests be filled on a forty-eight hours' notice in advance of the regular delivery date and that teachers be allowed to pick up materials at the department whenever they wish. The practice of advance booking of materials for a school term is to be avoided in order that the bureau may serve on a flexible "as needed" basis. A wide variety of teaching tools should be available from an efficiently operated centralized bureau. Projected visual aids—films, filmstrips, and slides—should be housed here. Until individual schools are adequately equipped, projectors and screens should likewise be circulated from such a depository.

Other materials should include apparatus for physical and chemical experiments, such as a telescope, barograph, polaroid and simple electrical equipment; natural science *realia*, such as minerals, mounted specimens, and habitat groupings; process exhibits which show steps in the manufacture of food and industrial products, as soybean derivatives and nylon; still pictures; colorfully illustrated booklets; phonograph records and radio transcriptions.

Information about Materials

A descriptive catalogue of materials and supplements in the possession of each teacher are methods of keeping teachers informed about available audio-visual aids. The plan of having a key teacher in each school act as liaison between the department and the faculty has proved highly successful as these teaching aids must be continually added to, revised, and withdrawn. If these materials are to make a child's environment more meaningful to him, it is necessary that they be geared to the changing civilization in which he lives.

RADIO IN ELEMENTARY-SCHOOL SCIENCE[4]

A number of educational agencies are sponsoring or promoting programs of science radio broadcasts designed for elementary-school children. In many cases these programs are intended to be used in the classroom. The number of possible listeners to these programs is very large. One educational agency which sponsors three science programs estimates a total of some 81,000 listeners.

One weakness inherent in the use of radio for classroom science in-

---

[4] The committee has profited from the collaboration of Charles K. Arey, University of Alabama, University, Alabama, in the following section of this chapter.

struction is that the teacher may leave science instruction to the radio entirely, thereby becoming merely a parasite. It must be emphasized that radio instruction, however skilfully done, cannot take the place of the classroom teacher nor can it build a curriculum in science. Few programs take into account the individual abilities, interests, and problems of the children, or the resources of the school and the community.

However, classroom listening to a series of radio broadcasts may have certain values for science instruction. If the series has balance among the various areas of science, it may serve to open up new areas of interest to children and to help them to orient themselves to a larger environment. If the series is designed to encourage children to experiment with the things around them, it may serve to relate science more closely to their everyday experiences. If the series is planned to encourage participation of the children in planning science activities, it may assist in improving the classroom instruction.

A second value which may come from a radio series on elementary science is related to the in-service training of teachers. Listening to such a series may well encourage teachers to broaden their teaching to new areas of experience or give them new ideas for teaching.

The agency responsible for the radio series in science should be aware of the characteristics of good instruction and should strive to remedy the weaknesses prevalent in the teaching of science in the school system. In this way science radio broadcasts can contribute to the development of science in the elementary school.

Summary

The objectives of science education to a large extent determine the pattern for the procedures of teaching science. In these procedures ample provision should be made for the utilization of the elements of the scientific method in the solution of problems. Children should become increasingly aware of these elements as they advance through the school and they should increase in ability to apply those elements to the problems they encounter in their lives.

The classroom should be a rich environment for learning science, with provision for a space for work with experiments. Much of the material utilized for experimentation can be secured from the local region, although some equipment may need to be purchased from scientific supply houses. Science can be of great assistance in making the classroom a more attractive place.

Authentic science material, such as books and visual aids which have been designed for children and classroom teachers, can provide motivation and guidance for the study of science. In utilizing such material, as much time as is needed should be taken to clear up each idea.

CHAPTER VIII

JUDGING THE RESULTS OF INSTRUCTION IN ELEMENTARY SCIENCE[1]

THE VARIOUS METHODS OF EVALUATION[2]

Evaluation as a Part of Teaching and Learning

Evaluation is inherent in all teaching and learning. It is not a post-process to follow elementary teaching and to serve as a basis for separating the "haves" and the "have nots." Rather, it is a vital and integral part of our efforts to insure continuous progress for each child. To this end, we evaluate the child's home and community background; his interests, beliefs, and understandings; his ability to apply and interpret; his social ideals and practices; his habits, skills, and needs—all these, in addition to the continual measuring of his progress in the more strictly limited fields of school learning.

Evaluation is an integral part of learning as well as of teaching. A purpose that enlists our best efforts and a sense of achievement make for effective learning. Children should participate in evaluation wherever possible, each pupil evaluating his own progress. The pupil needs to learn to evaluate as accurately as possible in terms of better living. Self-evaluation with the help of an understanding teacher will lead to intelligent self-direction.

Changing Concepts of Evaluation

The problems of evaluation are growing in scope and complexity as we learn more about the nature and objectives of education. When factual learnings were accepted as the paramount aim and responsibility of the schools, evaluation was based largely on the child's ability to reproduce facts. Education has progressed far beyond that simple concept of learning. Facts are still very essential. The factual knowledge needed by individuals for intelligent action is yearly growing more extensive and varied. But the emphasis in education today is on behavior.

The child is a growing organism continually interacting in an en-

---

[1] The reader will find many suggestions in respect to evaluation in chapter xv. Although that chapter is directed to the secondary-school level, many of the suggestions and devices will be found useful in the elementary school.

[2] The committee has profited from the collaboration of W. C. Croxton, State Teachers College, St. Cloud, Minnesota, in the following section of this chapter.

vironment. Objectives are functional. Social concern and contribution are essential for survival. Educational goals are progress goals toward better living. We need to find out many things about the growing, learning child. As we learn more about children and how they develop, evaluation becomes more important, more varied, and more difficult.

Evaluation in Terms of Functional Outcomes

Evaluation should be in terms of changes in understandings, actions, and outlooks. Some of these changes may be evident to anyone who knows his pupils intimately, but others can be judged only through carefully planned evaluation or after a period of time.

The reduction of accidents, rather than how much information can be recalled by pupils, is the most significant measure of the effectiveness of education for safety. Likewise, the degree to which conservation outcomes or recreation outcomes are achieved can best be judged by the attitudes which children manifest and by their acts. However, evaluation in terms of pupil behavior in situations as they naturally arise is essentially long-time evaluation. In many cases it seems desirable to devise methods which will yield more immediate, though admittedly less valid, evidence of achievement of the desired outcomes. It is most important that the situations in which the evaluating is done shall be as nearly as possible like those in which we hope that the learning will function.

Difficulties Involved in Evaluation of Functional Outcomes

Emphasis on functional outcomes in education introduces great difficulties in evaluation. As Burton has well stated, "Pupil behavior in any situation is controlled by a constellation of understandings, attitudes, abilities, and skills" (1). We are confronted with the integrated functioning of the whole child.

Evaluation of functional outcomes is comparable to diagnosis by a physician. The physician cannot measure the health of the child. He can make highly objective measurements of temperature, pulse, blood count, etc. He can also secure valuable subjective data by well-directed questions and observations. From all of these data the physician appraises the health of the individual, taking into consideration his hereditary endowment, his past experience, and the conditions under which he is living. Educational evaluation must be approached in like manner, but the problem is even more difficult.

Limited Progress in Evaluation in Elementary Science

Science is probably the least developed area of elementary education. It has only recently been introduced into many elementary curriculums. As might be expected of a newcomer, science has not as yet found its place in many schools, although much progress has been made within the past few years. The courses of study still reveal little agreement as to objectives, scope, sequence, suggested experiences, or grade placement of learnings. With this situation existing in elementary science, it is not strange that little progress has been made in evaluation.

Emphasis in the better elementary schools today is on sensing needs and developing purposeful experience units. Evaluation is useful both in sensing needs and as a basis for planning and directing our efforts. We sense needs, formulate our objectives in terms of functional outcomes, plan purposeful learning experiences, evaluate to discover how well we are doing in achieving our purposes, and redirect our efforts accordingly.

In some schools science instruction is carried on with little consideration of childhood living or social need. Progress in evaluation must await a clearer sensing of need and recognition of worthy purposes to be attained. Little is to be gained through time spent in attempting to evaluate achievements without relation to their functioning in life situations. Careful evaluation requires much energy and is time-consuming. It would seem to be wise to direct our efforts toward evaluation of important functional outcomes.

Many of the materials prepared for use in elementary science have been science-centered rather than life-centered. We have been slow to recognize the distinction between science in the abstract and science in elementary education. The science area offers rich opportunities for experiencing and for learning that are directed toward functional outcomes of elementary education, but the goals are not peculiar to science. They are common goals of the whole school program. General understanding of this fact is essential for improvement in materials of instruction, for teacher-pupil planning of purposeful experiences, and for evaluation.

Evaluation of the functional outcomes of elementary education in the science area is evaluation of the outcomes of childhood education. Very little has been done to evaluate the contributions of experience in science to the understandings, appreciations, attitudes, abilities, skills, habits, and participations of children that go to make up good living.

Preliminary Steps in Evaluation

The first step in evaluation is to determine the outcomes to be evaluated (8). Each specific outcome should be stated clearly. Such a statement might be related to the practice of covering coughs and sneezes with a handkerchief, the ability to read a thermometer, appreciation of the services of the janitor, or understanding that we depend largely upon the sun for energy.

Teachers will find many suggestions for exploring needs and formulating statements of functional outcomes in a publication entitled *Redirecting Science Teaching in the Light of Personal-social Needs* (**6**). The publication contains check lists of functional outcomes of science teaching at the various levels, prepared by a large number of teachers who were engaged in reconstructing their science programs. It is interesting to note that these statements of outcomes are similar to those developed by teachers in other areas.

The next step is to describe each outcome in terms of specific pupil behavior. For some outcomes this is a relatively simple task, for others it is not so easy. We cannot measure directly outcomes such as attitudes and appreciations. We can evaluate them only in terms of specific pupil behavior indicative of the desired appreciations or attitudes. This involves compilation of significant behavior items and the use of a number of evaluation procedures.

A preliminary step to evaluating comprehension of the broader generalizations is to analyze them into contributing understandings. Science is an especially fertile area for stimulating growth in understanding of the environment and for guiding the child toward an intelligent adjustment to his environment. There is, moreover, reasonably adequate evidence that elementary-school children are able to generalize if they have the requisite experience basis. The broader generalizations are essentially perspectives acquired by the individual through varied experiences and acquired understandings. Those that become incorporated and integrated in his thinking function cumulatively in an ever widening scope of relationships. The analysis of the broader generalizations into their contributing understandings is one of the most promising fields for contribution to the advancement of general education. It is an essential preliminary to the establishment of progress goals in generalization and to evaluation of our efforts to achieve intelligent outlooks.

Simplifying Evaluation Procedures

Most elementary-school teachers are general teachers, each of whom is responsible for a group of children throughout the school day. They have many scheduled and unscheduled duties. They do not have either the time or the energy to prepare elaborate measuring instruments. Evaluation procedures must, for the most part, be simple ones which can be fitted into the daily round of activities. There are few standard tests available which busy teachers will find very useful in evaluating functional outcomes of instruction at the elementary level. Tests of work-study skills, such as the Iowa Every-Pupil Tests of Basic Study Skills (**4**), may prove helpful. Some of the types of reading tests, interest inventories, scales of attitudes and beliefs, and self-rating scales can be used to advantage. Teachers will find helpful suggestions in some of the recent curriculum bulletins published by state and city school systems, in the Forty-fifth Yearbook of the National Society for the Study of Education (5), and in books such as those by Wrightstone (10) and Burton (1). With these suggestions and examples at hand, teachers must adapt and devise simple methods and instruments of evaluation suited to their purposes. Specialists in evaluation are needed in our schools to aid in, but not to direct, the efforts of teachers.

Use of Different Methods of Evaluation

Evaluation is still too much limited to traditional types of pencil-and-paper tests, although the trend is strongly toward appraisal through interpretation of pupil behavior. Records of the child's behavior, both in controlled and uncontrolled situations, are an important part of the work in modern elementary schools. They possess some important advantages. They yield evidence of the integrated functioning of the whole child—direct evidence obtained in certain life situations approximating others in which it is hoped that the learnings will function. They are relatively simple to use and they can be employed in evaluating a wide range of outcomes, many of which cannot be measured objectively.

Improved essay-type examinations have limited use in the upper elementary grades in testing understanding. The questions should be simple, clear, and specific. Each question should be such as to require the understanding and application of some fact, concept, or principle and to elicit a brief, clear statement. Enough questions covering the learning should be prepared to test adequately the child's comprehension and his use of the knowledge acquired. Questions calling for comprehensive discussion of a topic have little value at this level.

Every teacher should be able to construct several types of objective tests. The multiple-choice and best-answer tests are among the most valuable types of objective tests. Good objective tests are not easy to construct. However, many teachers today have had some instruction in devising and using this type of measuring instrument.

The newer problem-situation tests have important advantages. All teachers should learn about them. These tests are especially suited to the science area. They test the ability to evaluate data, to formulate hypotheses, to check interpretations and judgments against the evidence, and to employ understandings in new situations.

A problem-situation test presents a situation with sufficient and pertinent information to enable the pupil to solve the problem. The child may be confronted with an actual situation and be expected to decide upon an intelligent course of action through observation or experimentation and to act accordingly. More often, perhaps, the situation is described and the pupil analyzes it to decide upon a solution. For use in the elementary school, the problem situations should, in either case, be simple ones without too many complicating factors.

There are many other methods and devices for evaluation. The work products of the child both at school and at home are among the most significant evidences of his growing ability to employ his creative powers. Self-rating scales help in appraising the child's growth in ability to evaluate his own efforts. Interviews, inventories, and questionnaires all have their places. Case studies with the help of specialists are needed in some instances.

Intelligent Use of the Results of Evaluation

Evaluation is of little service unless the findings are wisely used. They are helpful in exploration and planning, in diagnosing difficulties, and in redirecting learning activities. They assist the teacher to understand each child and his problems. The teacher should have a folder for each child in which are kept all of the objective and subjective records pertaining to his development and progress.

As the teacher comes to understand his pupils better through careful evaluation and as he proceeds to plan additional learning experiences, the efforts grow more purposeful and the task becomes more professional and more interesting. As the pupil learns to evaluate his own achievements, desires for further learning develop which are potentially an incentive for continued progress. Evaluation can serve as the basis for pooling of efforts in teacher-child-parent planning. Joint efforts in purposeful planning, careful evaluation, and continual redirection can raise a school to new levels of service.

EVALUATION ON THE BASIS OF INTERPRETATION OF BEHAVIOR[3]

The observation of a pupil in various school situations may well give some clues to his progress. This is not a new idea. Teachers constantly observe the children in their classrooms and draw conclusions as to the growth of individuals in certain areas. However, many teachers are of the opinion that this procedure is an inaccurate method of evaluation. This opinion may have been formed because standards against which to judge the behavior of individuals have not been sufficiently defined.

---

[3] The committee has profited from the collaboration of Katherine E. Hill, Wheelock College, Boston, Massachusetts, in the following section of this chapter.

Basing Standards for Behavior on Fundamental Goals

Setting up a list of standards for behavior at a particular age level is primarily the problem of individual schools and teachers. The responsibility is theirs because the type of behavior held to be good in any situation depends upon the specific teaching aims of a school. Consequently, the teachers and principal must come to a joint decision concerning the behavior which is to be expected under given conditions.

An understanding both of the general facts of child development and of goals for science teaching is necessary. The standards for behavior of children in a situation should be based on a synthesis of information concerning the over-all growth of children at various age levels and of information concerning certain broad aims for science teaching. In other words, the teacher must first have the general facts concerning the development of children well in mind. For example, most five-year-olds should not be expected to connect wires to a dry cell with any considerable degree of success; the finger muscles of a five-year-old are not yet well developed. On the other hand, most five-year-olds are able to watch an older child or the teacher set up an electrical circuit, and they are able to use such a circuit after it has been put in order. The teacher of a ten-year-old group could expect most of the children to set up such a circuit as well as to be able to use it.

The teacher of five-year-olds knows that these children cannot usually carry on a general discussion of any one topic for more than a few minutes. The teacher of ten-year-olds knows that such children are capable, with some guidance, of carrying on a discussion of a particular topic for at least fifteen or twenty minutes.

Such general characteristics of child growth as these must first be taken into consideration. In addition, a teacher who is interested in the interpretation of the behavior of children in science situations must understand the basic aims of science teaching as they are set forth in chapter iii. Information which may be obtained by observation of the behavior of children will probably throw light on progress in relation to the development of scientific appreciations, interests, and attitudes.

Suggestions for types of responses which may be expected at various age levels. Certain groups of teachers who have considered both the general facts of child growth and the objectives of science instruction have emphasized the importance of the following goals: (1) Children should improve in their ability to attack a problem and come to a satisfactory conclusion in regard to that problem. (2) Children should become more and more responsible in carrying out their plans. (3) Children should grow in their ability to work together. (4) Children should become better able to make use of the materials of science as they work toward the solution of a problem. (5) Children should approach a discussion with an open mind and yet be critical of their own ideas and of the ideas of others.

Goals such as these may be constantly in the mind of the teacher; yet the determination of the degree of attainment to be expected at a particular age level in relation to any one of these goals may be difficult. There is, as yet, no definite set of standards which would give a teacher information as to the behavior which might be expected from a nine-year-old in relation to one of these broad goals. Perhaps there should be no set of standards as definite as this.

It may be that the standards with which individual work can be compared may evolve from the records of children in a particular school system or within single schools. In other words, "good" responses for particular age levels in terms of chosen objectives should probably be defined by the teacher in each situation. A careful study of cumulative records taken from year to year within a school should yield such standards. In this way, the standards for behavior at various age levels in a particular school would be in a constant state of evolution.

This kind of general preliminary study within a school should yield examples of the types of behavior which may be expected of the children in that school at various levels of development. For example, a study of remarks recorded verbatim and made by first-, second-, fifth-, and sixth-grade children (3) revealed a characteristic which might be called discrimination. Discrimination involves dealing with more than one idea. This characteristic was found more frequently in the remarks of fifth and sixth graders than in the remarks of first and second graders. The remarks of children who had had more science experience revealed a characteristic which might be termed "relatedness." Again, more than one idea is involved in such remarks. Also, the responses of children with more science experience seemed to show an awareness of the necessity to be specific in their statements. Perhaps we should expect progress of this type to be revealed as children advance from grade to grade.

Many of the questions of children with less science experience were requests for identification, such as "What leaf is that?" Many of the questions of the more experienced children revealed a struggle for proof. An example of such a question is, "How do you account for the light that comes from the sun (if it is not burning)?" This search for further knowledge often resulted in a request to resort to experimentation. In general, younger children seemed to ask questions of the "why-is-it" and "how-is-it-done" type.

When speculating, younger children's responses often revealed an "I think" characteristic. Older children weighed evidence by including in their statements a speculative reason to explain a phenomenon. In drawing conclusions, less experienced children often made blunt statements of fact such as, "Nothing will grow without water." More experienced children often included a reason on which the conclusion was based. An example is, "You can't see water vapor. Why, when I take a bath, drops of water collect on the ceiling, and I can't see the water vapor going up there."

In searching for standards against which the responses of children in science discussions may be judged, we should consider possible progress in regard to more discrimination, more recognition of relatedness of events, more desire for proof, more reasons for speculation, more factual evidence as a basis for conclusions, more evidence of responsibility, more co-operation, more initiative. In other words, perhaps we should evolve standards which will reveal the expectation of a more mature or considered type of thinking as we attempt to judge children's progress by observing their behavior.

Gathering Information concerning the Behavior of Individuals

Observation of the children in a group is necessarily a part of good teaching. In this way good teachers obtain information concerning the progress of individual children and of the whole group in relation to the goals under discussion. The teacher must first have basic teaching goals well in mind in order to make relevant observations. Then, a record of the behavior of individual children must be kept if their behavior is to be interpreted with understanding.

Anecdotal records give a good picture of individual behavior. A classroom teacher often has little help for the gathering of data concerning children. Consequently, a valuable method of recording information about children is to write a short, pertinent narrative describing the behavior observed as soon after the observation period as possible. Anecdotal records of this type should be kept for each child over as long a period as is necessary for the gathering of sufficient data to be informative concerning the progress of that child in relation to a basic goal. A teacher would not, of course, be able to gather information about all the children in his group in any one day. It is probably better to concentrate on the observation of a few children each day.

Records of this kind yield a great deal of material concerning the behavior of children. As is indicated in a recent report prepared for the Commission on Teacher Education (2), the value of this material lies in the insights it affords into expected behavior at a particular age level.

Information concerning individual behavior may be obtained by coding. Another method of gathering information concerning the behavior of individuals in relation to desired goals is known as the "coding" technique. This method has been discussed in a number of studies concerned with the behavior of children (**3, 9, 10**). The method of gathering data by coding is briefly this. First the teaching goals are determined. Then a code number is assigned to each goal. As a child exhibits a certain kind of behavior, the code number which most nearly fits that kind of behavior is entered on a data sheet opposite that child's name. Data of this type are gathered for several consecutive days and at a later date for several more consecutive days.

These records may then be studied to determine which children are making good contributions most frequently and what those contributions are about. This method of collecting information can probably be used with the greatest degree of success by teachers of older children since older children need less guidance from the teacher in carrying on a discussion. Hence, the teacher of older children has more freedom to record information.

Information concerning the behavior of individuals may be obtained by recording remarks verbatim. The method of gathering information by coding is limited in that it does not tell precisely what the child said or what he did. This limitation may be overcome if records of the conversation and activities of children are taken by an expert stenographer. However, very few teachers have assistance of this type.

An adaptation of the stenographic method may be made by teachers, especially teachers of older children. This adaptation involves the recording of the remarks of a child as soon as they are made. With practice, a teacher is able to gather a good deal of information in this manner concerning one child on several consecutive days. Records of this kind give the content of the remarks of a child. Such specific observation of a child from time to time during the year will yield important data concerning his progress.

Interpretation of Records

No matter how records are taken, they should be kept and consulted. It is advisable to have a folder for each child, since an analysis of the accumulated records which are taken at regular intervals gives the teacher a clue as to how that child may be helped. The teacher may wish to see that a particular child has more opportunity for work with materials; the child may need to be drawn into the general discussion more frequently; or the child may need help concerning his ability to work with others.

If records are kept to include discussions other than those in science, the results of a study of a child's contributions will be even more enlightening. Oftentimes it is found that children are able to investigate new material in one area but need the teacher's help to see that the same type of investigation may be used in other areas. At other times reluctance or lack of ability to deal with problems is apparent in several different subject-matter areas. The teacher who keeps and studies individual records is the one who is most often able to help a child effectively.

It is time-consuming and difficult to keep and interpret records of the behavior of individuals. Evaluation through the interpretation of behavior is especially useful, however, in attempting to determine individual progress in relation to such basic goals as those dealing with skills, appreciations, interests, and attitudes.

Summary

Evaluation in elementary-school science should be in terms of the fundamental purposes to be served by science in the lives of children. Teachers and other elementary-school workers with responsibility for evaluation should give careful attention to these purposes (see chaps. iii and v).

Evaluation should be an integral part of teaching and learning. Children should participate in evaluation whenever possible and feasible, with each child evaluating his own progress as well as the combined progress of his group.

Almost all methods of instruction can be utilized in evaluation. For example, art work which expresses children's ideas may give the teacher a means of diagnosing children's understandings in science. This is also true for oral and written expression.

Evaluation through the interpretation of behavior is especially useful in attempting to determine individual progress in relation to such basic objectives as skills, interests, appreciations, and attitudes, and in relation to the functional understanding of facts, large conceptions, and basic principles of science. In order to evaluate an individual's progress by observing his behavior, it is first necessary to determine the set of standards against which that behavior is to be judged. Such a set of standards should take into consideration the general facts of child growth as well as the general aims of science instruction.

Information concerning the behavior of individuals may be gathered in several ways. An analysis of accumulated data regarding a child will give some clue as to his progress. In addition, the teacher who makes a careful study of the behavior records of a child will be better able to help that child make progress in relation to the set of standards which have been found to be acceptable.

The utilization of previous learnings in new situations provides the teacher with an effective means of evaluation. This latter is especially applicable in a continuous program of instruction in science. The development of such a program seems to call for continuous evaluation and the refinement of evaluative procedure on the part of teachers working together in curriculum reconstruction. Data secured from evaluation are most essential to the planning for new instruction.

REFERENCES

1. BURTON, WILLIAM H. *The Guidance of Learning Activities.* New York: D. Appleton–Century Co., Inc., 1944.
2. COMMISSION ON TEACHER EDUCATION. *Helping Teachers Understand Children.* Washington: American Council on Education, 1945.
3. HILL, KATHERINE E. *Children's Contributions in Science Discussions.* New York: Bureau of Publications, Teachers College, Columbia University, 1946.
4. "Iowa Every-Pupil Tests of Basic Study Skills. Test B: Work-Study Skills." New York: Houghton Mifflin Co., 1940.
5. "The Measurement of Understanding in Science," *The Measurement of Understanding*, Chapter VI. Forty-fifth Yearbook of the National Society for the Study of Education, Part I. Chicago: University of Chicago Press, 1946.
6. NATIONAL COMMITTEE ON SCIENCE TEACHING. *Redirecting Science Teaching in the Light of Personal-Social Needs.* Washington: National Education Association, 1942.
7. "Science Course of Study for Elementary Schools, 1943." Cleveland, Ohio: Board of Education, 1943.
8. URBAN, JOHN. *Behavior Changes Resulting from a Study of Communicable Diseases.* New York: Bureau of Publications, Teachers College, Columbia University, 1943.
9. WEST, JOE YOUNG. *A Technique for Appraising Certain Observable Behavior of Children in Science in Elementary Schools.* Teachers College Contributions to Education, No. 728. New York: Bureau of Publications, Teachers College, Columbia University, 1937.
10. WRIGHTSTONE, J. WAYNE. *Appraisal of Newer Elementary-School Practices.* New York: Bureau of Publications, Teachers College, Columbia University, 1938.

CHAPTER IX

RESOURCE MATERIALS FOR ELEMENTARY SCIENCE IN RURAL AND URBAN SCHOOLS

ELEMENTARY SCIENCE IN THE RURAL SCHOOL[1]

The Instructional Setting of the Rural School

In the typical one-room school there is a range in ages from four-and-a-half to fourteen or fifteen years. Seldom are there many supplementary books or other library materials, and usually there is no museum to which the pupils have access. On the other hand, materials found naturally in the environment are usually present in considerable variety and abundance. Indeed, a rural environment affords great educational opportunities for children. Weather is an especially significant part of rural life because it is so closely related to the crops upon which occupational success depends. Plants and animals have to be guarded against various types of disease. Motors and other machines are in constant use about the farm. Rural children see and hear about these things constantly so that it is usually not difficult to find and to guide their interests in the science of the everyday world.

The Rural Science Curriculum

Use of community resources. In the rural school, the varied and abundant community resources for science teaching are the logical ones for use. Under the observation of the children, birds build their nests, raise their young, feed themselves and their young, and prepare for migration. Plants and animals get ready for winter or cast off the dormancy of an inactive season. Pets and farm animals must be fed, watered, and otherwise cared for. Children learn to look for flowers, for fruits and berries, for weeds, and for nightshade and poison ivy and learn to know different kinds of farm, garden, and orchard crops. Animal tracks convey information about species, size, speed of travel, and other habits. The constellations, undimmed by city lights, are seen overhead during all seasons of the year. After a storm, miniature river valleys are seen, and erosion and leaching are apparent.

---

[1] The committee has profited from the collaboration of Albert J. Huggett, Michigan State College, East Lansing, Michigan, in the following section of this chapter.

Use of readily available equipment. A small amount of equipment is needed for teaching elementary science. Most of this is inexpensive and much can be supplied by the homes of pupils. Magnetism can be taught through the use of horseshoe magnets, and electricity may be explained by means of flashlights, old dry cells, doorbells, Christmas-tree cords, and homemade push buttons.

Many of the basic principles of sound may be demonstrated by a vibrating stick, those of light by a candle, flashlight, and mirror. To rural youth, acids and bases are not mysterious materials secured from supply houses but are such common substances as vinegar, citrus fruit juices, limewater, and the liquid obtained by leaching ashes. Making soap is easily understood when it is made from beef fat or lard and the caustic potash obtained by having water run slowly through wood ashes. Carbon dioxide may be made and its properties demonstrated by the use of baking soda, vinegar, and candles. The properties of the air[2,3] can be shown by the familiar egg and milk-bottle experiment.

Daily happenings in science instruction. No instruction can be effectively carried out if based entirely upon daily happenings. If teaching is carried out entirely in this manner, it will be hit-and-miss and incomplete. In teaching, as in everything else, there must be planning, scope, and sequence. Opportunistic teaching is not to be commended.

On the other hand, there are times when plans may be modified because of special interest. It may be wise to defer teaching about the migration of birds if the children have become interested in what makes the leaves change color in autumn. Numerous daily happenings, such as a thunderstorm, a swarm of bees passing over the school grounds, or the accidental discovery of a woodchuck's den, may be used effectively in instruction. It is quite possible to utilize unexpected occurrences without discontinuing one's general plans for teaching.

Relationships with Other Fields

It is possible to mention only a few of the related fields with which science in the rural school may be effectively integrated. The ones which seem most important are named and a brief description given for each.

Conservation education. Nationally we are becoming increasingly conscious of the necessity for conservation. Rural children will be concerned about the depletion of our reserves of lumber, petroleum, coal, and iron

---

[2] Carleton J. Lynde, *Science Experiences with Inexpensive Equipment.* Scranton, Pennsylvania: International Textbook Co., 1939.

[3] Charles K. Arey, *Science Experiences for Elementary Schools.* New York: Bureau of Publications, Teachers College, Columbia University, 1942.

ore because their lives will be affected by a scarcity of these materials. They may have evidence that the fertility of the soil is being depleted. Wells are going dry, due to the lowering of the water table. Lumber for buildings is harder to get than was formerly the case. Some types of animal and plant life are vanishing because of wastefulness and greed. Conservation education fits into and becomes an integral part of science instruction in the rural school because the natural resources that have been mentioned make up such an important part of rural life (see chap. iii).

Safety education. City people are inclined to consider safety education as concerned primarily with safeguarding children and adults from automobile traffic dangers. To the rural boy and girl, safety education has a much broader connotation. Lives are lost each year through hazards connected with the operation of tractors, reapers, mowing machines, threshing machines, silo fillers, and other types of farm equipment. Domestic animals are sometimes a hazard. Safety education follows as a natural part of science teaching.

Sex education. To the rural child, the overt functionings of sex are not a mystery. Before him will occur all the stages of animal reproduction from fertilization to birth. Science is concerned with reproduction in plants and animals. It is also concerned with the reproduction of man.

Health education. The study of germs, of vitamins and hormones, of food-getting and storage, and of protection from cold and heat lead naturally to consideration of the health of people. The effects of alcohol and narcotics are best studied through scientific evidence. Size and bodily efficiency in their relationship to nutrition are logical applications resulting from the study of plants and animals.

Teaching Methods in the Rural School

Good teaching is good teaching whether found in the large city school or in the one-room rural school. Essentially, effective methods are the same everywhere.

It is desirable for efficiency in the use of time to provide study and activity in which all children can participate in some way. Suppose, for example, that the unit is "How Plants and Animals Prepare for Winter." Children in the primary grades as well as those in the later elementary grades can read selected materials pertaining to this topic. All can participate in the discussions and all can observe the migration flights of birds, the gathering of nuts by squirrels, the shedding of leaves, the storage of food by plants in stems and roots, etc. All can use this subject in their language study. Trips can be taken together. In fact, it is seldom that a single grade can be taken on a trip by itself because of the necessity that the teacher look after all of the children. Should there be construction work, such as the building of a bird-feeding station or a house for animal pets, this should be done largely by the older pupils. All of the children can, though, participate in some way in this type of work.

ELEMENTARY SCIENCE IN THE URBAN SCHOOL[4]

Similarity of village or urban schools and rural schools. The fundamental problems inherent in science teaching in elementary schools are essentially the same for urban and rural districts. The peculiar problem in either case is largely one of adapting the work to things with which children are associated and with which people work. However, a crowded area presents some situations that are unique. For example, in an average village or city, many of the interests and experiences of children and of adults pertain to phases of industry, such as manufacturing, processing, and laboratory testing; and to various types of transportation, as by air, water, motor, and rail. Such experiences require extended understandings relating to physical science. From the biological point of view, the types of situations in which children work range from crowded districts in which there are few parks or vacant lots to expansive outlying districts which have large parks, fields, swamps, orchards, and gardens. Every section of a city, whether a crowded area or an outlying district, is rich in materials and opportunities for developing scientific information and a point of view essential to understanding common experiences and to solving common problems.

A careful survey of opportunities offered by any city presents an extensive array of materials that may be used in teaching science. It is the function of the school to select those experiences that are most important in developing science understandings and attitudes. It is also the duty of the school to provide guidance in recognizing problems relating to these materials and to provide experiences in using the scientific method in solving them. Reflective thinking will be thought of, then, as a process or tool that conditions the outlook both mentally and morally and on which continuance and improvement of a democratic society is dependent.

Materials of special interest in urban regions. The following situations in cities contain resource materials appropriate for teaching science. No attempt is here made to arrange these in order of importance.

1. *Many kinds of industrial plants* exhibit applications of materials considered in class work, such as magnets, electromagnets, simple and complex machines, and huge furnaces for melting ore.

---

[4] The committee has profited from the collaboration of Florence G. Billig, College of Education, Wayne University, Detroit, Michigan, in the following section of this chapter.

2. *Commercial shops* use physical principles that are involved in things with which children play, such as those related to magnetism, electricity, floating, sinking, dissolving, balancing, pounding, pushing, pulling, winding, and air currents.

3. *Airports* offer centers of interest, such as the great planes equipped to meet flying conditions; weather information needed by pilots before taking off; methods of securing weather information for fliers; the method of giving weather information to pilots during flight; what a crew in an airplane needs to know about weather; knowledge of light, sound, magnetism, and electricity; strategic materials used in airplanes; and the effects of flying on the human body.

4. *Weather bureaus* offer a means of getting acquainted with air and water relations, with facts about weather, with methods of collecting weather information, with instruments used in collecting weather information, and with the prediction of weather.

5. *Museums* have departments where children may go as individuals or groups for instruction under the direction of authorities. Study may center around prehistoric animals, meteors, rocks, minerals, soils, machines, light, sound, magnetism, electricity, or animal and plant materials. Some museums maintain special science rooms or laboratories for children.

6. *Planetariums* maintain astronomical museums with the planetarium instrument as the principal exhibit and may sponsor programs and clubs for children.

7. *Observatories* are often located in areas accessible to cities and offer opportunities to gain understanding of the heavens and of the instruments through which astronomical data are secured.

8. *Radio broadcasting stations* provide practical information relating to sound.

9. *Photographic establishments* depend upon light and its chemical relations.

10. *Markets* sell food products to city people.

11. *City departments* are concerned with problems of preserving health by maintaining a pure water supply and by disposal of garbage and sewage; by eliminating vermin, such as rats, mice, flies, mosquitoes, cockroaches, and bedbugs; and by lighting the streets, alleys, and public and private buildings.

12. *Civic organizations, newspapers, and department stores* offer facilities to schools through printed materials, garden clubs, garden centers, flower shows, birdhouse contests, lectures, field trips, exhibits, and festivals.

13. *Backyards* have various types of trees, shrubs, and herbaceous plants; rocks in rock gardens; pools with plant and animal life; bird sanctuaries; vegetable and flower gardens; insect friends and enemies; and the garage with its many problems.

14. *Alleys* often have trees, shrubs, vines, weeds, grasses, and seedlings growing between cracks in cement and at the edge of the pavement.

15. *Parks and extensive boulevard gardens* help to arouse interest in and appreciation of plants and animals as living things. Some of the materials available are listed, though the list could be greatly extended.

a. *Trees, shrubs, and vines,* growing under excellent conditions and properly cared for by pruning, spraying, fertilizing, and watering.

b. *Herbaceous plants,* including those commonly used in home planting and showing different methods of propagation.

c. *Insects,* living under normal conditions in ponds, streams, trees, shrubs, herbaceous plants, meadows, and dry situations.

d. *Birds,* living in and around water, in thick woods, meadows, and swamps where they are free to nest under natural conditions.

e. *Bird sanctuaries,* offering protection to birds and illustrating ways to attract and to protect birds in home and community grounds.

f. *Toads, frogs, salamanders, snakes, snails, earthworms, squirrels, chipmunks, rabbits, and field mice,* living under normal conditions.

16. *Specialized parks,* such as zoological and botanical parks, exhibit *native and foreign animals* living under conditions simulating native habitats as nearly as possible.

17. *Bird sanctuaries* include habitats of birds with situations which birds like for living, nesting, and rearing their young. *Aviaries* provide opportunities to study native and imported birds.

18. *Departments of parks and boulevards* co-operate in other ways than in providing great parks, such as

a. Assisting in the development of garden clubs for children and assisting in out-of-door *school gardens* throughout the year.

b. Providing *well-selected plants* for science rooms that show such things as types of reproduction and requirements of light, water, and temperature.

c. Giving *advice* to teachers and children regarding soil and plant problems.

19. *Near-by farms and gardens and vacant lots* provide a variety of science materials.

a. *Modern farms* show typical farm buildings, machinery, and animals.

b. *Trees, shrubs, and herbaceous plants* grow under excellent conditions.

c. *Home gardens and orchards,* loaned by owners, offer children experiences with seeds, fruits, and vegetables.

d. *Farms in region surrounding city* present many problems relating to plants, animals, soil, weather, and machinery.

e. *Vacant lots and fields* offer materials relating to common weeds and their methods of propagation and seed distribution, birds that visit for food, and tracks of animals and their stories.

20. *Mines, quarries, gravel pits, and shorelines* are excellent sources of supplementary materials.

a. *Mines* provide knowledge about minerals, such as salt, copper, coal, and iron.

b. *Stone quarries and gravel pits* contain information about rocks and glacial action.

c. *Lake or ocean shorelines* tell much about the past history of the region. These are rich in interesting science materials, such as sand, rocks, pebbles, skeletons, plant and animal life, and the work of water.

21. *Boards of education* can provide many opportunities for science experiences, such as the following:[5]

  a. *Rooms*, in which science is taught, ranging from typical classroom to special science laboratory with adjoining conservatory, dark room, and storage and preparation room.

  b. *Classroom*, with simple equipment providing opportunities for experiences with biological and physical materials.

  c. *Special science room*, with gas and electric outlets, sink, running water, locked cabinets and cupboards, countershelves, bulletin boards, sand table, workbench, dark shades, screen and visual equipment, and room library. The science room is a laboratory or workshop in which opportunities are provided for experiences and for working out problems with various types of biological and physical environmental materials. There are opportunities for establishing aquariums and terrariums as homes of plants and animals; for making and arranging collections and exhibits; for making such things as electromagnets, telegraph sets, electric motors, toys, planisphere, star boxes, shadow screens, planting flats, and homes for animals; and for experimenting with air, water, magnets, electricity, soils, rocks, plants, and the like. A conservatory may open from the science room in which children propagate plants, make desert, water, and dry-land gardens, grow and care for plants to be used in home and school gardens, for school decorations, and for plant sales. There may be a dark room in which photographic experiences may be gained, and there may be a storeroom for equipment and supplies.

  d. *Garden centers*, equipped with toolhouses, compost pile, and water. Centers are located in different parts of the city. Children work as individuals or groups under direction of trained instructors.

  e. *Greenhouse facilities*, providing year-round plant projects directed by trained workers. Children may receive instruction in preparing soil, various means of propagating plants, transplanting plants, and proper care of plants.

  f. *Gardening*, an integral part of the science program, with actual out-of-door gardening carried on in home and school gardens with co-operation of parents.

  g. *Museums of different kinds*, including a children's museum where individuals and groups go for instruction in biological and physical science under the direction of trained curators; a museum used as a distributing center for living and physical materials; and a school museum developed and maintained by children.

  h. *School zoo*, directed by a trained person but cared for, in large part, by children. Animals, such as the following, are kept in the zoo: pony, calf, coyote, fox, small mammals, birds, and domestic fowls.

  i. *Exhibits of living animals* sent to schools, such as cow and calf, horse and colt, hog and litter of young, and ewe and lamb.

---

[5] The facilities listed here should not be considered as essential to good science instruction.

The use of community materials often involves a trip or excursion which presents problems in connection with time, transportation, and safety. The time necessary for the trip is handled by the administrative department of the school. Bus transportation for long trips is supplied by children, school, or the board of education. Careful planning and executing of plans by children and teacher result in development of patterns of behavior that help eliminate many safety problems.

A collection should be made of illustrative materials which relate to problems of conservation, trespassing, and wise collection and use of materials.

Teachers must select science experiences which present curriculum problems, if experiences are to be of the kind that children can use or adapt in free play, that suggest leisure-time activities, that answer needs, that satisfy curiosities, and that create greater interest and pleasure in the environment.

The list of opportunities relating to science is suggestive of the wealth of available materials offered by a city. While no one city has all of the resources mentioned, each city has them in varying degrees. It is clearly the obligation of teachers and supervisors to survey school communities and the city with its environs to find out what resources are available. These materials should then be used as a part of the science facilities. The peculiar problems in a city situation are concerned with adapting the science program to the resource materials available and with which the children are associated.

Summary

The recommendations for elementary-school science in earlier chapters of Section II are applicable to both rural and urban schools. It is in the resources for teaching science that the teachers and the supervisor must recognize a difference. The wealth of the resources for teaching science in both city and country should be revealed to teachers through preservice and in-service programs of education so that these resources will be utilized more effectively.

CHAPTER X

THE IMPROVEMENT OF INSTRUCTION IN SCIENCE IN THE ELEMENTARY SCHOOL[1]

THE PRESERVICE EDUCATION OF CLASSROOM TEACHERS IN SCIENCE[2]

It is the responsibility of the institutions engaged in preparing classroom teachers for the elementary school to see that their graduates are competent, with respect to both subject matter and methods, to teach the science which is appropriate for the grade level at which they expect to be employed.

Aims of Instruction in Science for Elementary-School Teachers

The elementary-school teachers need special preparation in college for the job of teaching science. The courses which are appropriate for the teacher at the secondary level or for engineers, or which are designed primarily for the liberal education of the general student, are usually inappropriate for the elementary-school teacher. They are inappropriate because of different objectives and usually different methods. The science courses which are intended for the elementary teacher must be so designed as to make clear to the prospective teacher the social function of science. They must also provide for breadth of subject matter in all areas of science rather than specialization in a limited number of areas and this must be done without sacrificing quality. The prospective teacher must be shown the oneness of science and must see how science contributes to the solution of problems which occur in the daily lives of the students. The courses must be taught in such a manner that the student learns the elements of the scientific method and acquires the most important attitudes and skills related to the scientific method. Too frequently in college teaching the intellectual significance of the subject matter is stressed to the neglect of the other values. Without neglecting the intellectual significance of science, its legitimate aesthetic, economic, and social significance should be emphasized as well.

---

[1] The reader will find many suggestions in respect to teacher education in chapter xvi. Although that chapter is directed to the secondary level, many suggestions will be found useful to the elementary school.

[2] The committee has profited from the collaboration of Victor Crowell, State Teachers College, Trenton, New Jersey, in the following section of this chapter.

Field and Laboratory Activities

In all of the science courses designed for the elementary-school teacher, a considerable amount of time should be devoted to field and laboratory activities. This is just as true in the physical sciences as it is in the biological sciences. In most instances these activities should be especially designed for the particular purpose of preparing teachers for the elementary school. In other words, these courses should be professionalized. By that is meant, first, a judicious selection of subject matter with respect to the use to be made of it and, second, a harmonious blending of subject matter and methods of instruction so that the student, while learning subject matter, will see how it can be taught in the elementary school. In many instances the basic principles can be illustrated by simple materials and activities which can, with slight modification, be used later by the student as a teacher in the elementary school. This can be done without sacrificing the scholarliness of the presentation or academic respectability. The laboratory should give the student some competence in the construction of simple equipment and considerable facility in the handling of apparatus. The prospective elementary-school teacher should know how to use dry cells, motors, balances, and other common appliances. He should learn to utilize the resources of the vicinity rather than to depend solely upon purchased material.

In the biological courses considerable attention should likewise be given to field work and to the care and handling of living plants and animals. The student should study the ecological relations of organisms by observing them in the field as well as by studying about them in the textbook. As an example, students from six teachers' colleges participated in a field trip. Nearly all of them had been exposed to courses in biology. When shown an illustration of symbiosis, in the relationship between aphids and an ant colony, only one out of thirty students recognized the phenomenon. About half of the others said, after having it explained to them, that they had studied about the subject in the classroom and in a textbook. This is not an isolated instance confined to the biological sciences but is one which is met with constantly in all areas. Many students can recognize Ursa Major or a terminal moraine on a lantern slide and not recognize it in nature. Most things take on new meanings when studied in the field in their natural habitat.

Specific Recommendations for Teacher Education

The following are specific recommendations for courses which will contribute toward the preparation of a well-educated classroom teacher who is at the same time qualified to teach science to elementary-school children. The importance of science in our daily lives justifies the suggestion that approximately twenty semester hours be devoted to science during the four-year college course. This represents approximately one-sixth of the total program and is more than is provided in the average curriculum today. It is suggested that these twenty hours be utilized in the following manner.

There should be three six-semester-hour courses in subject matter. In the three subject-matter courses, the subject matter will be organized in large units which will develop the major generalizations within each area and which will, to a large degree, cut across artificial subject-matter barriers. The criteria for the selection of subject matter will be: (1) Does the subject matter contribute to the development of a well-educated individual? (2) Does the subject matter contribute to the preparation of a well-equipped elementary-school teacher?

Each of these three courses should, as stated before, provide for laboratory and field work, and each should be professionalized. The content usually covered in courses of special methods and problems of teaching should preferably be combined with these courses, although it may be offered as a separate course.

One of the recommended courses should be concerned with the earth sciences. This would include materials from astronomy, geology, and meteorology.

A second course would include the study of the physical sciences incorporating material from chemistry and physics. Although chemistry is of importance in our culture, at least half of the materials of this course should be drawn from the field of physics.

The third subject-matter course should be biological science. As with the other courses, this course should be built around general problems without reference to subject-matter boundaries. In other words, one general course is preferable to several courses in the special fields of botany, zoology, physiology, etc. As previously stated, considerable emphasis should be placed upon the use of living materials rather than on the use of prepared slides, specimens, models, etc., exclusively.

In a special-methods course in the teaching of elementary science, the student should be given opportunity to see how the materials of the preceding courses in science can be organized into teaching units for the grades in which he is preparing to teach. The student should in this course have an opportunity to become acquainted with textbooks in science and other literature written for children, as well as with courses of study. He should learn about sources of materials, such as free and low-cost motion pictures, lantern slides, apparatus, and museum materials. Opportunity should be given to learn how to prepare homemade lantern slides and how to use visual-aid equipment in the field of science. Here also will be summarized the aims and objectives of science teaching in the elementary school and methods of evaluating these. The student should by all means observe a number of lessons taught by a superior classroom teacher and later discuss and evaluate the techniques employed.

A great deal of the success of a well-prepared teacher in the elementary grades depends upon the spirit in which children regard their science experiences. The student teacher must be given a background of vital experiences so that he acquires an inner urge and a compulsion to share them with his pupils in the classroom. He must want to make learning a co-operative process in which he and the children are continually exploring their environment in an ever-expanding series of pleasurable experiences.

THE IN-SERVICE EDUCATION OF CLASSROOM TEACHERS IN SCIENCE

The Continuous Nature of Professional Education[3]

The abilities that make for continued success cannot be learned once and for all in a four- or five-year course in a teachers' or liberal-arts college (**3**:61). The professional education of an elementary-school teacher must continue as long as the teacher is active in professional work. "The quality of teacher preparation is exceedingly important. But no matter how excellent, it cannot by itself determine what kind of job will be done by a given graduate either at the beginning of his professional career or as that career continues" (**2**:118).

Ideally, preservice education should blend into in-service education in such a way that it would be difficult to know where one leaves off and the other begins (**3**:61). One of the first steps in such a program is the organization of the undergraduate work so as to develop an early awareness of the importance of continuous professional education. When this is done, an individual is prepared to participate in a program of in-service education immediately upon graduation (**9**: chap. x).

The Universal Necessity of In-service Education

Every school system should have a program of in-service education in operation. This is true even in school systems that have a teaching personnel of the highest qualifications. Teachers must learn to work as a team. They must secure knowledge of the factors operating in the local situation. They must build an acquaintance with regional problems and resources. There is always a demand for the introduction of experienced

---

[3] The committee has profited from the collaboration of Franklyn Branley, Horace Mann School for Boys, New York City, in the following section of this chapter.

teachers to new practices and innovations as well as for the orientation of new teachers to the school system. "Moreover, our times demand a rethinking of the functions of schools in our society and a modification of school patterns to make them more effective in meeting contemporary personal-social needs. Such rethinking and modification call for a pooling of the powers of thought and action of all educational workers" (2:118).

While science has been a recognized field in the elementary schools for several decades, it is in reality an innovation as a functional subject in the curriculum. This in large part grows out of the fact that science is still new to society. As a result there is a growing demand from teachers and parents for practical in-service education. This demand is one of the most gratifying aspects of the development of elementary science in public education.

School systems too small to maintain the kind of in-service programs in science which they desire have achieved a degree of success by combining their efforts with those of neighboring systems.

Democratic and Co-operative Planning of In-service Education

Attention is being directed in public schools today to democratic means of improving instruction. This pattern is built on co-operation among individual teachers and between teachers and administrators (9: chap. x). The result is co-operative planning of the in-service program by the teaching and administrative staffs (3:61). Such planning does not deny to the administration the exercise of leadership within a democratic framework (2:174).

It is important to secure the enthusiastic support of teachers in developing a program of in-service education in elementary science. One way to secure enthusiasm and co-operation is to supply teachers with the kind of assistance in science they can easily recognize as immediately functional in the everyday task of teaching.

In many school systems co-operative planning is cared for by a central planning committee elected by the staff (2:141). Any program planned for improvement in science instruction should be presented and cleared through the central planning committee. In this way science would not become isolated from the remainder of the program of in-service education.

The Relation of Supervision to In-service Education

The improvement of instruction in the elementary school has been traditionally assigned to supervision. Emphasis on democratic and co-operative planning does not eliminate supervision. Instead, there is a movement toward a new kind of supervision, one in which supervisors work co-operatively and democratically with planning groups. The work of the supervisor consists in developing and in carrying out the programs approved by the planning groups.

Individual Professional Improvement

In many school systems in-service education is entirely an individual matter (**3:64**). A teacher may desire to improve his teaching in some area and will, on his own initiative, participate in extension and summer school courses. He may strive through reading and travel to improve his professional background.

At the present time there are many opportunities open to an individual for self-improvement in science. There is a substantial body of professional literature in science. A number of teacher-education institutions offer functional courses in science to teachers in service. A few school systems are remunerating teachers for individual professional improvement. Teachers accepting financial assistance are frequently held responsible in the ensuing years for leadership along the lines of the work pursued. They may be expected to make recommendations of changes in the curriculum and in school practices on their return to active service in the school. In this way the school system is quite free to offer the kind of guidance that will cause the individual professional program to conform to the over-all planning of the school system.

It is not at all uncommon for school systems to assist classroom teachers with the cost involved in summer school courses in science with the expectation that these teachers will become leaders in science in their school systems.

The Work of a Committee for the Improvement of Instruction in Elementary Science

A committee from the teaching staff may be established for the purpose of planning and developing a program for the improvement of instruction in elementary science (**3:62**). This committee may work with all agencies in the community that have contributions to make to the objectives involved. The committee in science should be composed of teachers at all levels of instruction in the elementary school (see chap. vi). There may be representatives from the parent association, from each field of secondary science, and from the scientific agencies of the community, such as public health boards and conservation societies. The committee should include in its membership the leadership that is emerging in the field of elementary science in the school system. It is important that membership in the committee be established on a voluntary basis (**3:63**).

The chairman of a successful in-service program in science need not be a member of the administrative staff (**3**:63). Some of the most success-ful programs have been those in which a classroom teacher, elected by the entire teaching body, served as a chairman.

This committee should develop all policies relating to in-service educa-tion in science. Such matters as arranging and promoting conferences, organizing clinics, and selecting consultants are within its province. The committee should work closely with the central planning committee. It should also keep in touch with the teaching staff so that it will formulate a program that has the enthusiastic support of the school system.

Use of Consultants

In a number of schools consultants or advisers from outside the system are employed to assist in the improvement of instruction in elementary science (**2**:150–55). The importance of long-term planning by the con-sultant, with the help of the planning committee and the committee in science, cannot be overemphasized.

Consultants may spend considerable time in schools observing work and conferring with principals and teachers (**3**:65). Luncheons and teas are frequently made the occasion for informal conferences. Teachers and principals are encouraged to state their problems frankly in such confer-ences. These problems may be given consideration at the larger staff conference at which the consultant may lead the discussion.

Consultants from outside the system are frequently utilized to train special leaders within a school system (**3**:166). This may result in the training of a teacher within the school system to become a consultant and to carry on after the outside consultant is no longer needed. This has been a successful procedure.

Professional Courses in Elementary Science

There is a large demand for courses of professional content in elemen-tary science for teachers in service (**5**). In a number of cases successful courses of this kind have been established by the use of leadership found within the school system. In other cases, outside consultants are em-ployed for such purposes. Experience indicates that these courses should be taught by an instructor with a thorough knowledge of science and of elementary education.

Observation of Teaching

Observation of teachers at work is an important means of in-service education (**3**:64). In some school systems individual schools have de-veloped programs with special emphasis on science. These schools may serve as centers for experimental work, the results of which are made available to all schools of the system. In other cases the schools may provide observational opportunities for teachers. In some systems these special schools which are devoted to science, have been very useful. In some they have tended to localize rather than to spread science throughout the system.

In some schools observations are carried on within a school by special arrangements. Teachers are freed from their regular duties at special times to observe different activities in classrooms within their own school. Such observations should be followed by evaluation conferences.

The Clinic in Elementary Science

Sometimes the outside consultant observes instruction with groups of teachers and participates in an evaluation conference. This has been successful in developing interest in science and in making teachers aware of good methods of instruction. It is necessary in this practice to develop an attitude of open-mindedness and critical-mindedness so that all participating will give and receive evaluation suggestions objectively and constructively. Greater sharing of successful methods should be promoted among teachers. There is no reason why clinics cannot be as successful in the educational field as they have been in the medical profession. At such clinics there can be exchange of experience among teachers.

Clinics are generally more successful when they are organized for a particular school than when they are on a system-wide basis.

Professional Improvement through Evaluation of Instruction

Closely associated with the clinics in elementary science is the focusing of education upon the evaluation of instruction. For instance, some schools at the present time are focusing attention upon the attitudes developed by children. These studies are followed by attempts to develop instruction suitable for the growth of children toward scientific attitudes. Such a procedure is particularly applicable to schools that have conducted studies of child growth and development (**1**). Consultants are usually employed to assist in the evaluation. In connection with this evaluation there must be extensive professional study of the objectives and content of science.

Workshop Conferences

Workshop conferences in science have been successful in many school systems (**2**:155–64). Sometimes arrangements are made by which teachers report for their workshop two or three weeks prior to the opening of school. Many school systems employ consultants for this work. The program in science may involve a variety of activities. There may be a study of community problems. There may be provision for instruction in the professional content of science. There may be a discussion of problems that face the teachers in a local situation. The science of the community may be studied through field excursions with consultants. Workshops should provide for conferences of large and small groups according to the demands. In a number of systems useful professional or regional material may be developed by the teachers. In some school workshops, handbooks for teachers have been prepared which were later mimeographed or printed for all teachers of the school system (**6;11**).

Use of Professional Laboratories in Elementary Science

One reason for the need of in-service education in science for elementary teachers is that the mores of our Western culture have encouraged women to avoid a firsthand acquaintance with science. There is frequently the hesitancy to manipulate the simple equipment needed for instruction in science. Oddly enough, this remains true in spite of the fact that the modern housewife is one who operates a wide variety of electrical and other equipment in her daily work (**7**:15). Such an attitude by no means represents an insurmountable obstacle to the development of vital instruction in science at the elementary-school level.

A number of public schools have arranged facilities by which teachers may secure experience with the equipment of science appropriate to the simple experiments that are utilized in the elementary school (**4**). In some schools a professional laboratory suitable for the use of both teachers and children has been established in a central location. Such laboratories may be utilized in connection with staff meetings and workshops. A handbook of experiments for laboratory experience in the workshop is sometimes prepared (**10**). The leadership emerging in elementary science in a school system can be utilized in establishing such laboratory centers.

Field Centers

There is a growing trend to develop natural-science field centers. One school system in a southern state has a large tract of land which has been developed as a field center. This center is so completely equipped that field work may extend over several weeks. Field and educational consultants at different periods go with groups of teachers to the field center for the study of science and related subjects. This center is also suitable for work with children. Teachers can return to the field center with their own classes for several days during each school year. Various teachers' organizations have utilized recreational parks in much the same manner.

Provisions can be made at field centers for the study of community problems, such as erosion and depletion of the soil and the spread of pests. Geologists, farm agents, plant and animal ecologists, agriculturalists, and other experts may be invited to the field center to work with the teachers for limited periods (**7**: chap. iv). In using experts from the field of science in this work, it is important that instruction be integrated with the assistance of someone who knows the field of elementary science.

A number of teachers' colleges and universities are establishing field centers for teachers in service.

SUMMARY

The elementary-school teacher needs special preparation in college for the job of teaching science. This preparation should include courses which provide for a breadth in all areas of science rather than a specialization in a limited number of areas. It is important that the social function of science be made clear to prospective teachers. The place of science in modern life justifies the suggestion that approximately twenty semester hours be devoted to science during the four-year college course.

In all science courses designed for the elementary teacher, a considerable amount of time should be devoted to field and laboratory activities. In most instances these activities should be especially planned for the particular purpose of preparing teachers for the elementary school. In other words, these courses should be professionalized.

The professional education of an elementary-school teacher must continue as long as the teacher is active in professional work. Ideally, pre-service education should blend into in-service education in such a way that it would be difficult to know where one leaves off and the other begins.

Every school system should have a program of in-service education in science in operation. Attention is being directed in public schools today to democratic means of improving instruction. The result is co-operative planning of in-service programs by teaching and administrative staffs. There is a movement toward a new kind of supervision, one in which supervisors work co-operatively and democratically with planning groups. Procedures for the improvement of instruction in elementary science through in-service education have been described in this chapter.

REFERENCES

1. AMERICAN COUNCIL ON EDUCATION. *Helping Teachers Understand Children.* Washington: American Council on Education, 1945.
2. ———. *The Improvement of Teacher Education.* Washington: American Council on Education, 1946.
3. AMERICAN COUNCIL OF SCIENCE TEACHERS, NATIONAL COMMITTEE ON SCIENCE TEACHING. *The Education of the Science Teacher.* Washington: National Education Association, 1942.
4. AREY, CHARLES K. *Science Experiences for Elementary Schools.* New York: Bureau of Publications, Teachers College, Columbia University, 1942.
5. BILLIG, FLORENCE G. *A Technique for Developing Content for a Professional*

Course in Science for Teachers in Elementary Schools. New York: Bureau of Publications, Teachers College, Columbia University, 1930.

6. *Cherokee County, Alabama, Workshop Report.* Jacksonville, Alabama: State Teachers College, 1946.

7. CRAIG, GERALD S. *Science in Childhood Education.* New York: Bureau of Publications, Teachers College, Columbia University, 1944.

8. CROXTON, W. C. *Science in the Elementary School.* New York: McGraw-Hill Book Co., 1937.

9. JOHN DEWEY SOCIETY. *Teachers for Democracy.* New York: D. Appleton–Century Co., 1940.

10. HARTIG, HILDEGARDE. *Suggestions for Classroom Teachers in Studying about Current Electricity.* San Diego, California: Office of Superintendent, Board of Education, 1945.

11. *Montgomery County, Maryland, Curriculum Bulletins.* Rockville, Maryland: Board of Education, 1934.

12. PRALL, CHARLES E., and CUSHMAN, C. LESLIE. *Teacher Education in Service.* Washington: American Council on Education, 1944.

SCIENCE IN THE SECONDARY SCHOOL

CHAPTER XI

TRENDS AND OBJECTIVES IN SECONDARY-SCHOOL SCIENCE

TRENDS IN SECONDARY-SCHOOL SCIENCE[1]

Trends in Enrolment

In spite of the rapid expansion of scientific knowledge and the even more rapid expansion in applications of science and practical invention, the percentage of high-school pupils enrolled in science courses has continued to decline.

From the latest available data (**13**) it is evident that there have been increases in percentages of enrolments in the generalized courses in science, general science, and general biology. In contrast, percentages of enrolments in specialized sciences have, in general, steadily dropped during a forty-four year period. Further, the evidence reveals that astronomy, geology, botany, zoology, and physical geography have practically disappeared from the science programs of the high schools. Physiology has almost gone, although a newer course in hygiene and sanitation continues. (There is a question of classification of this last course. It may belong more appropriately to the field of health and physical education.)

A further study of the data reveals that trends shown by percentages of enrolments in the sciences may represent losses that are more apparent than real. If the data are treated in another fashion, the situation becomes relatively more encouraging for the proponent of the values of the sciences. The absolute *numbers* of pupils enrolled in many science courses have increased rather than decreased. This is true even for some of the courses that seem to be losing ground when the percentages are compared. For example, the number of pupils enrolled in high-school physics was 281,928 in 1934 as compared with 79,720 in 1895, the year of the peak

---

[1] The committee has benefited from the collaboration of Ralph K. Watkins, University of Missouri, Columbia, Missouri, in the following section of this chapter.

percentage of enrolment in this subject. The number of pupils enrolled in chemistry increased from 20,503 in 1890 to 339,769 in 1934. Those enrolled in biology increased from 129,200 in 1922 to 653,530 in 1934. The enrolment in general science increased from 393,385 in 1922 to 798,227 in 1934.

If comparisons are made by high-school years a different picture appears. Two-fifths of the pupils in the seventh and eighth years in 1933-34 were enrolled in general science or junior high school science (**13**:14-15). Of the pupils enrolled in the first year of the four-year high school, the ninth grade, 54 per cent were in the general-science course. Of the pupils enrolled in the second year of the four-year high school, 53 per cent were in general biology. More than 51 per cent of all pupils in four-year high schools were enrolled in science courses.

According to the Office of Education report the typical junior high school pupil registered in science in either Grade VII or Grade VIII. The typical pupil of the four-year high school took two science courses during his four years of high-school experience.

A more recent, but less extensive, survey of science enrolments was conducted by Hunter and Spore (**8**). This study is based upon a questionnaire sent to a sampling of selected high schools scattered geographically over the United States. The data from this study, as of 1940, are consistent with the data gathered earlier by the Office of Education and show no new trends. Postwar data are at present unavailable.

Trends in Courses

The science courses of the junior high school have become relatively stabilized. The content is in effect a spreading and an enlargement of general science to cover the science needs of pupils of this maturity level.

The science of the senior high school (Grades X, XI, and XII) is typically biology in the tenth year and physics or chemistry in the eleventh and twelfth years. No complete data are at hand for the developing one-year course in general physical science for eleventh- and twelfth-year students. The course is not reported in the bulletin of the Office of Education (**13**). Hunter and Spore (**8**:22-23) report for the 655 junior and senior high schools of their survey that of 545 science courses offered in the eleventh year, 67 were in "new kinds" of physical science courses. For the twelfth year there were 82 physical-science courses out of a total offering of 549 courses. For the two years combined this represents approximately 14 per cent of the total offering.

Exact data on the present status of junior-college science courses are not available. The picture is a confused one. The results of the studies tend to be contradictory. For example, Clark's report of a survey of natural-science courses in public junior colleges of Southern California in 1936 (1) stated that "terminal courses are disappearing." Rennick (14) surveyed the chemistry and physics courses in 254 junior colleges over the United States, using data taken from 1938–39 catalogues, and found that only 15 per cent of the physics and chemistry courses were offered on a liberal, cultural, or semiprofessional basis. Eighty-five per cent of the courses in physics and in chemistry were found in 15 per cent of the institutions. In 1940 Watson (16) published the results of his study of the catalogues of 1,239 colleges, including junior colleges. He reports that the growth of survey courses in the physical sciences has been rapid in both high schools and junior colleges.

Without doubt, the general trend in science courses throughout the junior high school, senior high school, and the junior college has been toward generalized courses planned to meet the more immediate science needs of the common users of science. This movement has been underway since 1915. Accompanying it has been the development of a science program in the first six elementary grades. At present both movements are incomplete. The high-school science program attracts approximately half of the high-school pupils in any one year. The unified course in biological science in the senior high school is an accomplished fact, while the integrated course in physical science in the senior high school is only well started. Survey and terminal science courses still struggle for dominance with the traditional specialized courses at the junior-college level.

It is not surprising that there has been growth in the number of pupils taking science courses and in the variety of courses offered. The surprising fact is that the growth has not been more rapid. Two factors may explain the slow acceptance of the universal need for science instruction in the schools. One is the complacent adherence to the values of the traditional areas of the school program. The other is the preoccupation of educators with the socialization of the school program through the social studies.

Actually, science instruction in the schools offers means of socializing the program of studies as truly as do the social sciences themselves. The exploitation of the masses of humanity by the commercialization of scientific knowledge makes mandatory an attempt at universal science instruction in the schools. Modern advances in science serve only to make more acute a need that has existed at least since the middle of the nineteenth century.

Another reason for the need for greater emphasis on science instruction is the development of trained leadership. As scientific knowledge becomes increasingly complex—and the expansion takes place almost in geometric ratios—scientific leadership calls increasingly for expert specialization.

Adequate training of the young scientist may need to begin earlier than has been supposed. The movement toward the science education of the masses in the generalized science courses of the schools must be continued; but adequate provision for early specialization of selected individuals is also a "must." All this points to a careful reconsideration in detail of the objectives to be served by science courses, as well as of the kinds of human beings that are to be served in the particular courses set up.

The Relationship of Secondary-School Science to Areas of Human Experience

The problems associated with the education of young people for effective adjustment are highly complex. While the causes of this complexity may be manifold, at least two are clearly discernible: (1) the forces bringing about social and economic change are in themselves complex, and (2) each new problem calls forth its own unique type of behavior. It would, indeed, be rare to find a life situation that is not the focal point of factors from many areas of human experience. To anticipate any considerable number of these problems in the school situation and to give specific instruction bearing on their solution would be not only impossible but highly undesirable. It does little good to designate school problems and activities as "real life situations." As a matter of fact, it is practically impossible to set up classroom situations which actually duplicate situations and problems encountered outside of school. The best that can be done in this respect is to make as close an approximation of a "real life situation" as possible, but inevitably it must be more or less artificial. The various areas of the school curriculum should, therefore, rather aim at a set of objectives that will provide for the individual a flexible and adaptable equipment which may be called upon in the solution of many and diverse problems of adjustment.

Science problems of social significance may be found in certain broad areas of human experience such as health, consumership, conservation, vocation, family relationships, and citizenship. Some of these areas, elaborated in chapters ii and iii, show the great complexity and multiplicity of the problems that may arise and also show the relationship of these problems to science instruction. These areas of human experience have particular significance for science instruction at the secondary levels.

The problem of how best to meet the needs of young people in the above-mentioned areas of experience is somewhat controversial. In many schools specialized courses are offered in consumership, conservation, safety, and health, and for these courses special textbooks have been written. In other schools there has been an effort to fuse the materials from these areas into the more common courses of the curriculum such as science, physical education, social studies, and home economics. As noted in chapter iv, the latter alternative is recommended by the present year-book committee.

The fact, however, that so much attention is being directed toward education for effective adjustment carries a significant implication for secondary-school science. There are many problems with antecedents in science which arise in these areas. The war revealed an appallingly low standard of health among men drafted for service. Injury and death from automobile and household accidents are mounting annually. Our soil is being carried down to the sea at an ever-increasing rate. Inventions and changes in industry are continually creating problems in the displacement and readjustment of workers. Many forms of fraudulent advertising claiming scientific foundation are constantly being perpetrated on a credulous public by radio, newspaper, and magazine advertising.

The causal role of science as a basic factor in many of our present social and economic problems demands that the science teacher set the goals of instruction well beyond the narrow confines of the specialized sciences such as biology, physics, and chemistry. It is becoming increasingly more important that the science teacher seek out the social implications of his materials of instruction and deal with them in such a way that they give promise of having more carry-over values to aid the pupil as he attempts to adjust to the problems encountered in his daily living.

The Functions of Objectives in Science Teaching

The objectives proposed for science teaching by the committee have been clearly set forth in chapter iii. Here it is desirable to consider these objectives as they pertain particularly to the levels of secondary-science teaching, namely, Grades VII to XIV, inclusive. While the functions of these objectives at the secondary level are little different from those at other levels, emphasis at various points may need to be altered to fit the maturity of the pupil.

Objectives are directions of growth. As the pupil progresses through the grades of the elementary school and on to the secondary levels of instruction, objectives should take on enlarged meanings and there should be an ever-widening and developing pattern of relationships among them. Even at the completion of secondary education they will not have been fully attained, but growth toward their attainment should be constant.

In the early years of the elementary school the needs and interests of a child regarding some principle of science may, perhaps, be satisfied by the generalization of a few simple facts into a minor principle. The same principle encountered at a later level of maturity, and in a more complex setting, may require not only more facts but the understanding of a larger principle or generalization. At the same time the pupil may be called upon to use this principle in a new and unique situation which requires him to interpret the evidence, formulate a hypothesis, test it imaginatively, and act in accordance. Thus the emphasis on certain objectives may shift from level to level.

Acceptance of this view of learning robs the high-school teacher of any justification for the complaint that he has nothing left to teach. For example, the pupil in the elementary grades must inevitably learn much about air and learn it, not all in one grade, but from level to level throughout this period. When he enters the high-school class in science there is still much more to learn about air; so much more that there is abundant material for the enlargement of the concept through every subsequent grade. This enlargement will not take place by simply engaging again and again in the experiences of the lower grades. The responsibility rests upon the high-school teacher to select and order experiences which will insure growth.

The problems of young people, which have antecedents in science, grow out of their varied contacts in the many areas of human experience. Hence the objectives for instruction in science must be immediately derived from these areas. They must be so framed that growth toward them will insure an increasing ability on the part of young people to modify their behavior so as to cope more effectively with the problems confronting them. This point of view has been expressed by many writers in the magazines devoted to science education during the past decade. It has been summarized by Noll (**12**) in an article dealing with the relationship of science teaching and behavior changes in young people.

In chapter iii the committee has outlined the major objectives of science teaching as follows:

A. Providing opportunities for growth in the functional understanding of facts.
B. Providing for development of functional concepts.
C. Providing for growth in the functional understanding of principles.
D. Providing opportunity for growth in basic instrumental skills.
E. Providing opportunity for growth of skill in the use of elements of scientific method.
F. Providing for growth in the development of scientific attitudes.
G. Providing for growth in the development of appreciations.
H. Providing for growth in the development of interests.

In chapter iii these objectives were broken down in part for purposes of illustration. At this point the reader may desire to refer again to the discussion of Objectives A, B, and C, as there presented (pp. 28–32). It is desirable, however, to consider Objectives D to H in more detail and to analyze them into the elements which are essential for purposes of teaching and evaluation at the level of the secondary school.

A. *Providing opportunity for growth in the functional understanding of facts.*

B. *Providing for development of functional concepts.*

C. *Providing opportunity for growth in the functional understanding of principles.*

D. *Providing opportunity for growth in basic instrumental skills.* Growth in skill, as in functional understanding, is an ever-widening process. Many of the skills essential for effective work in the science courses of the secondary school will have been begun in the elementary school. The work of the secondary school should aim to develop these skills further and add new ones to the pupils' growing equipment.

Expanded in greater detail than was possible in chapter iii, some of the instrumental skills essential to effective work in science at the various levels of the secondary school are:[2]

1. *Locating source materials*
    a) Using various parts of a book
        (1) Using key words in a problem for locating material in an index
        (2) Using cross reference
        (3) Using a table of contents
        (4) Using a glossary
        (5) Using figures, pictures, and diagrams
        (6) Using footnotes
        (7) Using topical headings and running headings
    b) Using materials other than textbooks
        (1) Using encyclopedias
        (2) Using handbooks
        (3) Using dictionaries
        (4) Using magazines, pamphlets, and newspapers
        (5) Using various government publications
        (6) Using bibliographies

2. *Using source materials*
    a) Using aids in comprehending material read
        (1) Finding main ideas in a paragraph
        (2) Using reading signals such as italics and bold-faced type
        (3) Translating into one's own words statements from reading
        (4) Phrasing topics from reading

---

[2] The analysis of this objective is based on outlines originally prepared by committees of the faculties of Colorado College of Education, Greeley, Colorado, and the John Burroughs School, Clayton, Missouri.

(5) Skimming for main ideas

(6) Learning meanings of words and phrases from context

(7) Determining the main topics over several paragraphs

(8) Taking notes

(9) Outlining

  b) Interpreting graphic materials

(1) Obtaining evidence from various types of graphic material

(2) Noting relationships shown between factors

(3) Evaluating conclusions based upon data recorded

3. *Solving mathematical problems necessary in obtaining pertinent data*

  a) Picking out the elements in a mathematical problem that can be used in its solution

  b) Seeing relationships between these elements

  c) Using essential formulas

  d) Performing fundamental operations, such as addition, subtraction, multiplication, and division

  e) Using the metric and English systems of measurement

  f) Understanding the mathematical terms used in these problems, such as square, proportion, area, volume, etc.

4. *Using talks and interviews as sources of information*

  a) Selecting individuals who can contribute information to the solution of a problem

  b) Making suitable plans for a talk or interview

  c) Making arrangements with the person for the interview

  d) Selecting the main ideas from the activity

5. *Making observations suitable for solving a problem*

  a) Devising a suitable demonstration

(1) Selecting materials and equipment needed in the demonstration

  b) Observing demonstrations

(1) Identifying and selecting important ideas demonstrated

  c) Selecting the important ideas presented by charts, models, exhibits, pictures, slides, motion pictures, and radio

  d) Using the resources of the community for purposes of obtaining data pertinent to the problem

(1) Locating conditions or situations in the community to observe

(2) Selecting the essential ideas from such observations.

E. *Providing opportunity for growth of skill in the use of the elements of scientific method.* The scientific method of problem-solving is a composite of many skills of varying degrees of complexity. There is some evidence to support the inference that certain of the higher skills involved in use of scientific method may be employed by some pupils at the elementary-school levels. However, it is probably true that both the nature of the courses and the greater maturity of the pupils make the secondary school a propitious place for intensive development of these skills.

An examination of the literature of science education over the past few years reveals an ever-increasing number of titles pertaining to research or to general discussion bearing on the problem-solving objective. These articles range from attempts to analyze the specific elements of problem-solving behavior to experimentation in methodology related to the development of the skills. Among the investigators who have made analyses of this objective are Downing (**5**) and Keeslar (**9**).

This objective has, for a long time, been merely taken for granted. Most courses of study in science and many textbooks published within the last thirty years have listed problem-solving as an objective. Many teachers using these courses of study and many authors of textbooks have given lip service to the objective and then assumed that association with a course in science, a teacher trained in science, and scientific equipment and materials would, in some mysterious way, result in growth toward the objective. The elements of problem-solving behavior will be attained as objectives only to the degree that they are definitely sought and taught through appropriate learning experiences. These skills are potential, and they become habits only (1) as they are identified by the learner; (2) as they are correctly and repeatedly practiced; (3) as they are carried over into experiences outside the classroom. Watkins (**15**), for example, points out clearly that certain types of specific training in the aspects of this objective are essential if it is to become useful to the citizen in solving his problems. In a later chapter suggestive procedures for developing some of the elements of problem-solving will be discussed.

Since this objective is complex, it seems desirable to present one analysis that has been useful.[3] The analysis here presented follows the steps outlined in chapter iii, but it goes into more detail and describes the basic elements of each step in the process. With such an analysis at hand the teacher of secondary-school science should find it easier to plan learning experiences that will foster growth in the various elements. Since problems are not always solved by taking the steps in the order proposed, the suggested order is to be regarded primarily as one of convenience.

1. *Sensing significant problems*
   a) Sensing situations involving personal and social problems where science knowledge and skills can be profitably used
   b) Recognizing specific problems in these situations

---

[3] *Ibid.*

2. *Defining problem situations*
   a) Isolating the single major idea of the problem
   b) Stating the problem (question) in definite and concise language
   c) Selecting the key words of a problem
   d) Defining key words as a means of getting a better understanding of the problem
3. *Studying the situation for all facts and clues bearing upon the problem*
   a) Learning to recognize valid evidence
   b) Recalling past experiences which bear upon a problem
   c) Isolating elements common in experience and problem
   d) Using experimental procedures suitable to the solution of a problem
      (1) Devising experiments appropriate to the solution of a problem
         (a) Selecting the main factor in the experiment
         (b) Allowing only one variable
         (c) Setting up controls for the experimental factor
      (2) Carrying out the details of the experiment
         (a) Identifying effects and determining causes
         (b) Testing the effects of the experimental factor under varying conditions
         (c) Performing the experiment a sufficient number of times to insure reliable evidence
         (d) Determining and recording qualitative and quantitative data
         (e) Developing a logical organization of recorded data
         (f) Generalizing on the basis of data
      (3) Manipulating the laboratory equipment needed in solving a problem with understanding of its function
         (a) Selecting the kinds of equipment or materials that will be helpful in the solution of the problem
         (b) Appraising scales and divisions of scales on measuring instruments
         (c) Avoiding hazards and consequent personal accidents
   e) Locating source materials
      Note: Attention is here directed to the detailed analysis of the specific skills involved in this element, and the four which follow, that has been made in connection with the preceding objective (pp. 144-45)
   f) Using source materials
   g) Solving mathematical problems necessary in obtaining pertinent data
   h) Making observations suitable for solving a problem
   i) Using talks and interviews as sources of information
4. *Making the best tentative explanation or hypothesis*
   a) Selecting important factors related to the problem
   b) Identifying the different relationships which may exist between the factors
5. *Selecting the most likely hypothesis*
   a) Analyzing, selecting, and interpreting relevant data
   b) Judging pertinency or significance of data for the immediate problem
      (1) Checking data against authority
      (2) Recognizing and developing logical sequence of data

   c) Recognizing weaknesses in data
   d) Using resourcefulness in proposing new hypotheses
6. *Testing the hypothesis by experimental or other means*
   a) Checking the hypothesis with recognized authorities
   b) Devising experimental procedures suitable for testing the hypothesis
   c) Organizing data
   d) Rechecking data for errors in interpretation
   e) Applying the hypothesis to the problem to determine its adequacy
7. *Accepting tentatively or rejecting the hypothesis and testing other hypotheses*
8. *Drawing conclusions*
   a) Using the hypothesis as a basis for generalizing in terms of similar problem situations

F. *Providing for growth in the development of scientific attitudes.* Considerable research has been done on this objective beginning with the pioneer work of Curtis (**3**), and later by Davis (**4**), Noll (**11**), and Ebel (**6**).

If growth toward scientific attitudes is to be realized as an objective in science instruction, these attitudes must be taught as rigorously as we now strive for the functional understanding of content. Compton (**2**) has said:

Science is not a technique or a body of knowledge, though it uses both. It is rather an attitude of inquiry, of observation and reasoning with respect to the world. It can be developed, not by memorizing facts or juggling formulas to get an answer, but only by actual practice of scientific observation and reasoning.

The following analysis[4] of a selected group of attitudes is proposed as a guide rather than as a final list. The science program in the secondary school should foster and develop the attitudes which will modify the individual's behavior so that he:

1. Looks for the natural causes for things that happen:
   a) Does not believe in superstitions, such as charms of good or bad luck.
   b) Believes that there is no connection necessarily between two events just because they happen at the same time or one after the other.
2. Is open-minded toward work and opinion of others and information related to his problem:
   a) Believes that truth never changes, but his ideas of what is true may change as he gains better understanding of that truth.
   b) Revises his opinions and conclusions in the light of additional reliable evidence.
   c) Listens to, observes, or reads evidence supporting ideas contrary to his personal opinions.
   d) Accepts no conclusion as final or ultimate.

---

[4] *Ibid.*

3. Bases opinions and conclusions on adequate evidence:
   a) Is slow to accept as facts anything not supported by convincing proof.
   b) Bases his conclusions upon evidence obtained from a variety of dependable sources.
   c) Searches for the most satisfactory explanation of observed phenomena that the evidence permits.
   d) Sticks to the facts and refrains from exaggeration.
   e) Does not permit his personal pride, bias, prejudice, or ambition to pervert the truth.
   f) Does not make snap judgments or jump to conclusions.

4. Evaluates techniques and procedures used and information obtained:
   a) Uses a planned procedure in solving his problems.
   b) Seeks to use the various techniques and procedures which have proved valuable in obtaining evidence.
   c) Seeks to adapt the various techniques and procedures to the problem at hand.
   d) Personally considers the evidence and decides whether it relates to the problem.
   e) Judges whether the evidence is sound, sensible, and complete enough to allow a conclusion to be drawn.
   f) Selects the most recent, authoritative, and accurate evidence related to the problem.

5. Is curious concerning the things he observes:
   a) Wants to know the "whys," "whats," and "hows" of observed phenomena.
   b) Is not satisfied with vague explanations of his questions.

G. *Providing for growth in the development of appreciations.* This objective has come to be accepted as a worthy one in science instruction. It has long been accepted by certain other areas of the secondary-school curriculum, such as art, music, social studies, and English. Science teachers may have felt that appreciations are intangible and, therefore, somewhat remote from their field. Perhaps the main factor in this feeling has been the fact that there has been no agreement upon just what is meant by the term "appreciation." Another factor may have been that there has been little or no attempt made to analyze the objective into its specific elements. As related to science, Nixon (10) defines the term "appreciation" as follows: "Appreciation, which involves both intellectual and emotional elements, is a sensitive awareness to and perception of the importance or utility of information in its relation to other fields and in the development of attitudes and tastes."

A suggested list of appreciations, in which science instruction at the secondary level may well encourage growth, might include the following:

1. The contributions of science to the progress of civilization
2. The methods of problem-solving as they have been used by scientists in making discoveries
3. The potentialities of science for creating well-being or destruction for the peoples of the earth
4. The contributions of science to promoting good health and eliminating disease
5. The manifold applications of science through inventions
6. The causal role of science in creating social and economic problems and in aiding in their intelligent solution
7. The importance of conserving natural resources of many types
8. The importance of science for the consumer
9. The potentialities of science for raising standards of living

H. *Providing for growth in the development of interests.* Science teaching at the secondary-school level should seek not only to make the day-to-day learning of the pupil interesting but also to create abiding interests in science that may be pursued through life. These interests may well play an important part in the vocation of some pupils while in others they may continue into post-school life purely in an avocational role. Thus, the science teacher must be certain to point out to pupils the possibilities that the field may offer for a career and also to plan his teaching so that the avocational and recreational opportunities are brought out.

The career possibilities of science can probably best be provided for through individual counseling. The teacher will be in a strategic position to select from his classes those young people who, because of special aptitudes, may be well fitted to pursue study in the field leading to a life work. Interest in science for such pupils may be materially enhanced by selecting them for special responsibilities about the laboratory. They can save the busy science teacher many hours of work while learning to handle various pieces of equipment. In many cases such pupils have proved able to set up demonstrations and keep equipment in repair.

Avocational interests in science may be widely varied throughout all the recognized scientific areas and fields. Such interests can be effectively provided for during the school years through the science clubs and through the field trips that are taken in certain subject-matter areas.

Following is a list of some of the interests that science instruction at the secondary level may well promote:

1. Interest in some phase of science for a career such as engineering, chemistry, medicine, mining, agriculture, etc.
2. Interest in amateur photography
3. Interest in astronomy
4. Interest in microscopy

5. Interest in birds as a hobby
6. Interest in collecting rocks and minerals
7. Interest in chemistry as a hobby
8. Interest in botany as a hobby
9. Interest in gardening
10. Interest in making scientific equipment

SUMMARY

The trend in science courses throughout the junior high school, senior high school, and junior college seems to be in the direction of the more general type of course. These courses are commonly planned to meet the more immediate science needs of those who enrol in them.

The objectives for secondary-school science teaching are the same as those for other levels but perhaps with emphasis varying with the increased maturity of the learner. These objectives must be sought in the broad areas of human experience where young people meet their problems of adjustment.

Adjustment to new situations usually means a modification of the behavior patterns of the individual. Thus, the functional understanding of facts, principles, and concepts, the acquisition of skills, the growth in the use of scientific method, and the acquisition of scientific attitudes, appreciations, and interests are means to the end of more effective adjustment.

Growth in ability to use the scientific method and in the acquisition of scientific attitudes, appreciations, and interests has long been assumed to be a concomitant of growth in knowledge. This is a false assumption. If these so-called "intangibles" are to be realized as objectives they must be sought as vigorously in the classroom as is the functional understanding of facts, principles, and concepts.

REFERENCES

1. CLARK, H. N. "A Survey of the Natural Science Courses Offered in the Public Junior Colleges of Southern California." Los Angeles: University of Southern California (Manuscript).
2. COMPTON, KARL T. "Science in Education," *Science Education*, XX (April, 1936), 53–56.
3. CURTIS, F. D. *Some Values Derived from Extensive Reading of General Science.* Teachers College Contributions to Education, No. 163. New York: Teachers College, Columbia University, 1924.
4. DAVIS, IRA C. "The Measurement of Scientific Attitudes," *Science Education*, XIX (October, 1935), 117–22.
5. DOWNING, E. R. "Elements and Safeguards of Scientific Thinking," *Scientific Monthly*, XXVI (March, 1938), 231–43.
6. EBEL, ROBERT L. "What is the Scientific Attitude?" *Science Education*, XXII (January, 1938), 1–5; (February, 1938), 75–81.

7. ENGLEMAN, LOIS, and EELS, WALTER C. *The Literature of Junior-College Terminal Education.* Washington: American Association of Junior Colleges, 1941.

8. HUNTER, G. W., and SPORE, LEROY. "Science Sequence and Enrolments in the Secondary Schools of the United States," *Science Education,* XXV (December, 1941), 359–70; XXVI (February, 1942), 66–77.

9. KEESLAR, OREON. "The Elements of Scientific Methods," *Science Education,* XXIX (December, 1945), 273–78.

10. NIXON, ALFRED E. "The Meaning of Appreciation," *Science Education,* XXIX (February, 1945), 35–40.

11. NOLL, VICTOR H. *The Habit of Scientific Thinking.* New York: Bureau of Publications, Teachers College, Columbia University, 1935.

12. NOLL, VICTOR H. "Teaching Science for the Purpose of Influencing Behavior," *Science Education,* XX (February, 1936), 17–20.

13. *Offerings and Registrations in High-School Subjects, 1933–1934.* United States Office of Education Bulletin, No. 6, 1938. Washington: Government Printing Office, 1938.

14. RENNICK, HOWARD. "Survey of Chemistry and Physics Courses," *Junior College Journal,* X (March, 1940), 394–95.

15. WATKINS, RALPH K. "An Analysis of the Types of Scientific Method Used by Laymen in Typical Out-of-School Situations," *Science Education,* XXXIV (November, 1934) 804–11.

16. WATSON, D. R. "Survey Courses in Physical Science." Los Angeles: University of Southern California, 1940 (Manuscript).

CHAPTER XII

THE CONTENT AND METHODS OF SCIENCE
IN THE JUNIOR HIGH SCHOOL

THE DEVELOPMENT OF SCIENCE AT THE JUNIOR HIGH SCHOOL LEVEL

The problem of developing an adequate introductory course in science was generally recognized prior to the organization of junior high schools. Early in the present century dissatisfaction with science teaching was widely expressed. The famous report of the Committee of Ten (**37**) had produced improvements in the organization and teaching of separate sciences in secondary schools. Those improvements, though very real, had omitted entirely the benefits of earlier courses in natural science. Indeed, the Committee of Ten was adversely critical of general courses in natural science. One result of the work of that eminent committee was to make secondary-science teaching highly exacting in terms of special science subjects. Such exactions appear to have been more in the interest of the science subjects than in the interest of pupils. Thus, the courses in science did not produce the expected results in secondary schools. This situation emphasized the need of improved introduction to science.

In its earliest stages the problems involved were regarded as pertaining to the first year of the four-year high school, rather than to seventh and eighth grades which later became parts of the junior high school. Other reports dealing with improvement of science instruction show that the four-year high school and not the junior high school was then under consideration. Within a few years, however, it became evident that all of the junior high school years offered an excellent field for improved courses in introductory science, which soon became known as general science.

It is significant that science teachers in various parts of the country were independently trying out different types of content and methods for teaching introductory science. At least twenty-two such experiments were under way in the school year 1909–10 (**5**). Some of these experimental courses consisted of several short courses in special sciences. In others, one special science, such as physiography, physics, or chemistry, was used as the general outline with a small amount of related material drawn from other sciences. In some schools the course consisted of general lectures of an entertaining nature which did not require a considerable amount of student work, the lecture topics being in the fields of the science teachers who gave them. In other schools the experimental courses were composed of topical science, which used material from several specialized sciences.

Obviously, there was "in the air" a widespread sensing of the need for a new kind of course. It is equally obvious that there was no agreement as to the content or nature of such a course. In the cases of the twenty-two experimental courses referred to above, the schools recognized that highly specialized sciences were not meeting the needs of first-year pupils. Pupils showed interest in science, but interest often slackened or disappeared when the pupils were placed in courses in specialized science. It was concluded that new types of introductory science were imperative to meet the needs of younger pupils as well as to improve the results from the later courses in specialized sciences.

There was much discussion among science teachers about what science materials would best compose an introductory course. Different guiding ideas were used by different teachers. One plan of work is here given as illustration of selection of course materials. The first experimental work done in the University of Chicago High School was based upon short courses in each of five separate sciences. That plan was disappointing, though it was an improvement upon any previously-taught specialized science. The teachers in charge there assembled extensive questions and suggestions by a large number of pupils regarding scientific matters about which they wished to know. These questions and suggestions were secured by direct appeal to hundreds of pupils in their classrooms and in school-assembly meetings. When these items were tabulated, it was found that almost all of them could be classified under a half-dozen major topics. Those topics were then examined at length and under them were organized the subject matter, experiments, demonstrations, readings, and community illustrations for pupil work and classroom discussions. Those studies and pupil experiences were organized with little regard to what sciences were represented; coherence within the course, such as there was, was found in the relations of the topics and their contents, not in the usual relations of the parts of any specialized science. The results with the pupils seemed to justify the plans as thus developed. Criteria for the earliest selection of topics and their content for inclusion in general science can hardly be claimed to have been fully satisfactory.

The N.E.A. report, called *Reorganization of Science in Secondary Schools*, was published in 1920 (**36**). That report took account of experimental courses already being used and made definite recommendations of far-reaching import. The attitude of the committee is set forth by the following quotation from the Preface:

Some of the improvements that the Committee sought to effect have already been adopted by many of the best schools. The full report herein presented, formulated through this procedure, incorporates practices that have proved most useful. It asks for only those features of reorganization that have been found to work well or which, by a fair amount of trial, promise improvements. Further experiments with new courses in science, or with the readjustment of older courses, may make desirable and necessary a revision of the report before many years have passed.

There were forty-seven members of the committee which produced that report. Though most of the work was done by a few, the successive drafts were criticized by the entire committee.

At the time of publication of that report, general science was taught in many schools. Quotations from the statement about general science show that the point of view regarding the purposes of the subject and the topical nature and the scope of its content had reached a stage of considerable definiteness. For example:

Science is universal and constant in the life of our citizens, and hence to be useful to all pupils, general science must accept the science of common things as its legitimate field. The science of common use and that of the classrooms should be the same. General science should use any phase of any special science which is pertinent in the citizen's interpretation of a worth-while problem. . . . . In organizing this material, the topic should be the large unit to which many specific pieces of work are related.

Then there follow seven illustrative topics, each with outlines of its related subtopics. The seven major topics are combustion, water, air and the weather, light and its benefits, work and energy, magnetism and electricity, and nature's balance of life. The committee did not regard this list as complete and suggested inclusion of units on astronomy and on household science. It appears, therefore, that more than twenty-five years ago general science had ceased to be a series of short courses in the separate sciences, was composed of topics or units related to the citizens' needs in science, and drew its materials from any specialized science which helped to meet those needs.

The development of junior high schools called for the organization of appropriate science courses for Grades VII and VIII, or both, as well as for Grade IX which had been the first year of the four-year high school. The first general science courses had been organized for the first year of the four-year high school. It was natural that the ninth-grade course should be readjusted for use in the earlier junior high school years. This was done. In many junior high schools general science is taught in but one or two of the three years; in others it is taught in all three years. In some junior high schools science is taught for two or three periods each week during the seventh and eighth school years and for five periods during the ninth year. In schools which continue the 8-4 plan, general science is commonly taught as a full-time subject in the ninth year. Obviously this confused situation calls for further study and experimentation. Such sequences of science subjects as those recommended by the Thirty-first Yearbook (**34**) appear to have but partial approval in actual *school* practices. As often remarked, it is still much easier to see what seems good to do than it is to do those things. Adjusted, reorganized, or newly developed courses are urged. An important field, for careful and prolonged experimentation, needs working in order that the most worthy and useful courses in science may be available for the junior high schools. The progress already made does not fully meet present needs.

Selecting and Organizing Content for Junior High School Science[1]

The earlier research on the selection and organization of content for junior high school science was summarized and reviewed in a previous yearbook of the National Society (**34**). *The Third Digest of Investigations in the Teaching of Science* by F. D. Curtis (**9**) brings the research down to the end of 1937. The trends reported here have to do with those supported by the research done since. Summaries of the more recent research on junior high school science are provided in a mimeographed report by David J. Blick (**4**) and in two numbers of the *Review of Educational Research* (**28**).

A series of unpublished studies done by Huffman, LeCocq, and Van der Ploeg (**48**) indicate a degree of uniformity of content in the science textbooks for the seventh, eighth, and ninth years as wholes. According to these studies, greater uniformity of content has been achieved in books for the eighth year than in books for the seventh and ninth years of three-book series.

The number of analyses of textbooks for junior high school science seems out of proportion to the relative importance of this problem. For example, studies of the fundamental needs of pupils for solutions to science problems, or of the adjustment of content to the varying maturities of pupils, seem to be needed more than do studies of agreement of current books.

The results of investigations on agreement among textbooks for particular grades are divergent. Pettit (**32**) finds no definite agreement on grade placement in three-book series. Sisson (**44**) also reports considerable variability in content, especially in seventh-grade books. On the other hand, Gervers (**13**), Graham (**14**), Hurd (**17**), and Sim-

---

[1] The Committee has profited from the collaboration of Ralph K. Watkins of the University of Missouri in the preparation of this section.

mons (**43**) find essential agreement among textbooks in general science or, at least, a trend toward uniformity. Apparently there is greater uniformity in the content of textbooks in general science than in the content of individual books for particular years of a three-year sequence. In other words, there is better agreement in the total content for the whole junior high school than there is in the grade placement of details for a particular year.

A survey of content by Hunter and Parker (**18**) merely confirms the fairly well-established pattern of content for general science that can be discerned by an examination of the textbooks.

In searching for a criterion for use in determining content in general science, Novak (**29**) resorted to the analysis of newspapers. Of fifteen major topics occurring in the *New York Times* he found most space devoted to health and medicine and to transportation and communication. If relative newspaper space is accepted as a criterion of importance, general science should be divided approximately half and half between the biological and physical sciences. This is in contradiction to the customary emphasis on physical science.

Ruffner (**39**) found the science interests of ninth-grade pupils sufficiently lasting to use them in determining the areas to be taught in general science. Her findings are in disagreement with some of the earlier studies and indicate a need for further investigation on the stability of the science interests of junior high school pupils, especially if these interests are to be used as criteria in selecting content of courses.

Matteson and Kambly (**26**) found that the topics covered by a test of 199 items were not learned by children below the seventh grade. The implications are that these topics remain to be taught as a part of the content of junior high school science.

The more significant recent studies of learning in the area of junior high school science have had to do with the relative difficulty of science concepts and with the relationship of such difficulty to the maturity of the pupils. In general, the various investigations are in agreement in pointing out that the science concepts and the accompanying vocabulary burden of junior high school science are too difficult for the maturity levels of the pupils for which the text materials are written.

Bailey (**2**) worked with the concepts of power selected from eighth- and ninth-grade general science. He tested the abilities of pupils of varying mental ages to learn these concepts and concluded that they cannot be learned by pupils with a mental age of 160 months or less and that they are still very difficult for pupils with a mental age of 190 months. He also indicates that factual material is easier to learn than principles.

Smith (**45**) discovered that the difficulty of sampled items of general science was too great for the average ninth-grade pupil to master with 50 per cent success. He concluded that the most important factor in facilitating the learning of general science is the selection of the items of content. He believed the selection factor more important than the conditions of learning and the effort of the pupil in learning.

Winters (**54**) with samplings from seventh-, ninth-, twelfth-, and thirteenth-year science found that at all levels of the secondary school many of the science meanings are not adapted to the grade level of the pupils or that pupils had not attained the mental age to comprehend the meanings at the grade levels where they were introduced. The elaborate studies of textbook vocabularies of Curtis (**10**) support the notion that the terminology of junior high school science is too difficult for the pupils. Curtis also found that vocabulary difficulties exist in nontechnical terms as well as in the technical.

Closely related to the vocabulary studies are two studies of the reading of science materials. Shores (**42**) reports that science reading is related to science vocabulary, general vocabulary, and ability to interpret graphs, tables, and charts, and that it is relatively specific and not highly correlated with an index of general reading ability. Swenson (**46**), on the other hand, points out the high correlation between general reading ability and science reading ability. Obviously further investigation on this point is needed.

In spite of studies of science interests of children and adolescents and a considerable exploration of reading and vocabulary difficulties in science, relatively little has been done with the problem of planning science experiences suited to the needs of young people of varying maturities. Instead of placidly accepting trite science experiences pushed down from the grade levels above, good teaching demands that science experiences be planned for the maturity of the particular pupils involved. The immediate pressing need is at the elementary and junior high school levels. However, the same issue can be raised concerning the smug acceptance of the adequacy of existing college practices in teaching science, especially at the junior-college level.

Psychologically the great barriers to a satisfactory grade placement of content for science courses are in the large variations in individual abilities and in the varying rates at which different pupils mature. There are also the factors of opportunity and the variations in physical and social environment. As a result of such factors, many pupils enrolled in the seventh grade can learn science more readily than some older pupils enrolled in the eighth grade. At the same time there are pupils in ninth grade who can learn science much less readily than many younger pupils of the seventh grade.

The difficulties of placement created by these conditions have led most workers in the field of science education to abandon the attempt to allocate a given selection of content to one particular grade and to omit these items from the next grade. There is no assurance that most pupils in a given grade can best learn item "x" at that particular grade level.

Most curriculum workers in the field of junior high school science are now committed to a policy of spiralling placement. In this solution of placement, many of the same principles, concepts, or generalizations of science are included in each year's work. The experiences of the pupils and the applications of these concepts or generalizations vary from year to year. There is the expectation also that the added experiences of pupils with a given concept in succeeding years will enlarge understanding and control of the concept or principle.

In searching for a practical pattern upon which to develop such a spiralled grade placement of junior high school science, course-of-study planners and authors of textbooks have arrived at the following general formula:

First year: Science experiences having to do with the immediately personal problems of the learner and with simple understandings.

Second year: Science experiences dealing with the physical and community environment.

Third year: Science experiences dealing with the wider social significances of science and the use of science for the control of environment.

Such a formula seems to be psychologically sound but in all probability is more empirical than scientific. It may have the defect of moving more rapidly toward adult experience than the maturity of junior high school pupils will warrant. At least it offers a present practical framework, albeit tentative, upon which to erect the spiral of experiences dealing with the enlarging concepts and generalizations of science.

The rather wide acceptance of the scheme presented may explain the fact that the general outlines of content for junior high school courses in science show better agreement than the details of selection of experiences for a particular year. On the other hand, the lack of assured knowledge concerning the way young people mature and evidence of their specific needs may explain the lack of conformity in details of selection for particular years.

In 1934, Hurd, as chairman of a research committee of the National Association for Research in Science Teaching, presented a report of an investigation of expert opinion on the problems of selection and organization of content for science courses below the college level (16). Hurd's list of criteria for selection and organization of content were based largely on a list prepared by Pieper (33). The revised list of criteria was sent to the members of the N.A.R.S.T. The findings of this study represent probably the nearest possible agreement on criteria for the selection of content for science courses.

The following criteria for the *selection of content* for junior high school science, condensed from the foregoing sources and agreed upon by the yearbook committee, are suggested.

Content for junior high school science should:

1. Be in harmony with the accepted objectives set up for the pupils.
2. Lead to the inculcation of appropriate scientific attitudes and the understanding of the methods of science.
3. Encourage the belief in, and practice of, desirable social ideals involving science.
4. Be of direct use to pupils in their daily living.
5. Be appropriate for the ability level of the pupil.
6. Aid pupils in the interpretation of the local and world environment.
7. Be in harmony with the needs and interests of the pupil.

From the research available and on the basis of a considered judgment of the committee, the following principles are recommended as guides for the *organization* of science content for the junior high school:

1. Content should be organized into large areas or units, each of which represents some major problem of living, area of human experience, or aspect of environment.
2. The content of any single area or unit should be broken down into smaller learning problems which have interest, significance, and usefulness to the learner.
3. The learning experiences in any single problem should be organized to promote functional understandings, growth in instrumental skills, growth in the processes of problem-solving, and the development of attitudes, appreciations, and interests.
4. Abundant opportunities should be provided both for building and applying principles and concepts.
5. Provision should be made for effective evaluation including self-evaluation.
6. The sequence of units should be planned to give recurrent contacts with facts, concepts, and principles of science and to provide a spiralling and enlarging pattern of growth in concepts and principles.
7. Problem situations should provide definite training in one or more of the elements of scientific method.
8. The courses in science should be organized to provide frequent opportunity for pupils to participate in planning and to engage in individual and group projects.

METHODS AND MATERIALS FOR JUNIOR HIGH SCHOOL SCIENCE

Determining classroom procedures. Problems of selection and organization of junior high school science are tied inextricably to the teaching methods used. There is always a question of whether or not content and method can be separated at all.

The present concept of method is that of a procedure which directs the experiences of young people immediately toward the attainment of objectives of science teaching. There are two phases of this concept: (1) method is primarily the direction or guidance of the experiences of the learners; (2) the learning experiences are to be selected to go as straightforwardly as possible toward the desired learning outcomes.

In accordance with this interpretation, general names for teaching methods tend to lose their significance. We speak not of laboratory or demonstration methods but of what laboratory or demonstrational experiences may possibly contribute to the desired learning for a particular group of young people. A method is good if the experiences involved produce the needed learning outcomes with a minimum of time and effort. A method is bad if the experiences it provides fail to produce the desired learning results or if it is relatively wasteful of time and energy in reaching the goals.

Junior high school science teaching tends to emphasize lecture-demonstration, text-recitation, class discussion, and supervised study. Apparently, laboratory work is at a minimum. Hilgers (**17**) reports that almost all teachers use lecture-demonstration. For a further discussion of the research bearing on this issue the reader is referred to chapter iv.

Factors contributing to the teacher's reliance on lecture-demonstration are: (*a*) the series of investigations showing the superiority, for immediate retention, of lecture-demonstration over the traditional type of laboratory experiences; (*b*) classes too large for successful laboratory work; and (*c*) lack of equipment for individual laboratory work.

A check on the kinds of demonstrations included in the teaching materials commonly available to junior high school science teachers shows that the more common demonstrations are those which the teachers learned to do in college science classes. It will be agreed that this is a poor basis for selection. There is a great need for the development of an adequate series of demonstrations to be used in junior high school classes for building up very specific understandings of particular science concepts, principles, and applications.

The rise of lecture-demonstration procedures and the decline of laboratory experiences during the period of the development of junior high school science has meant a minimizing of notebooks and drawings in science classwork at this level. The notebooks and drawings of the traditional science class were adjuncts of the laboratory. If laboratory work is not done, notebooks and drawings seem to have little justification. Educational experimentation on the value of these aids to learning science fails

to support their value. For example, see the findings reported by Kraus
(**23**).

The workbook. Workbooks have tended to supplant both notebooks
and laboratory manuals. Most existing science workbooks are yet largely
question-and-answer devices. They call for little more than the filling in
of blanks. (This is, however, less true of junior high school workbooks
than of those for the senior high school.) Little experimental evidence on
the learning value of science workbooks is available. Anderson (**1**) finds
that using workbooks in science gives better results than classwork without workbooks and that superior pupils profit more than others in the
use of workbooks.

The ideal science workbook should be built around a set of varied
experiences which, if properly carried out, would insure the learning desired. There should not be a complete dependency upon the workbook
for all that is done in the science class. No one method nor no one tool
can be expected to care for all learning situations. It is impossible to
build a teaching device outside the classroom situation that will care for
the individual needs of the pupils as the teacher can see them. A good
workbook should contain many suggestive learning activities from which
suitable assignment materials can be selected by the teacher and adapted
to the needs of the pupils in his classes. For a further discussion of the
workbook in science teaching the reader is referred to chapter iv.

Multi-sensory aids. Military and industrial training experiences during
the war have stimulated enormously the interest of school people and
that of laymen in the use of sensory aids to learning. In the science field
these aids have taken the form of silent motion pictures, sound motion
pictures, filmstrips, and micro-projection, models, charts, field trips, and
the like. Apparently the stimulation of public interest is being accompanied by something of a commercial boom in the manufacturing of
multi-sensory aids for classroom use. Increasingly, motion-picture films
and filmstrips are being built for specific instructional purposes.

So far the obstacle to greater use of films is the expense of purchasing
and maintaining a suitable film library. Schools that are parts of city
systems with central distributing organizations can readily meet this
difficulty. Smaller schools, or schools in isolated areas, cannot yet achieve
an adequate library at reasonable expense. They must struggle with the
scheduling difficulties inherent in a film supply from rental libraries and
regional distribution centers.

There is considerable evidence available to show the learning value of
experiences with motion pictures. Latest evidence indicates clearly that
other teaching along with the use of film enhances the learning value.
Evidence of the comparative value of sound and silent motion pictures is

inconclusive. The findings of recent investigations might be summed up by saying that both silent and sound pictures, if well selected, have educational worth. Intelligent teacher comment and class discussion based upon the pictures add to their usefulness. Motion pictures are not substitutes for all other forms of teaching and need to be woven into the total educational experiences of pupils with careful planning and with good judgment.

On the issue of sound versus silent films, Maneval (**25**), working with eighth-grade pupils, achieved superior results with silent films both for immediate and delayed recall, but the differences noted were not statistically significant.

In attempting to find a good way to use motion pictures in science instruction, Krasker (**22**) found that a preliminary showing followed by discussion and a reshowing of the film gave superior results over merely showing the pictures. He concluded that the showing of a film without discussion or review did not achieve enough learning to justify the time taken.

A comparison of the uses of motion pictures with other optional teaching techniques was made by Maneval (**25**) who found that for immediate recall study sheets were superior to sound films in learning the same material. There were no differences for delayed recall. Pupils liked the sound films better than the study sheets.

Certainly the available investigations do not support the current enthusiasm for sound motion pictures in teaching science. Neither do they support the carry-over of supposed superior results claimed for the use of motion pictures in the armed forces during the war. The total accumulated evidence is small. Further extended investigation is needed.

Among special types of visual aids, micro-projection has great promise for certain phases of science teaching. Equipment for micro-projection is much less expensive than the cost of equipping individual workers with microscopes. Besides, junior high school pupils may be too immature to work with expensive microscopes. With micro-projection it is easily possible for the teacher to determine the reaction of the pupil to what he sees. Teacher and pupils see the same thing at the same time. With beginning learners the greater magnification should be a definite advantage in many cases. Still, Hilgers reports that teachers make very little use of micro-projection (**15**). This may be due to inadequate experiences with the manipulation of the necessary equipment in teacher-training institutions, including both the college classes in the sciences and student teaching.

Extensive reading. A methodology including a much greater use of extensive reading of books and magazines in the science fields should be adopted by science teachers everywhere. There is a considerable body of experimental evidence to support the learning values of a wide range of reading in science (**9, 38**).

At present a wealth of non-textbook material is available for reading. Much attention has been given to the needs of children and adult lay readers. Well-edited booklists are accessible to the science teacher. Among these the annual list of H. A. Webb deserves special mention (**53**). Teachers in training should have experience with science-library materials and should learn to make purchase lists for building up local science libraries.

The most serious limitation on the use of extensive reading in the teaching of science is the inadequacy of the existing library facilities in most schools. Administrators should give due consideration to the great need for building the science sections of the local school library.

Many teachers have not yet learned the relatively simple techniques for individualized assignments which make use of library facilities in science, nor have they developed techniques for effective use of classroom libraries. Here is a need for both in-service training and for improved cadet-teacher training.

The use of extensive reading for science instruction immediately raises the issue of need for improvement in reading processes and in vocabulary building for junior high school pupils. This need is shown by a number of recent studies (**9, 42, 46**). The use of extensive science reading, improved reading procedures, and science vocabulary-building can be readily developed as a part of any acceptable procedure in teaching science.

Related to the teaching problems included in science reading are the findings of a number of isolated studies having to do with study sheets, work sheets, and illustrations. Olson and Kambly (**31**) have shown that individual assistance in study is superior to group assistance or to assistance given when called for. Significant differences have been found in favor of pupils using illustrated text material over those using the same material mimeographed without illustrations (**20**). The Morrison "unit" attack with a "lesson guide method" is reported as superior to "conventional procedures" (**12**).

The laboratory. Laboratories, as they are commonly thought of, rarely exist in junior high schools. If the major purpose of junior high school science is that of teaching facts, or possibly the interpretation of principles, it is probable that other instructional procedures may be quite effective. If, on the other hand, pupils are to learn to solve science problems for themselves or to manipulate apparatus skilfully and intelligently, there seems to be every reason to provide some firsthand laboratory experiences. The case for laboratory instruction at junior high school level must be built on this assumption.

The young worker is not to go into the laboratory to *prove* an established law or principle of science. He may illustrate a known principle. He does not *prove* it. The incentive to proof in the sense of dependence upon one's own data is totally lacking. How can pupils learn scientific methods for out-of-school uses under such conditions?

Although laws and principles of science are interpreted in many available textbooks, the applications of principles to homely living situations are practically untouched. Many of these are appropriate centers for laboratory investigations by teachers and pupils. If the current concern for training in scientific methods and scientific attitudes is to be actually implemented, there are great possibilities in the development of such laboratory experiences with junior high school pupils.

Problem-solving. In spite of the interest in problem-solving expressed by teachers of science, the number of studies of this phase of science education is decidedly small. Keeslar (**21**) has a useful and suggestive analysis of elements of scientific method which emphasizes the multiplicity of methods of attack used in modern science. The analysis is too long to reproduce here but its reading is recommended for study to the student of scientific problem-solving. Curtis (**8**) reports an analysis of the types of thought questions found in the textbooks of science. According to his data the textbooks and workbooks for junior high school science make insufficient use of types of questions that stimulate reflective thinking. In a report of an attempt to teach scientific analysis of advertising, Scott (**40**) concluded that a school study of advertising is worthless unless it is accompanied by laboratory work on the advertised commodities.

Attitudes and appreciations. More investigative work has been done on the accompanying phases of scientific attitudes and appreciations, although some of the findings are contradictory and indicate need for further research. Blair and Goodson (**3**) found that mere exposure to a course in general science does not develop scientific attitudes but that marked improvement in scientific thinking can be achieved by direct teaching. On the contrary, Eberhard and Hunter (**11**) noted no significant advantage for an experimental group with respect to scientific attitudes after seven months of direct teaching. There may well be a question concerning the comparability of the attitudes taught in these two investigations. Certainly the findings of Eberhard and Hunter are inconsistent with earlier investigations in which the direct teaching of attitudes is reported as successful. In agreement with the study of Blair and Goodson (**3**), McKnelly (**27**) found that scientific attitudes are not formed by free reading in science.

The interest of investigators in superstitions and unfounded beliefs continues. Vicklund's (**49**) work to reduce credence in superstitions and unfounded beliefs by direct teaching is comparable with that of Blair and Goodson on the direct teaching of attitudes. In six weeks of direct teaching, Vicklund reports, unfounded beliefs of the subjects were considerably diminished. Beliefs in health and mental telepathy and those which relate to religious faiths seemed to be most difficult to change. Ter Keurst (**47**) tested pupils in Grades VII, VIII, and IX for superstitions and observed that superstitions do not decrease with grade level. Apparently there was no direct teaching with the subjects of Ter Keurst's investigation.

Zim (**55**) has made the most elaborate of the recent interest studies. The findings indicate the extent of appreciation of science on the part of young people and the areas in which interests and appreciations are found. He discovered that interests are expressed in relation to specific phases of science rather than to general areas or subjects. Moreover, science interests seem to arise from other sources more often than from experiences in school science, strong preferences being noted among both boys and girls for science as related to health, growth, reproduction, and animal life.

Pupil planning. A recent development in teaching methods is the increased attention to the participation of the pupils in planning their own work, called "the pupil-planned unit" in modern parlance. Science teachers, along with others, have for a long time encouraged pupil planning. An obvious criticism of these attempts can be found in the need for a better pattern of logical sequence of science experiences than most pupil planning seems to achieve. According to reports of reactions of pupils (**52**) to such planning, the pupils themselves seem to be impressed with the inadequacy of the science interpretations built up in very loosely integrated science experiences. The science experiences chosen by the pupils and their own statements on the completion of the work both point in this direction.

The core curriculum. An even more complex problem in the selection and organization of content and in the accompanying methodology is found in the development of core-curriculum experiments in an increasing number of schools. To date most core-curriculum enterprises have involved the fusion of materials from other subjects around centers drawn from the social studies and English. There have been few attempts to include needed scientific facts and interpretations in these fusions. Some schools have tried to develop a science core in which some significant scientific development becomes the center of organization rather than experiences drawn from the social studies. To date, there are no published investigations which adequately evaluate the introduction of needed science education into the units of a core curriculum (**19**).

Certainly, if the curriculum of the school of the future is to be organized on the pattern of the present experimental cores, scientific facts, principles, interpretations, understandings, and attitudes will need to be incorporated in the units.

GROWTH OF SKILLS IN THE USE OF THE ELEMENTS OF SCIENTIFIC METHOD

The techniques which may be useful in developing some of the skills of scientific thinking or problem-solving require special consideration. The importance of this objective of science teaching and the fact that its methodology has been somewhat specialized justify this separate treatment.

In a previous section of this chapter it has been pointed out that the proper selection and organization of the content of general science may well contribute to growth in the skills of problem-solving. For example, if the content of a given unit in general science is so organized that the pupil must use problem-solving techniques in arriving at a solution, it may be assumed that he will grow toward this objective. However, as a teacher attempts to organize materials of instruction for teaching the skills of this objective, he will soon discover that it is not always possible to introduce a complete cycle of the steps in problem-solving in each specific situation.

This condition prevails whether the teacher is teaching from a course of study or textbook based on a topical organization or from one based on a problem organization. The fact that not all problem situations require the use of every element of scientific method should not be a serious handicap to the teacher who wishes to strive for this objective. It should be emphasized at this point that nearly every lesson in science has in it rich potentialities for developing one or more skills in problem-solving if the teacher is sensitive to these opportunities in lesson-planning. Even the most prosaic and conventional discussion, recitation, demonstration, or experiment may hold a great many opportunities for practicing some of the elements of the problem-solving technique. Teachers must assume responsibility for finding these occasions and then for shaping the development of the lesson in such a way that pupils may secure practice. One situation may be used for defining a problem, planning a controlled experiment, or formulating hypotheses, while other situations may be more promising for experience in collecting evidence, in testing hypotheses, in interpreting data, or in formulating conclusions. Skills in problem-solving, like other skills, are developed only by repeated use day after day in the classroom.

Limitations of space will not permit the detailed treatment of methods relative to the development of all the specific skills of problem-solving. The following discussion will, therefore, be only suggestive.

Sensing a Significant Problem

Interest is one of the principal factors in developing problem-solving skills. Without the full co-operation of the learner there can be little growth. This means that the approach to setting problems in the classroom should be developed co-operatively so as to allow student and teacher together to explore a given area of learning to locate and to define problems for study. The teacher should continually encourage sensitivity to problems on the part of learners by managing situations in which they must use their various senses and by proposing an analytical approach. During this period of raising questions, the teacher must do skilful steering. He may perform several challenging demonstrations to raise questions, or relate an experience, or read a newspaper clipping, or show pictures or a movie associated with the area under study, all with the purpose of evoking fruitful questions. Sometimes an exploratory trip into the community will serve to generate interest in the problems for study of a given topic.

A general-science class was about to study some of the problems of community health and sanitation. The center of motivation for the study was a clean-restaurant ordinance that was being considered by the town council. Pupils were asked to visit restaurants, hamburger stands, and soda fountains, and to report to the class any unsanitary conditions or practices observed. After a lively discussion, several problems were defined not only in relation to unsanitary practices but also with reference to bacteria, rats, garbage, and insects. After a study of these problems, the pupils deluged the town council with letters demanding action on the measure.

Defining Problem Situations

When problems of study are being defined the teacher has an excellent opportunity to teach the use of clear and concise English. Pupils may be asked to write their problems for a home assignment. These may be read and criticized in class, and the final selection of problems may then be listed.

Adjustment to problems arising out of the environment of pupils regularly demands some change of behavior. The expected change in behavior may often be expressed in verb form. The resourceful teacher can find a wide variety of verbs to use in stating worth-while problems. Following are a few such verbs, selected at random, around which problems from many areas could well be stated:[2]

avoid	generate	organize	repair
build	grow	perform	rid
care for	identify	plant	safeguard
cause	improve	predict	select
change	inspect	prepare	supply
collect	maintain	provide	take apart
conserve	make	purify	train
control	manipulate	rear	transfer
destroy	measure	recognize	transmit
devise	obtain	regulate	use
feed	operate	remove	work

For example:

How does one *avoid* a contagious disease?
How may harmful bacetria be *destroyed?*
How may we *identify* harmful mosquitoes?
How do communities *obtain* pure water?

The analysis of a problem is an essential step toward its definition and solution. When the pupil has isolated the single major factor in a problem, further study will reveal the key words or ideas in the situation. Some teachers, for example, suggest that the pupil underline the key words in the written problem. At this point it is essential to be sure that every pupil in the class knows the meaning of all words in the problem and especially of the key words. The teacher can do a great deal here in helping pupils learn the technical vocabulary so essential to successful work in science. He may, for example, propose the use of the glossary in the textbook or the dictionary. When key words in a problem are defined, a step has been taken toward better insight into the perplexity involved.

Studying the Situation for All Possible Clues and Facts Bearing upon the Problem

The resourceful teacher will find, in this element of problem-solving, many opportunities for guiding pupils in the development of a variety of skills and techniques. In collecting evidence bearing on the solution of the problem, the pupil will be called upon to use many sources such as books, interviews, field trips, experiments, catalogues, models, graphs, moving

---

[2] This list is based on one prepared by Charles J. Pieper, New York University, New York City.

pictures, filmslides, and so on. Each of these types of material calls for a specific technique or a special set of skills for which the pupil must have careful help and guidance.

The student should be taught to collect information bearing on the solution of a problem from as wide a variety of sources as possible. One of the shortcomings of present-day science teaching is the tendency to rely on one or two sources. Pupils should learn early to be critical about books as authoritative sources of information. They should be encouraged to check up on authors and to look for publication dates of books as well as to check on the reliability and recency of information.

Teachers of general science frequently find that pupils are not aware of the sources of the information they desire. It may be wise to have the librarian acquaint them with the library and with techniques for using such aids as card catalogues, guides, and encyclopedias. In turn, the science teacher may profitably spend time teaching the effective use of a book, such as use of a table of contents, index, chapter summaries, glossary, appendixes, etc.

Some teachers have found the instructional test a useful device in teaching these instrumental skills. These tests are usually short and so constructed that they may be easily scored. It is often a good plan to have pupils score their own tests, since the object is to reveal weaknesses rather than to secure "marks." Such a test might contain items of the following type:

1. The part of a book which would be most helpful in turning quickly to the chapter called 'Communicable Diseases" would be (*a*) index (*b*) table of contents (*c*) glossary (*d*) appendix (*e*) title-page (*f*) preface.
2. Write in the blanks the two key words you would use in locating information about each of the problems listed:

.... 1. What effect does tobacco have on the growth of young people?
.... 2. Why are vitamins necessary in the diet?
.... 3. How may burning be controlled?

Tests of the above form may also be used as drill material for promoting growth in the skill. A short time each day devoted to drill exercises of this sort at the beginning of the year will save much time later on.

The science teacher must also assume responsibility for teaching the pupil the skills of reading for exact meaning. Many pupils experience difficulty with science subjects because they fail to make the distinction between reading for pleasure and reading for exact information. This difficulty results from the fact that they fail to read analytically and with purpose. The teacher must motivate the purpose to a large degree and then teach the pupil to read in a questioning manner. What is the author driving at? How do his statements check with other information on the problem? How does this material bear on the solution of my problem? What is the kernel of this paragraph? Pupils must be taught the skill of thinking while they read.

Lists of questions of various types, prepared on the reading related to a given problem, have proved useful in teaching pupils the skills of reading for exact information. Curtis (**8**) listed the various types of questions appearing in science textbooks. Such questions are a stimulus for the development of habits of reflective thinking.

The experiment offers a splendid opportunity in science for collecting reliable information bearing on the solution of problems. Much of the so-called "laboratory work" in general science is merely "busy" work. Teachers should see to it that experiments are used to supply information useful in the solution of problems. Through the medium of the experiment, teachers may find many opportunities for developing the skills of accurate observation, efficient arrangement of data, interpretation of data, and drawing reasonable conclusions.

Teachers often assume that young people studying general science are familiar with good experimental procedures. This, however, is not true. They must be taught efficient laboratory techniques, such as the use and care of equipment. Experience has shown that, in a discussion of an experiment, pupils can learn to isolate the experimental factor and propose ways of controlling other factors. Often in such a discussion, the entire procedure of an experiment may be worked out by the pupils, thus doing away with "cook book" directions so often found in books. Sharpe (**41**) reported some interesting and unique ways of using controlled experiments. Obourn and Montgomery (**30**) have also reported suggested classroom procedures for developing understanding of controlled experiments.

A home assignment may be made in which pupils are asked to formulate a controlled experiment for testing a given idea or hypothesis. This practice also has great potentialities for developing resourcefulness in pupils.

It is very essential that pupils learn at an early time in their general-science course what *good evidence* is and how to judge it. As the teacher guides pupils in the acquisition of the skills essential for collecting evidence, he should use every opportunity to point out the earmarks of reliable data. The following excerpt is taken from an article by Ward (**50**).

(1) Science cares only for indisputable evidence. (2) If the evidence is conflicting, science balances the probabilities without running headlong into a conclusion. (3) Unless the evidence so cumulates that almost all competent observers are forced to agree, science suspends judgment. How small a proportion of the population now has any conception of suspending judgment! How salutory it is

for any of us to learn to suspend! (4) Whenever new evidence appears, the true scientist welcomes it; he is as ready to have his previous theory demolished as to have it corroborated. He is guided by a curiosity that cares only for what the new evidence indicates. (5) Science recognizes that no amount of evidence is ever certain, that no knowledge is everlasting and immutable. The teacher who can give his class an inkling of what true evidence is has made their intellectual lives safer and better. If he tries to expound the abstract principle, he will accomplish nothing. He can convey understanding only by putting before the class one concrete illustration after another, and so gradually bringing out the difference between empty "thinking" and real proof. The humbler the demonstration the better.

Making the Best Tentative Explanation or Hypothesis

It should be stated once more that the present order in discussing the various elements of problem-solving behavior does not mean that the steps must always occur in the same sequence in solving problems. Very often, for example, the step of formulating hypotheses follows directly upon the statement of a problem before any evidence has been collected.

Probably the most neglected skill in teaching problem-solving is the formulation of hypotheses. This judgment is borne out by the lack of research studies related to the skill in question. In the usual classroom procedure pupils do not formulate hypotheses but go directly to the statement of conclusions from evidence collected. The skills involved in proposing hypotheses are important in modern life and should, therefore, receive more attention in the classroom. These skills have been analyzed in chapter xi.

To develop these and other skills of problem-solving, it is not necessary for the teacher of science to abandon or sacrifice the content courses as now organized in favor of some radically different plan. A large proportion of high-school science lends itself to the purposes here discussed with but a slight change of emphasis and approach. The important factor is a teacher who is alert to the potentialities of the situation as it arises.

A class in ninth-grade general science was beginning the study of plant responses. In a preliminary discussion several types of stimuli to which plants might respond were suggested by the class. Among these were air, water, light, touch, and gravity. The home assignment for the next day was to propose hypotheses of just how (positively or negatively) plants respond to these stimuli and then to devise controlled experiments that would serve to test the hypotheses. The following day the pupils came into class arguing with each other about their proposals. The teacher had a difficult time getting the class quiet, for all wanted to talk about their hypotheses and experiments at the same time. The class hour was spent in the critical examination and selection of what seemed to be the most promising hypotheses and the controlled experiments to test them. Some of the hypotheses were restated for greater clarity and some of the experiments were deemed inadequate. The next home assignment was to refine the controlled experiments for testing the various hypotheses and to make out detailed directions for building or manipulating the equipment needed.

The next few days were spent in setting up the experiments. The week following was a bedlam in the laboratory at the beginning of each day and of each class period as the interest rose to fever-pitch while the pupils awaited the results of their experiments.

To give practice in formulating hypotheses the teacher may prepare a list of problems within the ability range of general-science pupils and have them propose hypotheses for their solution. Any question that requires the pupil to explain a situation on the basis of his experience is in reality one in which the pupil formulates hypotheses. Such questions are common in most textbooks of general science and may be used to advantage for purposes of practice in this skill. The teacher may, however, be sure some extraneous situations will need to be introduced to afford adequate practice for most of the skills of problem-solving. Situations often arise in the classroom when an experiment or a demonstration fails to work. By turning over to the class the question of why it failed, the teacher may set a perfect opportunity for the proposing and testing of hypotheses. Also, in the course of a controlled experiment, conflicting data may result at times. This type of situation may again be used to formulate and test new hypotheses.

Selecting the Most Likely Hypothesis

Teaching to develop the skills of problem-solving is a time-consuming process and, if it is used for this purpose, something must be sacrificed in the amount of content covered in a given period of time. The slow and careful guidance that a teacher must use in leading a class from the formulation of a certain group of hypotheses, through the steps of selection, testing, and rejecting, and finally to a conclusion, may require several class periods. In the same time much more ground could have been covered by the usual classroom procedures.

Selecting the most likely one of several hypotheses for the solution of a given problem may involve several special skills, such as the analysis and interpretation of data, judging the pertinency of the data for the immediate problem, and checking the data against recognized authorities.

A class in general science had been studying the unit on air and air pressure. Toward the close of the study a problem about the workings of a vacuum cleaner was stated as follows: How is dirt picked up by a vacuum cleaner? The teacher asked the class to give the best explanation. Several hypotheses were proposed but after careful consideration all were rejected except two:

1. The dirt is pulled into the bag.
2. The dirt is pushed into the bag.

It seemed that these were the two most likely hypotheses. At this point the period ended and so the teacher asked each pupil to devise tests that might be used to check these hypotheses so that the better one might be selected.

Testing the Hypothesis by Experimental or Other Means

At the next meeting of the class several clever experiments were proposed and suitable controls were discussed. Some of the proposed experiments were:

1. Measure the pressure in front of and just behind the fan while the fan is turning.
2. Remove the bag and trace the air with smoke.
3. Observe the motion of flour when it is picked up by the cleaner.
4. Observe the bag behind the fan when the motor is started.

A vacuum sweeper and a small rug were brought into the classroom and several of the experiments were tried out. From these tests the pupils were able to prove the hypothesis—that the dirt was pushed into the bag by the air pressure outside.

This situation is not novel; it is, in fact, quite commonplace and could be found in almost any classroom when air pressure is being studied.

Space will permit only one other example of a situation that might be used for proposing, selecting, and testing hypotheses. A girl was using a short, narrow rubber tube to siphon the water from a heavy aquarium. The water was flowing too slowly. She observed that the water was very dirty.

The problem: How can the siphoning be speeded up?

Evaluating the data. Check the items given in the following list that are important in the solution of the problem.

a) The tube was too short.
b) The aquarium was heavy.
c) The water was dirty.
d) The tube was too narrow.
e) The tube was not filled with water.
f) The tube had a hole in it.

Hypotheses. The siphon could have been speeded up by:

a) Using a longer tube.
b) Lowering the outlet of the tube.

c) Using a glass tube of the same size and length.
d) Using clear water.
e) Using a larger tube.

With these or other hypotheses before a class, the time is ripe for using the skills of selecting the most tenable hypothesis, for proposing controlled experiments for testing, and finally for the testing itself. Such experiences are dramatic for the pupil and are filled with thrill and suspense.

Accept Tentatively or Reject Hypotheses and Test Others

Although this step of problem-solving is listed separately and no doubt requires a certain group of special skills, it will often be performed during the processes of selecting and testing hypotheses. The above examples are adequate in suggesting how the skills of this step might be developed in the classroom.

Drawing Conclusions

To draw a clear-cut conclusion it is essential that the problem first be carefully defined, that evidence be collected, and that a hypothesis be formulated and tested. Pupils must be taught to interpret the evidence which has been tested and to seek relationships which are shown between factors involved.

The demonstration and the experiment offer numberless situations where teachers may teach the skill of framing conclusions and generalizing from data. Some teachers find it a good idea to have each individual frame conclusions from the data while others prefer to evaluate the evidence and reach a conclusion in a class discussion. In either plan the teacher must see to it that the conclusion is consistent with the data and with the problem being solved.

Once more, in the development of this skill, as of others, the teacher may provide additional practice material by having pupils respond to evidence that is introduced from outside sources. The daily newspaper and many current magazines carry articles in which evidence and conclusions are published. These printed materials provide excellent opportunities for practice in drawing conclusions. The resourceful teacher can also frame many situations that will be equally valuable. In one class in general science the teacher collected a large number of situations in which the data were graphed. These graphs were mimeographed and a list of questions was made out for each situation. Another plan that has been used successfully is to cite the evidence and then list five or six conclusions, some that are irrelevant, some that are partly supported by the data, and one that is true. The pupils are asked to check the one that is correct and to cite their reasons. Reasons, good and bad, may also be written out for the pupil to check.

In using extraneous exercises in the development of any of the skills of problem-solving, the teacher will do well to look outside the immediate science subject for material. The result is that the skills of problem-solving are seen to be applicable in situations that are not essentially science situations.

Applying Principles

It is, perhaps, debatable whether or not this step is truly one of the elements of problem-solving. It is, however, one of the most vital and important steps in the learning process and, therefore, should be considered at least as an adjunct to the specific elements of problem-solving. It is equally true of this aspect of learning that the pupil attains the skill to the degree that he practices it. When principles have been learned, it requires a definite and conscious effort on the part of the pupil to make them function in new situations.

Effectiveness in this skill depends directly upon several identifiable abilities, among which the following may be typical.

1. Ability to recognize the common and related elements in the principle and in the new situation.
2. Ability to analyze or interpret new situations in the light of conclusions reached.
3. Ability to synthesize elements in a new situation toward the formulation of new and unique problems.

In his study of the types of thought questions found in science textbooks, Curtis (8) lists "applications in new situations" as one of the types. Most textbooks contain many questions of this type. The following are illustrative:

1. Suggest ways of correcting a bad case of reverberation in a hall or church.
2. Why does sprinkling the street on a warm day cool the air?
3. What measurements would you make to find the mechanical advantage of a screwdriver?
4. Can you prove that transpiration in plants is carried on more rapidly in the daytime than at night?

Teachers can well make use of such questions in giving practice in the application of principles. Some teachers prepare lists of such questions for each major principle studied and have pupils respond to them, either in oral discussion or in writing.

Tyler and associates (35), in an analysis of pupil responses to test items involving the application of principles, found that inadequate responses of pupils were due to one or more of the following causes:

1. Lack of complete knowledge of the principle involved.
2. Failure to see that the principle applies in a given situation.
3. Inability to tell why a given thing happened, even though the pupils can explain what happened or predict what will happen.

Teachers can make use of the above findings in teaching the ability to apply principles. It would appear that all three of the causes listed result from the failure to learn principles to the point that they become functional in the thinking of the pupil.

GROWTH IN SCIENTIFIC ATTITUDES, APPRECIATIONS, AND INTERESTS

Attitudes

Again the reader's attention is directed to the fact that this section has been set apart for a discussion of some of the methods used for developing attitudes, appreciations, and interests. These objectives of science teaching have long been assumed to result concomitantly when content is learned. As this book has pointed out repeatedly, they must be taught directly. A few promising methods will be discussed here.

It is probably safe to assume that the attitudes of young people are pretty well fixed when they have reached the senior high school and that little change ordinarily takes place in them after the completion of the ninth grade. This is far from meaning that attitudes cannot be modified. Provided the motivation for change is strong enough, attitudes can be altered at *any* age. In this connection it is well to keep in mind, however, that the mere verbal expression of an acceptable attitude is no valid indication that it has become a part of the individual's behavior pattern.

One need not look beyond the display of magazines devoted to astrology at the newsstand to learn that a real problem exists. The studies of Caldwell and Lundeen (6) show that junior high school pupils possess unfounded beliefs to a marked degree and that such beliefs influence the behavior of these young people. Nevertheless, there seems to be some doubt concerning the problem of method with regard to the development of attitudes.

Both Wessell (51) and Lichtenstein (24), although carrying on independent investigations, suggest that direct teaching fails to produce effective changes in pupils' attitudes and, further, that uncontrolled out-of-school experiences and such factors as maturation are very important in the development of attitudes held by young people.

On the other hand, a study by Curtis (9) and more recent studies by Blair and Goodson (3) and Vicklund (49) seem to indicate that direct teaching does modify the attitudes sought.

It is safe to assume that young people studying science in the junior high school have far too little contact with desirable scientific attitudes.

Thus, whatever can be done, either through the atmosphere of the science room, or through methods used by the teacher, to give pupils more experience with them, will be of value and will go beyond present practice.

To confront pupils with varied exercises which will elicit their use of desirable attitudes is good practice and has been employed by many teachers. A teacher, for example, brought some small mirrors into the classroom and during a very clever bit of teaching dropped and broke one mirror. The discussion of the common superstition was on, and before the hour was over nearly every pupil had smashed a mirror with a hammer that was handy. Perhaps this is a homely example, but it certainly had the merit of presenting an immediate situation in which superstition and unfounded belief played a prominent part.

Newspapers and magazines are fruitful sources of materials that may be saved and presented to classes for attitude reactions. One teacher keeps a file of several folders with pictures and cutouts from these sources. It is always a reservoir for new experiences. A glance through one of these folders reveals pictures of people walking under a ladder, an article on astrology, and an advertisement of an oil company showing an oil prospector using a divining rod for locating oil, and many others. This material has been used over and over until it is well worn. It has been used both for the bulletin board and for direct teaching situations. In either case, it never fails to create dramatic interest and keen discussion in the classroom. Almost annually it leads to a survey of all the superstitions known to the class and their associates. These, kept from year to year and compiled, form a fine source of teaching materials.

Some textbooks in general science and biology have sections devoted to practice on attitude situations of the following type: Some people believe that if a bird happens to fly into the house through an open window or door, a death is certain to occur in that family unless something is done to thwart the mysterious influence. Which of the following statements do you think would most nearly represent the reactions of a person who has a scientific training:

a) There is probably no reliable foundation for the belief.
b) For some people the belief is probably well founded.
c) The belief is silly.
d) There can be little doubt but that it is a sound belief.
e) While I do not believe in this, yet I am disturbed when a bird flies into the house.

Perhaps the most vital force at present in the development of desirable scientific attitudes in young people in school is a teacher who exhibits them day after day. The atmosphere of such a classroom will be charged with a spirit of friendly criticism; will encourage an intelligent questioning of authority; and will lead to a healthy skepticism concerning re-ported evidence. Emotional and wishful thinking will be questioned, and prejudice and intolerance will find no place. Facts and assumptions will be clearly differentiated, and hypotheses will be modified in the light of new evidence. Radio, magazine, and other forms of advertising also pro-vide situations which may be used effectively in developing critical think-ing.

Appreciations

Basically, appreciation is an outgrowth of understanding. An individ-ual cannot appreciate the importance and the many contributions of sci-ence unless he has some understanding of his environment and the way science affects both the environment and his own life situations.

The methods used for developing appreciations in young people through the study of general science may vary from level to level with their maturing interests. In the seventh grade, pupils seem to have a flare for the aspects of romance and adventure in anything they do. This inter-est may well be utilized by the science teacher.

In this day of jet-propelled devices, the story of a rocket trip to the moon or space-ship visit to the planets or into interstellar space may develop in the child an appreciation of the tremendous distances that lie outside our solar system.

The history of science is filled with incidents which the skilled teacher can transform into thrilling experiences for pupils by the use of in-genuity. Such experiences need be no less exact, nor need they be dis-torted. It is only good teaching to lay hold of the current interest of the pupil and convert it into a drive that makes his science experiences more meaningful and lasting.

As the pupil matures through the years of the junior high school, it will be possible to use more mature methods in developing appreciations, such as the consideration of cause-and-effect relationships, of the impor-tance of conservation of our natural resources, of the importance of sci-ence for the consumer, of the potentialities of science for raising living standards, and many others.

Interests

There has been considerable research devoted to the problem of the science interests which children have at different ages. There has been much less study of the problem of methods of stimulating and developing abiding interests in science. This latter problem is a very real one. It is the problem of this section. It is so important that it may spell the success of a given lesson.

Many teachers have the notion that materials to be learned must in some way be made "rose-colored," "glamorized," or "sugar coated" to enlist the interest of pupils. This fact is evident when teachers go to extremes in opportunistic teaching or in the use of spectacular experiments or demonstrations. Once the idea of expectancy for this type of science teaching is set up, it may prove to work out in reverse, for the learner's interest may fall to lower levels if each day's lesson fails to produce something of the bizarre.

This is not to argue against the occasional use of unusual demonstrations in science teaching nor the use of unique procedures at those levels of learning where there is inherent interest in the romantic and adventurous aspects of the subject. The real problem exists where these methods are used to the exclusion of all others.

Somewhat in contrast to the methods of sustaining interest mentioned above is the idea that satisfying learning in itself may be dramatic and challenging to the interest of the learner. Every teacher has at sometime had the experience of a drab and routine lesson being suddenly transformed into a thrilling experience with pupil interest at a very high level. Perhaps it is more than we may expect that each day's work can be of this nature.

A class in general science was showing only average interest in the study of bacteria cultures as related to a problem in health until a pupil raised the question of the dangers of kissing. The next day another pupil brought in pictures of cultures taken from the lips of college men and women. The class interest was high at once. They wanted to try the experiments. Several members of the class gave up a movie on Saturday to come to school and prepare more culture plates for the experiment. The experiments were tried and the days while the plates were incubating were "red letter" days as far as pupil interest was concerned. When problems become real to young people their interest in the solution will always follow.

Problem-solving methods offer many opportunities for enlisting student interest. Defining problems, proposing hypotheses, planning controlled experiments, testing hypotheses, evaluating data, and others, are co-operative classroom undertakings which go a long way toward keeping student interest at a high pitch. Once the interest of the pupil is aroused the questions of application and effort disappear.

The idea that science may hold both vocational and avocational interests for young people was pointed out in chapter xi. In fostering these interests the science club is perhaps the most fruitful device. In the larger city schools this may be a diversified activity in that there will be many clubs related to specialized science interests, such as radio club, a photography club, or a chemistry club. However, in the smaller high schools the single science club must be the rule because of the lack of trained faculty personnel for sponsoring more than one.

For a more detailed discussion of the science club the reader is referred to chapter xiv.

REFERENCES

1. ANDERSON, FRED C. "An Experiment To Determine the Effect of the Workbook on Achievement in General Science." Stillwater, Oklahoma: Oklahoma A. & M. College, 1938 (manuscript).
2. BAILEY, RALPH G. "The Difficulty Level of Certain Science Concepts," *Science Education*, XXV (February, 1941), 84–89.
3. BLAIR, GLENN M., and GOODSON, MAX R. "Development of Scientific Thinking," *School Review*, XLVII (November, 1939), 695–701.
4. BLICK, DAVID J. "Digest of Investigations in the Teaching of Science, 1937–43." Storrs, Connecticut: University of Connecticut, 1944 (mimeographed).
5. CALDWELL, OTIS W. "General Science for the First Year of the High School." Proceedings of the Central Association of Science and Mathematics Teachers. *School Science and Mathematics*, IX (1909), 115–27.
6. CALDWELL, OTIS W., and LUNDEEN, GERHARD. "A Summary of Investigations Regarding Superstitions and Unfounded Beliefs," *Science Education*, XX (February, 1936), 1–4.
7. CURTIS, F. D. *Third Digest of Investigations in the Teaching of Science.* Philadelphia: Blakiston Co., 1939.
8. ———. "Types of Thought Questions in Textbooks of Science," *Science Education*, XXVII (September–October, 1943), 60–67.
9. ———. *Some Values Derived from Extensive Reading in General Science.* New York: Teachers College, Columbia University, 1924.
10. ———. *Investigations of Vocabulary in Textbooks of Science for Secondary Schools.* Boston: Ginn & Co., 1938.
11. EBERHARD, J. W., and HUNTER, G. W. "The Scientific Attitude as Related to the Teaching of General Science," *Science Education*, XXIV (October, 1940), 275–81.
12. FORSYTH, KENNETH E. "A Comparison of the Relative Effectiveness of Two Methods of Teaching General Science." Ann Arbor: University of Michigan, 1939 (manuscript).
13. GERVERS, VIRGINIA. "Materials and Methods Found in General Science Textbooks Published since 1910," *Science Education*, XXIV (April, 1940), 202–3.
14. GRAHAM, CHARLES C. "Some Data Pertinent to Textbooks of General Science," *Science Education*, XXV (January, 1941), 35–41; (February, 1941), 65–68.
15. HILGERS, ROBERT J. "Practices and Techniques in Science Teaching," *Science Education*, XXVI (January, 1942), 16–21.
16. HURD, A. W. "How Shall Science Instruction Be Organized?" *Science Education*, XVIII (April, 1934), 106–12.
17. HURD, JEROME R. "An Evaluation of Certain General Science Textbooks on the Basis of Their Contributions to Health Education," *Science Education*, XXV (November, 1941), 327–30.
18. HUNTER, G. W., and PARKER, ALICE L. "The Subject Matter of General Science," *School Science and Mathematics*, XLII (December, 1942), 869–77.
19. "Illustrative Practices in the Core Curriculum, Springfield Senior High School," *Co-operative Curriculum Making in Missouri.* Jefferson City, Missouri: State Superintendent of Public Schools, 1945.

20. KAMBLY, PAUL E. "Science Textbook Illustrations," *Science Education*, XXVII (February, 1943), 17–19.

21. KEESLAR, OREON. "The Elements of Scientific Method," *Science Education*, XXIX (December, 1945), 273–78.

22. KRASKER, ABRAHAM. "A Critical Analysis of the Use of Educational Motion Pictures by Two Methods," *Science Education*, XXVII (February, 1943), 19–22.

23. KRAUS, PHILIP E. *Evaluation of the Pupil-made Notebook in Relation to Certain Measurable Outcomes in the Teaching of Science.* New York: New York University. 1943.

24. LICHTENSTEIN, ARTHUR. "The Effect of Teaching Stress upon an Attitude," *Science Education*, XIX (April, 1935), 73–75.

25. MANEVAL, ROY V. "The Relative Value of Sound Motion Picture and Study-sheets in Science Teaching," *Science Education*, XXV (February, 1939), 83–86.

26. MATTESON, HARVEY D., and KAMBLY, PAUL E. "Knowledge of Science Possessed by Pupils Entering Seventh Grade," *School Science and Mathematics*, XL (March, 1940), 244–47.

27. McKNELLY, CAL. "An Experiment in the Use of Free Reading in General Science," *Science Education*, XXV (January, 1941), 7–9.

28. "The Natural Sciences and Mathematics," *Review of Educational Research*, XII (October, 1942), 359–452; XV (October, 1945), 269–332.

29. NOVAK, BENJAMIN. "Science in the Newspaper," *Science Education*, XXVI (October, 1942), 138–43.

30. OBOURN, ELLSWORTH S., and MONTGOMERY, GAYLORD C. "Procedures for Developing the Elements of Problem Solving," *Science Education*, XXV (February, 1941), 72–80.

31. OLSON, MYRIN S., and KAMBLY, PAUL E. "A Comparison of Three Types of Teacher Activity in Directing the Study of General Science," *Science Education*. XXIII (November, 1939), 304–8.

32. PETTIT, DONALD D. "The Content of Junior High School Science," *School Science and Mathematics*, XL (October, 1940), 643–54; (November, 1940), 763–77.

33. PIEPER, C. J. "Science in the Seventh, Eighth, and Ninth Grades," *A Program for Teaching Science*, 193–220. Thirty-first Yearbook of the National Society for the Study of Education, Part I. Chicago: Distributed by the University of Chicago Press, 1932.

34. *A Program for Teaching Science.* Thirty-first Yearbook of the National Society for the Study of Education, Part I. Chicago: Distributed by the University of Chicago Press, 1932.

35. PROGRESSIVE EDUCATION ASSOCIATION. *Application of Principles.* Evaluation in the Eight-Year Study. Bulletin No. 5, P.E.A., 898. Columbus, Ohio: Ohio State University, 1936 (mimeographed).

36. *Reorganization of Science in Secondary Schools.* Committee of the National Education Association. Commission on Reorganization of Secondary Education. Washington: Government Printing Office, 1920.

37. *Report of the Committee of Ten on Secondary-School Studies* (with reports of the conferences arranged by the Committee). Published for the National Education Association. New York: American Book Co., 1894.

38. RICE, R. S. "Extensive Reading vs. Intensive Textbook Study as a Means of Acquiring a Knowledge of Scientific Facts," *Journal of Experimental Education*, IV (June, 1936), 376–402.

39. RUFFNER, FRANCES E. "Interests of Ninth-Grade Students in General Science," *Science Education*, XXIV (January, 1940), 23–29.

40. SCOTT, W. FRANCIS. "A Study in Teaching the Scientific Method and Scientific Attitude in the Junior High School," *Science Education*, XXIV (January, 1940), 30–35.

41. SHARP, PHILIP B. "Why Not Use Control Experiments," *Science Education*, XXII (January, 1938), 19–22.

42. SHORES, J. HARLAN. "Skills Related to the Ability To Read History and Science." *Journal of Educational Research*, XXXV (April, 1943), 584–93.

43. SIMMONS, MAITLAND P. "Changing Conceptions of Topic Illustrations in General Science Textbooks," *Journal of Experimental Education*, V (June, 1937), 368–72.

44. SISSON, JEROME C. "Selecting Functional Subject Matter for a General Science Course," *Science Education*, XXVII (February, 1943), 22–26.

45. SMITH, VICTOR C. "How Is Difficulty of Subject Matter a Factor Affecting Learning in General Science?" *Science Education*, XXX (February, 1946), 19–23.

46. SWENSON, ESTHER J. "A Study of the Relationship among Various Types of Reading Scores and Science Materials," *Journal of Educational Research*, XXXVI (October, 1942), 81–90.

47. TER KEURST, A. J. "The Acceptance of Superstitious Beliefs among Secondary-School Pupils," *Journal of Educational Research*, XXXII (May, 1939), 673–85.

48. University of Iowa Masters' Theses:

HUFFMAN, OSCAR T. "Integration of Science Concepts of the Major Science Fields in Ninth-Grade Science." Iowa City, Iowa: State University of Iowa, 1938 (typewritten).

LeCOCQ, C. LOUIS. "Integration of Science Concepts of the Major Science Fields in Eighth-Grade Science." Iowa City, Iowa: State University of Iowa, 1938 (typewritten).

VANDER PLOEG, EDWARD P. "Integration of Science Concepts of the Major Fields in Seventh-Grade Science." Iowa City, Iowa: State University of Iowa, 1939 (typewritten).

49. VICKLUND, C. U. "The Elimination of Superstitions in Junior High School Science," *Science Education*, XXIV (February, 1940), 93–99.

50. WARD, C. HENSHAW. "The Goals of High-School Science," *Harvard Teachers Record*, III (October, 1933), 179–83.

51. WESSELL, GEORGE. "Measuring the Contribution of the Ninth-Grade General Science Course to the Development of Scientific Attitudes," *Science Education*, XXV (November, 1941), 336–39.

52. WATERS, EUGENE A. *A Study of the Application of an Educational Theory to Science Instruction.* New York: Teachers College, Columbia University, 1942.

53. WEBB, H. A. "The High-School Science Library for 1943–44," *Peabody Journal of Education*, XXII (January, 1945), 199–215.

54. WINTERS, ELWOOD J. *The Determination of the Meanings Which Students of Science at Different Grade Levels Associate with Selected Scientific Concepts.* New York: New York University, 1939.

55. ZIM, HERBERT S. *Science Interests and Activities of Adolescents.* New York: Teachers College, Columbia University, 1940.

CHAPTER XIII

THE CONTENT AND METHODS OF SENIOR HIGH SCHOOL SCIENCE

It was pointed out in chapter xi that the sequence of science courses in the senior high school has traditionally been biology in the tenth year and either physics or chemistry in the eleventh or twelfth year. Some of the smaller high schools alternate physics and chemistry in one of the last two years.

During the last decade a fourth science subject, physical science, has come into this sequence and has gained considerable recognition.

Each of these sciences may well contribute to the major objectives of science teaching as set forth in chapters iii and xi. In general, they might well have certain things in common, such as the principles of selecting and organizing content, the methods used to reach the general objectives, etc. However, there is a quality of uniqueness about these areas of learning that makes it desirable to consider each of them separately in this chapter.

THE COURSE IN HIGH-SCHOOL BIOLOGY[1]

The Selection and Organization of Content

In the past the course in high-school biology was planned to meet the supposed needs of pupils who expected to pursue the same subject in college. Though it replaced separate courses in botany and zoology as such, it often kept both those subjects and treated them separately, perhaps adding a section on human physiology.

As the high-school population became less selective, significant modifications of the biology course were instituted. From necessity, the subject matter has become less technical, more practical, and the trend has been toward a unified course, with increasing emphasis on its functional values. For example, the Thirty-first Yearbook (**46**) called attention to the value of fundamental generalizations in the field of science. It was suggested that experiences of all relevant kinds should be made to contribute to the understanding of the generalizations, which might then

---

[1] The committee has profited from the collaboration of J. Gordon Manzer, Central High School, Trenton, New Jersey, in the preparation of this section.

be expected to make other experiences meaningful and to determine appropriate action in problem situations.

The kind of thinking that is represented in the Thirty-first Yearbook has resulted in considerable change and improvement in science courses. However, it is quite possible to "teach" even a major generalization without making it functional. Pupils may be able to state a principle correctly and to answer questions about it, but if they do not use it in ordinary life situations, they have not truly learned it. For example, the present state of personal (and community) health and the prevalence of prejudice and intolerance demonstrate the inadequacy of the materials taught and learned in biology classes.

During the past ten years, particularly, the trend has been toward focusing attention less on the organization of subject matter and more on the results in the lives of the learners (1). It has been demonstrated that changes in behavior can accompany learning (2, 62).

More specifically, the subject matter of the high-school biology course should include materials related to:

1. Health (personal and public, including physical fitness, food and nutrition, disease, safety, mental health, etc.)
2. Reproduction, heredity, and the effect of the environment (as related to personal and social problems, individual and group differences, improvement of living organisms, etc.)
3. The conservation of living things
4. The structure and functions of living things, especially of the human body
5. The conditions necessary to support life, and adaptations of living things
6. Living things of the past, and the changes that have occurred
7. Relations between individuals, between groups, and among living things in general

The items just enumerated overlap, and certainly they do not exhaust the possibilities (41). It is assumed that all learning should contribute to scientific attitudes, the use of scientific methods, and a developing philosophy of life. The items here given are far too general to serve as a guide to the teaching of subject matter; they are intended to suggest some of the situations and problems in which biology may help.

It should be remembered that the selection and organization of content for a course in high-school biology is a means to an end—the desired end being, so far as this discussion is concerned, the statement of the objectives listed in chapter iii. Since the logical development and mastery of the subject matter of biology is not of itself a primary goal, and since in any event the field is far too broad to be covered adequately in the time provided in school, then it follows that considerable variation in topics covered and in the order of topics will be legitimate and desirable, as circumstances vary.

Understanding of Facts, Concepts, and Principles

The next problem is how to teach so that the learning and the materials learned will be of the greatest use to the learner. Every teacher knows that in some cases the "learning" stops with a certain amount of memorizing of facts. It is well established that facts so learned are soon forgotten, leaving little or no useful residue. On the other hand, if functional understanding of principles is attained, the ability to use them and to apply them is retained remarkably well (61). In general, it takes conscious effort, on the part of pupil as well as teacher, to make the proper connections for building up concepts and principles. The need is to encourage and assist the making of those connections, and the problem is to find methods that will make the process as easy and certain as possible.

While a biology class was considering the normal functioning of the human body, the question arose: "Why do we breathe?" The first answer, that we have to breathe in order to live and would die if we didn't breathe, was obviously inadequate. Next, a pupil suggested that we need to breathe in order to ventilate our lungs. That still left the question "why do we need to ventilate our lungs, and what is it that causes trouble if we do not ventilate them?"

Information was sought and obtained from pupils' memories of previous experiences, from textbooks and reference books, and from experiments, such as:

1. Breathing on a cold polished metal surface or mirror
2. Bubbling breathed-out air and ordinary air, separately, through limewater, and comparing results
3. Comparing breathed-out air and ordinary air in the amount of oxygen taken out by moist iron filings, or phosphorus, or in ability to support the burning of a candle

These experiments were in most cases not quantitative, but they did provide evidence that a change, or at least an exchange, occurs during breathing. Explanations suggested to account for the observed changes pointed eventually to oxidation of carbon and hydrogen in body compounds or in food. Results of experimental burning of food materials in air tended to support this explanation; so did texts and references.

At this point someone solemnly suggested that if the purpose of breathing is to supply oxygen for oxidation of food (or material derived from food) and to remove the products of oxidation, then one should be able to stop breathing if he also stopped eating—and that would save a lot of trouble. This led to a consideration of the purpose of oxidation in the body. Experiments, more or less quantitative in nature, showed a relationship between the amount of work done and the amount of air needed

—or the rate and depth of breathing. The class then engaged in the following exercises:

1. Measured the amount of air breathed in and out in one breath by various pupils both normally and during deep breathing.
2. Discussed, and tried to illustrate, what causes air to enter and to leave the lungs.
3. Discussed different ways of breathing and the effects of posture and clothing.
4. Investigated the need for ventilation in buildings and the way the need was being met.
5. Discussed respiratory diseases and the effects of various gases and dusts.
6. Compared breathing in man with breathing, or a corresponding function, in other animals.

The class also investigated where the oxygen went from the lungs, where the carbon dioxide came from, and where the oxidation occurred—and thus were led to other problems.

In the situation just described, the need for breathing was known to all, but the reason for the need was not entirely clear at first. The challenge lay in the natural desire to understand.

If the need for using a certain principle is felt, the gathering of the facts that lead to an understanding of the principle is well motivated. Under these circumstances, information gathered from textbooks, from reference books, from experts, from observations, and from experiments will contribute to the building of the concepts and understandings of the principles which the pupil needs to use. The idea is to *start* with the problem, or difficulty, and then seek facts, principles, methods, or anything else that seems necessary for solving the problem. The method may be applied partially, as when textbook writers list problems at the beginning of a unit, and then proceed to answer their own questions—usually in a quite orthodox manner. Here the advantage is chiefly in making clear, at the beginning, the goal toward which the build-up of the unit is directed. From this point of view, most science textbooks consist of ready-made solutions to problems. From them one can find how someone else solved a problem or, at least, what the solution was. But that is quite different from finding a solution for one's self.

Problem-solving may lead to disappointing results in terms of the number and importance of the problems solved. It may not be practical to limit the activities of a class entirely to problem-solving. Probably most of us try to teach too much and, as a consequence, neither teach it well nor develop properly the concomitant values which are likely to be more useful, as well as more lasting, than the technical details of the day's lesson. This is not an argument for fewer facts or for "snap" courses; rather, it is a plea for useful facts, used to develop concepts, principles, and functional understandings—and happy, successful individuals and good citizens.

We have plenty of problems, of all types and all grades of difficulty. Some of them are right on the surface and recognized as problems by all; others are less noticed, perhaps because we are accustomed to the ills they cause, perhaps because the effects are complex, or indirect.

Facts, concepts, and principles are functional only if they are actually used. We learn to use them effectively by *using* them and in no other way. Their use is in helping to solve our problems. It follows that the practical way to acquire functional understanding of facts, concepts, and principles is in connection with problem-solving.

Since so many of man's problems are related to the subject matter of biology, the biology class seems a particularly appropriate place to deal with them on a high-school level. Most of the pupils in our biology classes will study no more biology in school or college, many of them will study no more science, and some of them will have no more schooling at all. In other words, it may be their last chance to tackle biological problems under favorable conditions and (presumably) competent guidance. The subject matter and organization of the course are not so standardized as to offer any great hindrance; in fact, the most "regular" high-school biology course can hardly help running into pressing human problems at almost every turn.

Methods as Related to the Development of Growth in Habits of Thinking, in Attitudes, and in Appreciations

It should be evident that the same considerations that support the use of problem-solving methods for developing functional understandings will also support the same methods as means of aiding in the development of attitudes, appreciations, and habits of thought. The more artificial the learning situation, the more artificial the learning. In fact, there are school situations in existence today which have little value along these lines. And it is not merely a case of learning more or learning less, for some pupils surely do acquire undesirable attitudes toward schoolwork and book-learning in general. Habits of thinking are developed by thinking, not by reading, or by listening, or even by repeating what has been "learned."

In the study of breathing, previously mentioned, a number of situations arose in which the necessity for straight thinking was obvious—or became so. Pupils, who assumed (as some did) that all the oxygen was removed from the air that they breathed in the lungs, soon found that their conclusions were at variance with the facts. Individuals were found to differ so much that findings based on one or two cases could not safely be stated as general conclusions.

In the case of ventilation it was found that the apparent conclusion was not the true one. After a careful explanation of the fact that the water vapor added to the air in the lungs could come from oxidation of hydrogen in hydrogen compounds, the class was forced to admit that a good deal of water enters the body as a liquid and in moist foods.

As a rule, with proper guidance, pupils will detect and correct one another's (and even their own, and the teacher's) errors of fact and of reasoning. Thus they set up for the class, and for themselves, relatively high standards in habits of thinking and in attitudes of various kinds.

One method that has value in several directions is that of planning the course *with* the pupils instead of merely *for* them. In some school subjects the pupils know so little when they begin the course that they do not feel competent to prescribe for themselves; but in biology the possible topics or problems are more familiar, and the possible values are more evident.

Time is needed for survey, discussion, and decision, but it can be time well spent, for it goes without saying that pupils who participate in the planning of their course are likely to have a better idea of the whole field, as well as more interest in the topics chosen for study. Atkins (**4**) found that pupils who helped to plan their own work excelled in interest and effort and also in scientific attitudes. If the organization of the school permits this amount of freedom, or can be changed so as to permit it, teachers should be free to co-operate with their pupils in this manner. In general, the more interested and more conscientious teachers are the ones most likely to take advantage of such an opportunity; and the pupils are commonly found to be conservative rather than radical in their choices.

Although all the activities of the course should contribute toward the development of the so-called (and wrongly so-called) "intangibles," *class discussion* may be mentioned as an activity with special possibilities in this direction. It is assumed that in most cases the class will be working together rather than individually or in groups. (This is stated as the situation that exists, not necessarily as the one that should exist; and the principles of group discussion are similar for groups of different size.) Frequently questions that have arisen in the minds of various members of the class offer a fruitful basis for discussion. Such questions are likely to be concerned with apparent inconsistencies, with the reason for some statement or its implications, or with how it is illustrated (or contradicted) by some experience known to the pupil. One question may lead to another, and the answers to still others, until a concept or even a principle has been pretty well covered. In the process, erroneous information and ideas may be aired and corrected; personal or local applications of a principle may come to light; pupils may hear their classmates express ideas that they had not thought of but can understand. Not all questions or comments are of equal value, not all are relevant, so that there must be regulation and direction. On their wisdom and effectiveness the results of the discussion largely depend. There is no reason why the teacher should keep silent, but he should not do anything that can be done by members of the class. Purely factual questions can often be handled by referring to a textbook or some other easily available reference source.

Reports on current biological events and articles, especially in newspapers and magazines, offer an excellent opportunity for critical thinking of a kind that will be needed in the life of every individual. Study of personal and community needs should tend toward appropriate action; and individual and group projects may provide for, and help to develop, special interests.

Materials, Equipment, Multisensory Aids, Science Clubs, and Other Activities

Biology can be taught and learned with very little equipment, but it can be learned better and more efficiently with the help of the various aids that are available. The cost is insignificant in comparison with the benefits that can be derived.

First, of course, come living things themselves. Insects, especially, are available in great number and variety, and they exemplify life processes and principles very well. The smaller organisms, and the details of larger ones, require microscopes, models, and charts. Pictures, including moving pictures, are needed to bring to the classroom types not otherwise available. Field trips, including visits to museums, laboratories, hospitals, etc., have value, particularly if taken for a recognized purpose—not just to see what happens to be there. (The same remark applies to the use of motion pictures.)

Textbooks (including some college texts) and other reference books should be *available*, preferably in the classroom. The same is true for a few biological magazines (**1**). The book-review sections of science magazines are helpful in listing and commenting on biological literature as it becomes available.

Science clubs make it possible for interested pupils to do considerably more than may usually be accomplished. Also, they help to show the teacher what pupils can and will do.

In the classroom and the laboratory, reading and talking are not enough. Other and more concrete experiences are necessary. The paramecium should be seen in action, not merely in diagrams; the change from starch to sugar should be shown with appropriate tests instead of being allowed to remain an abstract idea. In most cases the concept or the principle is built up most fully, most accurately, and most surely when based, at least in part, on actual experiences.

Problem situations readily suggest activities which may contribute to a solution of the problems. Books are available which give helpful ideas and specific advice and directions for experiences in biology (**42**). Also, there are books for science in general, including biology (**31, 68**), and there are magazines (**53**) for the science teacher.

Time spent in preparing for suitable experiences in biology is time well spent. If a teacher demonstrates that he is making good use of the materials at his disposal, he is likely to receive all possible help in getting additional materials for which he can show a need. Moreover, he will have the satisfaction of making a real and appreciated contribution to the welfare of the pupils in his classes and, through them, will help to make the world a better place in which to live.

The Course in Physical Science[2]

The Place of Physical Science

Recent years have witnessed numerous well-defined efforts by workers in education, by policy-making committees, by science teachers themselves, and by writers of science textbooks, to broaden the scope of high-school science instruction to the end that it may become more functional in the everyday life of the student. These efforts have produced several types of generalized science courses that may be listed in the category of "physical science." Familiar titles of such courses are senior science, consumer science, survey science, fused physical science (combining only the elements of chemistry and physics), and physical science. In most instances the course in physical science takes the place of chemistry and physics in the eleventh or twelfth grade for non-college preparatory pupils and follows the course in general biology.

Physical-science courses were becoming increasingly popular until their temporary displacement, largely by the pre-induction courses, following the onset of World War II. Hunter and Spore (**35**) reported over 7,000 high-school students enrolled in physical science courses in California alone in 1938–39. Watson (**65**) reported in 1940 that physical-science courses were offered in the high schools of 54 cities of over 25,000 population distributed among twenty-six states. According to word-of-mouth

---

[2] The committee has profited from the collaboration of Robert H. Carleton, Newark College of Engineering, Newark, New Jersey, in the preparation of this section.

reports from publishers having textbooks in this field, such courses largely dropped out of the picture during the war but at the time of this writing are definitely "on the way back." Indeed, there is reason to believe that the physical-science course in one form or another will not only regain but far surpass the position it held among the high-school science offerings of 1940. Reasons for this belief include, first, recognition of the superior possibilities of a composite physical science over the separate traditional chemistry and physics courses in contributing to the aims of general education, and, second, the disposition of colleges to recognize the physical-science course as a bona-fide college-entrance unit for the nonscience major (21).

The implications of the Educational Policies Commission report (27) definitely favor a generalized-science type of course, rather than chemistry or physics, for the high-school student whose major abilities and interests are outside the realm of science. Turning to the Harvard Report (50) we find these comments:

Science instruction in general education should be characterized by broad integrative elements—the comparison of scientific with some other modes of thought, the comparison and contrast of the individual sciences with one another, the relations of science with its own past history and with general human history, and of science with problems of human society. These are areas in which science can make a lasting contribution to the general education of all students.

Below the college level virtually all science teaching should be devoted to general education. . . . . In high school . . . . for those especially for whom secondary education is terminal, and possibly for all students, a course in a particular science does not really fulfil the aims of general education.

Those students preparing to enter college but who have no direct interest in the sciences might also stop at this point [biology]; or for those who have had biology in the ninth grade a further course in physics or chemistry might be advised. Better still for such students would be a systematic presentation of concepts and principles of the physical sciences, such as is now being experimented with in a number of schools—its primary aims should be those of general education, not the development of the skills and technical knowledge of the potential physicist and chemist.

One may differ with the specific recommendations of the Harvard Report for the content and organization of the physical-science course and still recognize that this report promises to add considerable impetus to the physical-science movement. An important implication of this report is that the generalized physical-science course can be just as valuable for the college-bound students with nonscience interests as for those high-school students for whom secondary education is terminal.

The Selection and Organization of Content

There is as yet no "standard" course in physical science such as we have in both chemistry and physics. An examination of the few published textbooks in this field and of the suggestions for physical-science courses that have appeared in the periodicals reveals considerable difference of opinion as to what subject-matter content is appropriate. Whereas one course is heavy on the consumer slant, another is set up with the primary aim of "presenting" the important scientific principles and revealing their applications. The principles selected in some instances are taken only from the fields of chemistry and physics, while in other cases they come from all the physical-science fields, including, besides chemistry and physics, geology, astronomy, and meteorology. Again we find courses organized with the purpose of surveying, one by one, the various specialized sciences, while other courses offer integrations of the various facts, concepts, and principles drawn from all the fields of physical science for the purpose of helping young people gain competency in solving their problems of adjustment in the world of today.

The latter point of view is the one favored by this committee as best fulfilling the needs of general education in its broadest sense. The subject matter and activities of the physical-science course must be selected and the methods of instruction must be adapted so as to reveal the importance of science in contributing to more adequate adjustment. The real problems of adjustment arise from the experiences and felt needs of daily life such as the following: to provide the materials necessary to life (food, air, water, energy, etc.); to maintain better health; to develop wise consumership and increased economy; to promote more effective conservation; to secure greater comfort, convenience, and safety; to participate more fully in socioeconomic adjustment in a democracy; to understand more completely the science world-picture; and to substitute action based on critical thinking for action based on intolerances, prejudices, traditions, superstitions, and misconceptions. These are the criteria by which to judge whether or not particular materials and activities should go into the physical-science course. No subject matter can be justified solely on the ground that it is "good science" of a traditional sort or because it can be "presented" in the classroom with a minimum of effort and planning.

The present state of flux in which we find physical science and the lack of a "standard" course are really more of a boon than a detriment to the conscientious science teacher. He is thus free to cogitate, explore, and experiment, to start with the interests and problems of his own pupils, and to draw on his own community for source materials without being hampered by the old bugaboo (real or imagined) of having to "cover" so much "ground" or of having to prepare his pupils to meet the demands of certain established examinations. He is at liberty to select and organize his own content of subject matter and activities in terms of his own reasoned philosophy. He can, of course, get some help in this task by reviewing the relatively few published research studies relating to physical science in general education. As far back as 1933, Wray (**69**) attempted to find out what items of chemical information stood relatively high in functional value in the opinion of nonscience specialists. Later, Brown (**15**) developed a two-year physical-science course for his particular school situation, utilizing nine interpretive generalizations in physical science, ten needs of pupils, and three major types of educational values in working up the fifteen unit-areas of his course. In two studies by Wise (**66, 67**) 264 principles of physical science were evaluated in terms of their importance for general education. The highest ranking half of the principles included 108 from the field of physics, 28 from the field of chemistry, and 6 from geology. This study made no attempt to organize the principles into units of instruction. In Petersen's study (**45**) twelve instructional units were developed, including only principles of chemistry and physics. Other courses that offer helpful suggestions based on classroom experimentation, rather than on the findings of research, have been developed and reported by Bailey (**6**), Carleton (**20**), and Skinner (**56**). Finally, but by no means last in importance, mention should be made of the helpful guidance offered by the statement prepared for the Consumer Education Study (**43**) and by other publications previously referred to in this yearbook (**2,3,48**). The objectives and criteria proposed in chapters iii and xi of this yearbook and those presented in the Thirty-first Yearbook (**46**) merit careful consideration by persons engaged in developing courses in physical science.

Methods for Developing Functional Understanding of Facts, Concepts, and Principles

"Lesson-hearing" should be a thing of the past, at least in science teaching. It is not enough that students are able to "recite back" textbook statements and definitions of scientific facts, concepts, and principles. It is time to teach science scientifically. True enough, we have had comparatively little research in this field to provide a reliable basis for procedures, but we do have the suggestions of numerous workers in science education and we have descriptions of classroom-tested techniques of many science teachers to guide us.

The "best thinking" at present favors a developmental method (**31**) of increasing students' functional understanding of facts, concepts, and principles of science. The implication is that progress toward attainment of this goal is best made by guiding students through an extensive array of interrelated activities of many types, all of which point toward and contribute to the solution of large, over-all problems previously set up as worthy of consideration. An example of the developmental method in action in physical science seems appropriate at this point.

A class was working on problems within the unit area of "fire, fuels, and heat." The big problem under consideration was stated in the question, "How do we control fire and burning?" Discussion soon indicated the dual nature of the problem, one aspect of it being the control of fire and burning in instances where the process serves as an intentional source of heat energy, the other aspect being the control of fire in situations where it might prove harmful or disastrous to life and property. In connection with the latter aspect, class discussion directed attention to several disastrous fires within the experience and memory of the students: fires in their own and in near-by communities, the Hartford circus fire, the Boston night-club fire, forest fires in their own state, and others. Disastrous fires of years gone by were recalled and described by the teacher. The teacher also showed the class a file of clippings from the local newspaper which he had kept for the preceding fall and winter season in which were reported fires and fire fatalities for the surrounding area. It was pointed out to the class that in the United States fire destroys someone's dwelling every two minutes and causes a horrible death toll at an average rate of one person an hour. A striking impression of the magnitude of the destruction and loss of life caused by fire was created when the teacher read the following passage from a circular issued by the National Bureau of Standards:

The $500,000,000 annual property loss (based on a typical decade) can be represented by the fire ruins of dwellings placed in a solid row on one side of a highway extending from New York to Chicago, a distance of about 900 miles. An observer in an automobile would require perhaps three days to travel the length of this avenue of desolation. At intervals of about 600 feet, or at the rate of three or four a minute, there would be seen the graves of fire victims, mostly women and children, who died from burns, suffocation, panic, or other cause directly attributable to fire.

By this time the class had pretty largely agreed that the problem under consideration really was important. To facilitate the solving of the large problem, "How do we control fire and burning?" a number of smaller problems to be investigated were proposed, among them the following:

1. How do fires get started?
2. What part of the air makes a fire burn? (Some of the students had some previous knowledge of fire and burning, of course.)
3. What is oxygen like?

4. How does burning illustrate chemical change? (Suggested by the teacher.)
5. When things burn up, where do they go and what becomes of them?
6. How can we put out unwanted fires or bring them under control?
7. How do fire extinguishers work?
8. What should one do in case of fire when he is in a theater or elsewhere among a large gathering of people?
9. What kinds of first-aid treatment should be given to fire victims?
10. What methods are used to avoid fires in public buildings?

Answers to these and other questions were largely worked out by means of experimental activities, including individual experiments, student demonstrations, and teacher demonstrations, supplemented by reference to the textbook and to other source materials provided in the science room and in the school library. Two or three appropriate motion pictures were shown in connection with the study. The selected experimental activities and their sequence were about as follows:

1. A demonstration of chemical matches and their comparison with modern matches as devices for starting fires
2. Boiling water in a paper bag
3. A demonstration of how various materials differ in kindling-point temperature
4. Placing a burning candle in a large jar and covering tightly
5. A quantitative determination of the percentage of oxygen in air
6. A demonstration of how Priestley first prepared oxygen by heating mercuric oxide
7. An experimental study of the preparation and nature of oxygen and how things burn in pure oxygen
8. Mixing magnesium powder and iron filings and weighing the mixture in an iron dish before and after igniting
9. Weighing a photoflash lamp before and after flashing it, noting evidence of chemical change associated with the flash
10. Showing that water and carbon dioxide are the products of ordinary combustion
11. Demonstrating spontaneous combustion by two or three different methods
12. Demonstrating the dust explosion by using powdered sugar, cornstarch, and flour as well as lycopodium powder
13. Putting some gasoline into a pyrex beaker and igniting it; trying to extinguish with water squirted from a wash bottle; "smothering" the fire by covering with a cardboard cover; relighting the gasoline and trying to extinguish the fire with carbon tetrachloride squirted from a wash bottle
14. Boiling some carbon tetrachloride in a beaker and testing the vapor by inserting a burning splint; pouring some of the vapor down an inclined trough or large glass tube, allowing it to flow over a lighted candle at the lower end
15. Generating some carbon dioxide in a large jar by mixing baking soda and vinegar; testing the gas with a lighted splint; pouring from beaker to beaker

or otherwise demonstrating the density of carbon dioxide; pouring some of the gas down the inclined trough or tube onto a candle as was done with the carbon tetrachloride vapor

16. Demonstrating a working model of a soda-acid fire extinguisher; examining actual fire extinguishers of this and other types as may be available

17. Putting about one cup of lard into an iron dish or frying pan; heating strongly and igniting the vapors (Caution!); standing safely away and squirting water from a wash bottle onto the burning grease; tossing about a teaspoonful of baking soda onto the flaming grease

18. Demonstrating the reaction underlying the foam type of fire extinguisher

19. Demonstrating the nature of low-melting-point alloys

20. Demonstrating the principle of the "short circuit" and the way in which fuse links afford protection from electrical fire

21. Demonstrating a comparison of some samples of flame-proofed fabrics with some untreated samples

The pupils organized and summarized the results of their study of burning in written reports on questions of the following kinds:

1. What disadvantages of the chemical match and of the early phosphorus matches have been eliminated in modern types?

2. Why is it possible to boil water in a paper bag?

3. Why will wet or green wood not burn?

4. What is meant by kindling-point temperature?

5. How do we apply our knowledge of kindling points in starting fires, as in a furnace or a fireplace?

6. How is our knowledge of kindling points applied in modern matches?

7. How would believers in the phlogiston theory explain the behavior of the burning candle placed in the jar and then covered?

8. What are the essential factors or conditions necessary for ordinary burning?

9. What are some reasons why the percentage of oxygen in air as determined in our experiment does not agree with the accepted value as given in the text?

10. A higher temperature can be obtained by the use of an oxyacetylene torch than by the use of an air-acetylene torch. Why?

11. Write your own definitions of *chemical change* and *physical change* and state what you think are the chief differences between them.

12. What plans have you formulated for getting yourself and your family safely out of your dwelling in case fire should break out during the night?

13. Summarize recommended first-aid treatment for the victims in fire, burning, and scalding.

The following types of evaluation exercises were introduced at appropriate times during the study, more as learning activities than as tests, however.

1. An "interpretation of data" exercise based on the laboratory study of oxygen and burning in pure oxygen

2. An "understanding of concepts" exercise, covering such ideas as physical states of matter, elements, compounds, mixtures, etc.

3. An exercise involving "recognition of valid generalizations" which focused attention on the nature of chemical change and methods of controling chemical changes
4. An exercise involving "applications of principles," in which numerous examples of physical and chemical changes were to be identified and classified
5. A test, "What is your Fire I.Q.?" based on a test published by the National Fire Protection Association

Other activities accompanying the study included the following:

1. A report on the local fire laws and fire code
2. The school's provisions for fire drills and meeting fire emergencies during assemblies and passing periods
3. Selected motion pictures
4. Talks and demonstrations by some members of the class to be given to classes in safety and first aid, not all of the members of which take physical science

Two comments relative to the foregoing description are quite common and should receive consideration. The first reaction very often is, "It sounds like glorified general science," to which the answer is, "That is what it is intended to be, inasmuch as the underlying philosophies of general science and of physical science stem from the same considerations —namely, the objectives of general education." The second reaction is, "That can all be done in the regular chemistry class," to which the answer is, "Certainly, except that the average chemistry teacher might feel that he could hardly give this much time (perhaps two weeks) to such a limited area—what with so much ground to be covered in other parts of the course."

Methods of Developing Growth in Habits of Thinking, in Attitudes, and in Appreciations

The developmental method in itself does much to further the growth of students in developing the skills and abilities involved in scientific problem-solving. In the example described above, it is obvious that the teacher was concerned not only (a) with the students' acquisition of ideational content, but also (b) with giving them practice in using elements of scientific thinking and (c) with engendering an appreciation for the work of eminent scientists such as Priestley and Lavoisier.

Admittedly, conclusive evidence as to the effectiveness of this method in attaining goals of these types is meager. In Petersen's study (45) the outcomes compared were mostly concerned with subject-matter achievement rather than with growth in the skills and abilities involved in problem-solving and with the development of appreciations.

Perhaps one more example of procedure in a physical-science class in which the primary objective was the further development of understanding of scientific method and of scientific attitudes is in order. While working in the area of "sound," the class fell into a controversial discussion as to the effects of noise on personal health and efficiency. As a result of the discussion, two girls in the class who were also taking typing and stenography arranged to conduct an experiment on the problem. Acting on suggestions from Brown's report (**16**) of an experiment on noise and with some help from the teacher, the girls devised an experiment in which ten typists recommended by the typewriting teacher took two standard fifteen-minute speed and accuracy tests. Desks and typewriters were brought into the physical-science classroom, and various noise-making devices were arranged—such as a noise produced by directing a beam of light onto and through a siren disk and then focusing on the photoelectric cell of the sound motion-picture projector; whistles, bells, and organ pipes, and phonographic recordings of noise. One group of five student typists took the test under quiet conditions first and then under conditions of noise; the other group of five reversed the procedure, taking the test first under conditions of noise and then under quiet conditions. Records of speed and accuracy for each typist were computed.

The results of the experiment showed that six of the typists did appreciably better under conditions of noise, two showed little change one way or the other, and two did better under quiet conditions than under noisy conditions. These findings did not agree with the implications of the source materials which the physical-science students had consulted, hence much additional discussion followed. Reports on articles dealing with noise and its effects on health and efficiency of people were heard at this point. Finally, the class wrote up the experiment using the following questions as paragraph headings:

1. What was our problem in this experiment?
2. What was our working hypothesis?
3. In what ways was our experiment conducted according to the scientific method?
4. What was the *control* in our experiment?
5. What was the variable factor in our experiment?
6. In what ways would our experiment have to be refined or extended to make it more truly "scientific"?
7. How do you account for the discrepancy between our findings and what you have read or heard about the effects of noise on the efficiency of workers?

Materials, Equipment, Multisensory Aids, Clubs, and Other Activities

The materials and equipment required for a laboratory and demonstration course in physical science need not be so highly specialized as for chemistry or physics but obviously should be of greater variety than that for either of these courses alone. Probably all of the chemicals and chemical equipment can be borrowed from the school's chemistry room; the mechanical and electrical equipment and the equipment for the study of sound and light can be obtained from the physics room; materials and equipment used in the study of the earth sciences and astronomy may be available from the general-science room. As for all science teaching, much useful material and apparatus can be obtained from the local five-and-ten-cent stores, from hardware stores, from garages, etc.; likewise, much can be constructed by the students themselves at small cost.

Multisensory aids, clubs, field trips, and similar types of activities have much to offer for the physical-science course, contributing directly to ideational learnings and providing for extending and exploring the ramifications and implications of various subjects brought up in the course. If there is anything unique about the role of such activities in the physical-science course as compared to courses in chemistry and physics, it arises from the larger amount of time that can be devoted to such activities, particularly films, recordings of radio broadcasts, etc., having to do with the more general and cultural aspects of science. Valuable suggestions and bibliographies relative to science clubs, trips and journeys, multisensory aids, and materials in general for use in science teaching will be found in the work by Heiss, Obourn, and Hoffman (**31**). The role of individual laboratory work and of demonstrations has been well described in the Thirty-first Yearbook (**46**).

The Course in Chemistry[3]

We turn next to the high-school course in chemistry to consider how it can make its greatest contribution toward the accomplishment of the general objectives stated in chapter iii.

The secondary-school chemistry course has usefulness for the purposes of a general education. Its function is especially important for students who enter chemistry without first having taken the more general physical-science course. Accordingly, chemistry teaching should clarify the relations of chemistry to health, vocational pursuits, and to the other aspects of living to which the subject matter of chemistry relates and to which it contributes understandings.

The Selection and Organization of Content

The traditional chemistry course has strengths as well as weaknesses. Many of those who hold to this traditional chemistry would set up the curriculum as a series of projects with little regard for sequence. As

---

[3] The committee has profited from the collaboration of Harry H. Williams, Horace Mann School for Boys, New York, in the preparation of this section.

Buswell points out (19) this type of approach has on many occasions led to superior results by way of stimulating interest, inducing self-activity, and calling forth vigorous student response. As the same author goes on to point out, however, this is not enough. If, as is generally agreed, learning is growth and is progressive in the sense that it involves continuous reorganization of experience, appropriate organization of materials is highly desirable within the educational process.

In line with this view of education the trend in organization of chemistry courses has been toward the development of related units. True, some teachers and authors have sometimes adopted a unit plan without much serious consideration of their relatedness, either within units or between them. This practice is unfortunate, since the desirability of relatedness in learning is one of the points at which most psychologists agree. Each newly introduced concept should be seen as a part of an unfolding pattern, not as an isolated item.

Ideas vary as to what type of integrating theme a unit should have. It is still quite common to find chemistry units organized around material substances such as oxygen and hydrogen. In recent years, however, there has been a growing tendency to organize units about principles. Thus, the first unit may be built around the role of oxygen in burning, the control of burning, and the nature of chemical change. The latter type of organization tends to make more explicit the relationships to be established. Moreover, this type of organization makes more apparent the fact that the assumed subject matter has some bearing upon real-life situations.

An examination of the texts in which an attempt has been made to use principles and generalizations as the basis of organization shows that the plan has not been followed consistently. The traditional units on sulfur and on certain other elements are still likely to be included—this in spite of the fact that the really functional aspects of these units can be incorporated into more meaningful contexts around interpretive generalizations. No doubt we can afford to drop some of the traditional material for which no place is found in such a scheme. In some organizations, an over-all unit on metallurgy which stresses the general principles involved in obtaining, using, and protecting the metals has superseded the uninspiring and deadly treatment in which the metals are given extended study, one after the other, each as an isolated item.

As indicated above, choices must be made relative to course materials. Here the following principles are proposed:

1. The course content should help to satisfy real needs of the students.
2. The course content should be of a proper degree of difficulty, adequate consideration being given in its selection to the maturity level of the pupils.

3. Economic and social applications should be developed and stressed, particularly those relating to everyday life.
4. The content should include a wealth of materials and activities designed for use in developing the abilities and attitudes associated with the scientific method of problem-solving.
5. Content that appeals to pupil interest is more likely to influence pupil behavior than that which does not.

Opinions vary also as to the sequence of the units. Some prefer to introduce chemistry with a unit on the structure of matter. Proponents of this practice emphasize the logic of this approach, pointing out the fact that the material of this unit helps to clarify the concepts in all succeeding units. This is undoubtedly true. Such mode of procedure, however, suffers from a very serious handicap in that an unusually large percentage of the ideas presented must be taken by the student "on faith." Little can be done in this unit by way of laboratory experimentation; moreover, the number of teacher demonstrations is also limited. There is real danger of giving the initial impression that, for the most part, chemistry teaching is "telling." For these reasons it seems better to initiate the student into some unit in which he can begin to set up his own inquiries and to follow them through, at least in part, on an experimental basis. However, the unit on structure of matter should follow as soon as the need for its clarifying concepts becomes evident. Other units involving solution, ionization, etc., can then be arranged in a developmental sequence. While there has been a tendency to deal with consumer units in the last half of the course, present indications are that it is better to diffuse consumer chemistry throughout all units of the course.

Associated with the strength inherent in the organization of chemistry as a subject are certain pitfalls. One of the most crucial is the tendency to look upon the organization as the important item per se. In doing this we may seem to present chemistry content as something to be memorized and may forget that it is only a framework which gives direction to growth and understanding.

Chemistry teachers, like all other teachers, are no doubt justly accused of failing to develop adequately a pupil awareness of the extent to which facts, principles, and generalizations of chemistry relate to everyday living. These relationships are frequently less obvious in chemistry than in physics, although actually they are just as real. To take a specific example, in chemistry we teach about the presence of acids in foods, about the relative activity of the metals with acids, about the corrosion of products, and elsewhere we commonly discuss the toxic nature of compounds, particularly those of certain metals. Yet, if we then cite a case of "copper" poisoning traceable to the cooking of food in corroded copper utensils, most of the students are unable to explain the elementary chemistry of the situation. A leading question as to whether the copper or the corrosion was involved is also likely to prove baffling, even to a large proportion of those who can recite the facts needed for the explanation.

In summary, the following principles are suggested for the organization of the chemistry course:

1. The content should be organized into fairly large units, each focused upon some functional understanding or principle.
2. The sequence of units should be planned to proceed from the generally less difficult principles to those of greater difficulty.
3. The organization should stress relationships (between units as well as within units).
4. The organization should stress problem-solving as such with emphasis upon the associated skills and attitudes.
5. The classroom work should be constantly related to the larger life outside.
6. The organization should stress the development of interests and attitudes.

Methods for Developing Functional Understanding of Facts, Concepts, and Principles

Teachers have received more adequate training in the methods of teaching for assimilation and retention of information than they have in methods of dealing with other important objectives of science instruction. Similarly, the emphasis in textbooks has been preponderantly upon the information objective. Quite naturally, perhaps, teachers have usually devoted the greater part of their teaching efforts to this objective.

When we consider that, other things being equal, the more facts one can recall the better, the common teaching practice may appear to be entirely as it should be. Certain studies are, however, quite disturbing to any complacency that we may have when we accept this viewpoint (60). This research seems to indicate that development of the ability to recall information and of the ability to use this same information in inferential and applicational behavior do not necessarily go hand in hand. Students may make considerable progress with the former ability and relatively little with the latter. Since the facts, concepts, and principles which we have emphasized in our teaching are really only the raw materials needed for carrying on the intellectual processes which govern behavior, we should recognize the incompleteness of teaching methods which place almost exclusive emphasis upon memorization and recall. In the light of these considerations it seems advisable to devote the bulk of what space is available to a discussion of those important aspects of chemistry teaching with which we have been least successful.

Methods Related to Developing Growth in Habits of Thinking, in Attitudes, and in Appreciations

The process of developing understanding with respect to scientific facts, concepts, and principles is essentially the same as that of developing growth in certain habits of thinking, in attitudes, and in appreciations. The latter habits are those relating to problem-solving by scientific method. Our efforts at making the chemistry course a course in problem-solving have not been very productive. Familiar quotations from writings of outstanding leaders in education, such as John Dewey, to the effect that the heart of science is its method can be found in the prefaces of textbooks and in other equally accessible places. That teachers have read these statements is evidenced by the fact that they practically always rate the teaching of scientific method high on their lists of objectives. But when asked what they do in their courses to further this end, teachers are likely to be "on the spot," as were the teachers questioned by Beauchamp (7). If workers in education have really recognized the method of science as the most important item that science has to offer, it seems difficult to explain the scarcity of substantial research in science relating to problem-solving. The relative lack of curriculum materials developed for the expressed purpose of improving the problem-solving abilities of children is likewise disconcerting. This lack is no doubt largely explained, as Brownell (17) points out, by the complexity of the process of problem-solving and by the variability of the students whom we are attempting to develop into more efficient problem-solvers. This does not mean that research in this area should be discouraged. On the contrary, its importance certainly justifies the opposite point of view.

The conclusion to be drawn from this brief and incomplete analysis of the high-school chemistry course is, perhaps, that we should attempt to permeate this course with the method of science and with concepts that relate to real-life situations while retaining the merits of systematic development. For example, take the unit on structure of matter. The chemistry texts leave no doubt that this unit lends itself to a systematic development. Can we as confidently maintain that we have adequately explored the possibilities of this unit for accomplishing the objectives of problem-solving? We shall consider next some suggestions as to how some implementation can be given to the point of view that has been recommended.

Chapter xi has analyzed problem-solving and has set forth a list of behavior patterns. The practical question is what can we do about these objectives in the chemistry course. Very often in the past our efforts with problem-solving have consisted chiefly of breaking up the process into a number of idealized parts and then insisting that the student be able to recite these formalized steps. The results of this practice have been inadequate, to say the least.

Certain types of abilities are fundamental to problem-solving behavior. Some of the most fruitful suggestions for classroom procedure have come from those who have sought out these key abilities and have indicated how we can work for their improvement. In the past we have done a better job with some of these abilities than with others. Strauss (57), who administered Downings' test, "Some Elements of Scientific Thinking," to 19,343 pupils, came to the conclusion that the "ability to recognize a problem and the ability to observe seem to be the best mastered of the elements studied." Among the least developed seemed to be the abilities to reason, to analyze, and to see relationships. These studies seem to justify the attempts of those who have striven to develop methods for improving other key abilities involved in problem-solving.

Attempts to improve an ability needed for problem-solving should be centered about behavioral situations which encourage the student to exercise that particular ability. Take, for example, the ability to apply principles. It has been pointed out that we use this ability in two ways (32). Either we use it to explain something that has happened under a certain set of conditions or to predict what would happen under a given set of conditions. Thus, two types of problem situations are suggested as curriculum materials to be used in the improvement of this ability. Such application materials should make use of the facts and principles already met in the chemistry course but in unfamiliar context. For example, at the appropriate time the following situation calling for explanation might be used in chemistry:

A newspaper account of a man found dead in a room with a gas stove burning and windows closed ended as follows: "It is believed that the gas had used up all the oxygen in the room, and, hence, the occupant was asphyxiated while asleep." Would your analysis of the probable cause of death be the same as that above? If not, give your own analysis.

Another such application situation calling for prediction might be phrased:

Special recipes have been developed for making cakes and other baked goods at high altitudes. One of the chief differences between these and ordinary recipes is in the amount of baking powder used. Would you expect these special recipes to require more or less than the usual quantity of baking powder? Explain.

The improvement of ability to interpret data can be approached in a similar manner. This ability may well be conceived of as being complex and as including more specific abilities such as the ability to perceive relationships, the ability to recognize the limitations of a set of data, etc. Such analysis proves helpful to the teacher in that it suggests the specific behavior patterns to be encouraged and the types of situations to be used.

The following is an example of an interpretation of data exercise.

Substance	Solubility at 20° C	Solubility at Boiling Point of Saturated Solution	Boiling Point of Saturated Solution in Degrees C
NH_4Cl	37.2	88.9	114.2
$BaCl_2$	35.7	60.1	104.4
$CaCl_2$	74.5	325.0	179.5
$Ca(OH)_2$	0.165	0.05	100.0
$FeSO_4$	26.5	177.8	102.2
K_2CO_3	110.5	205.0	135.0
KNO_3	31.6	284.6	114.5
K_2SO_4	11.11	21.21	101.7
$NaCl$	36.0	41.2	108.4
Na_2SO_4	15.0	43.0	103.0

Which of the following conclusions (1) are clearly indicated as true by the data above; (2) may be true but are not proved by the above data; (3) are unsupported by the above data?

1. The greater the weight of solute present, the higher the boiling point of the saturated solution.
2. All substances increase in solubility as the temperature is increased.
3. Potassium salts undergo the greatest increases in solubility as the temperature is raised.
4. Sulfates have the lowest boiling points found among saturated salt solutions.
5. Chlorides have the highest boiling points found among saturated salt solutions.
6. The boiling points of saturated solutions do not depend upon the rates at which their solutes increase in solubility with increase in temperature.

Chemistry textbooks, workbooks, and laboratory guides do not provide much by the way of exercises for application situations, the interpretation of data, and other material relating to the various abilities used in problem-solving. Teachers commonly indicate a willingness to use such material but confess an ignorance of where to look for it or a lack of time to make the search. However, a group of science teachers in a concerted effort can usually produce a considerable amount of such material from past experience. Search through the periodicals of chemistry is also fruitful. Another significant source for suggestions is the testing material available for evaluating progress in the problem-solving abilities. Teaching and testing materials in this area are basically similar. The chief difference lies in the form of the material and the way in which it is used.

The chemistry course should provide some opportunity for actual problem-solving. This may seem too obvious to require statement, but the fact remains that little real problem-solving is done in most high-school chemistry courses. The laboratory immediately comes to mind, but in practice the laboratory has usually turned out to be a place for gaining practice in following directions, for learning certain laboratory skills, for learning to observe more accurately, and for confirming and illustrating what the textbook says. While certain aspects of problem-solving are involved in traditional laboratory work, it is rather rare to find chemistry students working on the solution of real problems.

There are very practical reasons why the high-school chemistry laboratory is not functioning on a problem-solving basis. Among these are the directives from those in positions of authority who tell teachers what and how much should be taught in the chemistry course. Then there are the practical difficulties involved in running a laboratory in which all or even a fair percentage of the members of a large class are working on different problems. Again, little has been done to indicate to teachers what kinds of problems are suitable for solution in high-school chemistry laboratories.

In some studies relating to science teaching attention has been given to the more effective use of the chemistry laboratory. One of the most fruitful of these is Horton's (**33**) study. This research seems to indicate that the fifty-five or so laboratory techniques to be mastered by doing the conventional laboratory exercises can be attained in a fraction of the school year. Moreover, enough research has been done to indicate that teacher demonstration is just about as effective as individual laboratory work for teaching the facts.

There is also some evidence to show how we might put the chemistry laboratory on a more defensible footing. Schlesinger (**54**), for example, indicates that this frequently can be done by small changes in the directions that we now give to students and suggests steps to be followed for the improvement of laboratory work. He includes illustrations of types of investigations that can be undertaken with profit. Units on consumer chemistry suggest the kinds of investigations that can be carried on with familiar materials. Examples of these are the determination of the percentage of acid in a sample of vinegar or the juice of a lemon, the relative amounts of carbon dioxide liberated by various baking powders, analysis of dentifrices, the hydrogenation of vegetable oils, recovery of silver from a silver coin, etc. It is true, of course, that the amount of suggestive material now available to teachers is inadequate.

It is not our intention to imply here that chemistry teachers should immediately revolutionize their procedures by dropping all conventional laboratory work. Indeed, it may well be that it will prove advisable to retain a certain portion of the present type of laboratory work with only slight modification. If, however, the present type does accomplish its purpose in only part of the year, then there is left time which can be devoted to the solution of problems whose answers are not known by the students beforehand.

Because real experiments usually require more time than laboratory exercises, the suggested procedure may seem to involve some sacrifice of quantity for quality and some loss in coverage. This criticism, although of questionable validity, can be met by additional demonstrations. Since the traditional way of teaching is likely to be the accepted way, any innovation of this sort involves a problem of re-education of teachers, administrators, and the public. The important thing is that the teacher begin to develop his own methods of dealing with objectives to which he has always subscribed but about which he has in most instances done very little.

Materials, Equipment, Multisensory Aids, Clubs, and Other Activities

The value of the materials that a teacher uses should be judged on the basis of the contributions that they make toward progress in accomplishment of the objectives of the course. Thus the showing of a film which offers entertainment only is hardly justifiable in a course where entertainment is not one of the important objectives. Consequently, in classes where films are used, the teacher continues to have an active role in the situation by way of planning, selecting, organizing, evaluating, etc. The fact that children are exposed to such materials is not in itself indicative that good teaching is taking place. If such were the case, the supplementary materials now available might well vie with the teacher for his place in the classroom. As a matter of fact, a well-known writer on the teaching of chemistry some years ago expressed the opinion that the moving picture would eventually reduce the number of teachers employed by at least 25 per cent. Today, however, there seems little likelihood that enrichment materials will have this tendency. Indeed, the teacher's responsibilities have tended to increase rather than decrease as new materials have become available.

A great variety of materials and devices for teaching science are available. Most of these, together with their sources, have been carefully catalogued in a number of places (31). In general, teachers appreciate the value of visual and other sensory aids that provide concrete experiences which help in establishing relationships. The generalizations of chemistry are abstractions toward a functional understanding of which appropriate demonstrations, field trips, films, slides, graphs, and other visual aids are making a valuable contribution.

Although abundant in quantity, the sensory-aid materials are very heterogeneous. This condition poses problems relating to selection and effective use of these aids. It also suggests the need of references to which the teacher can turn for evaluation of different types of materials. Much of the evaluation now available is in terms of general platitudes which are not very helpful. To read that a film, for example, is "good for use in chemistry classes" does not prove very valuable to the teacher who wishes to know with what specific course objectives the film deals effectively. The efforts of those who have attempted to provide this latter sort of evaluation are to be commended. One of the universities (29) with a large film library has, for example, published a film-utilization guide which includes the following information about each film described: maturity range, some reported applications, some reported teaching objectives, and some teacher comments. The advantage of such data to the teacher who must select films from the hundreds at hand is obvious. It is to be hoped that the initial efforts toward more critical and specific appraisals will be continued.

A wide variety of chemicals and equipment materials should be available at all times since students will not at all times be lock-stepped to the same activity. This can be arranged by having adequate and accessible shelf and storage space where the frequently needed chemicals and supplies are readily available to the students.

The chemistry club should arise ideally as a natural outgrowth of the regular chemistry course and should contribute to the objectives of the course. Special interests develop which the more formal classroom program encourages but for the exercise of which it fails to provide adequately. Clubs organized merely for the sake of having a club usually need a great deal of artificial stimulation to keep them going. In any club the need arises for a variety of activities such as visual programs, field trips, special speakers, contests, assembly programs. Effective organization and unobtrusive but positive faculty guidance are needed for the successful operation of clubs and related organizations.

THE COURSE IN PHYSICS[4]

Selection and Organization of Content

In the report of his 1932 study which dealt with the organization of physics courses, Beauchamp (7) said:

---

[4] The committee has profited from the collaboration of H. Emmett Brown, New York State Teachers College, Buffalo, New York, in the preparation of this section.

Courses in physics present a marked contrast to the courses in biology and general science. The topics in all the courses were classified easily under the headings: mechanics, heat, magnetism and electricity, sound, and light. There was some difference in the order of the topics presented and also in the divisions which were included under the main headings, but in general one obtains an impression of order and uniformity. . . . . It may be that the final word on the organization of a course in physics has been said. On the other hand, the decline in the enrolment in the subject at least suggests that a reorganization with change of emphasis might be desirable.

Others, as, for example, Brown (**12**), have criticized not only the unchanging nature and the order of the physics units but also their separation one from the other, each unit being a little textbook unto itself.

Weaver[5] found the space allocated to the various divisions of physics in twelve textbooks to average as follows:

Mechanics	36 per cent	Magnetism and electricity	24 per cent
Heat	15 per cent		
Sound	6 per cent	Modern physics	6 per cent
Light	13 per cent		

Texts and courses of study follow each other so closely that Beauchamp (**7**) found no need to study them separately. The picture we get is of a subject, physics, gone stale through adherence to a set and largely nonfunctional pattern of organization. A thorough overhauling both as to the content and organization seems in order. To this end, the following principles would seem to apply.

a) Unification about a central theme. The Thirty-first Yearbook (**46**:255) urged:

The integration of the physics course can be greatly improved if a very few large concepts be accepted as the basic organizing themes running through all the instructional units. For the high-school course it is suggested that the concept, *the indestructability of matter and energy*, and the concept, *all physical phenomena are based upon energy transformations*, be accepted as tentative organizing themes.

In another report (**15**) it is shown that the unifying theme of man's use and control of energy may be used for this purpose. It would seem that such an organization would help the student to sense the fundamental unity of the whole course and to see interrelationships between the various divisions. That the organization of the physics course around major generalizations may also be a factor in helping students to think scientifically is suggested by the work of Kilgore (**38**).

---

[5] J. F. Weaver, "The Distribution of Emphasis in Ten Physics Tests and in Twelve Physics Textbooks," *Journal of Educational Research*, XXXIX (September, 1945), 42-55.

b) Social implications of the material. In 1938, seventy-nine members of the National Association for Research in Science Teaching (**51**) were reported as in rather unanimous agreement that "Secondary-school content shall be modified from present practice to include materials of greater social significance." This statement means that we should teach the technical aspects of a machine and the meaning of such concepts as mechanical advantage, efficiency, and power. But beyond this it means that we, by a variety of techniques, should endeavor to bring home to students the significance of the fact that each person in the United States controls, on the average, about 10 h-p. (this is the equivalent of about 100 slaves); that electricity is not merely something measured in volts, amperes, and watts but a form of energy which had to be available before modern urban civilization could develop at all; that atomic fission is not merely an interesting nuclear process but perhaps the beginning of a new source of energy for man.

c) Material should be of immediate personal interest and value to students. In 1937, Hartmann and Stephens (**30**) rated 144 physics principles both as to difficulty and as to pleasure-value as determined from student ratings. Using the ratings, the authors determined the teaching order to be mechanics, heat, light, sound, electricity. The study gives little suggestion as to desirable change or new materials since the 144 principles were simply those found in common in all of the six popular texts analyzed.

That material which will be of greatest interest and value to students will (1) help the student the better to understand his own behavior; (2) help to explain, through reference to large underlying principles, the common phenomena and devices of his own environment. Material that does not meet these criteria becomes of suspect-value and may be considered for deletion.

Accepting this principle, we will pay increased attention to such topics as the effects of noise upon man, voice production, human and animal hearing, human vision, eye defects, lighting conditions in the home, man as a machine and a prime mover, motion in relation to safe driving and reaction time.

d) The number of topics or units taught during the year must be reduced. For years physics teachers have been bewailing the steady increase in the amount of material in their courses. New material is often added; little is ever dropped. It is time to realize that it is far better to leave out *whole sections* (e.g., all of the treatment of vector forces or of pneumatics and hydraulics) than to teach so much so poorly. In this connection it is encouraging to note the insistence of Vordenburg (**64**), reporting for the Committee on Physics Teaching of the Central Association of Science and Mathematics Teachers, on the need for "fewer concepts."

e) The course should be organized largely or entirely about problems. This principle suggests a method of work rather than material to be taught. Class activities—demonstrations, experiments, discussions—as well as student activities outside the classroom are carried on in order to obtain answers to certain large questions which have been accepted by the class as defining worth-while problems. The seventy-nine members of the N.A.R.S.T., previously referred to, strongly favored this type of organization for physics.

f) Students should have a considerable share in setting the goals of class instruction. Although this principle is almost ancillary to the previous statement, it does not mean that students are to plan the course. The teacher, as expert, usually suggests the main lines of class endeavor. Student advice is sought, and often taken, concerning details and the working out of class procedures.

g) Physics teaching at the high-school level should largely reject the preparatory function and stress the contributions of physics to the general education of American youth. In view of the discussion in chapter iii, further elaboration seems unnecessary here. Let us note, however, that this position is not at all inconsistent (in fact, quite the contrary) with the plea of the chairman of the Committee on the Teaching of Physics in Secondary Schools of the American Association of Physics Teachers (**40**) when he urges revision of the science curriculums to establish minimum essentials in all sciences.

Methods for Developing Functional Understanding of Facts, Concepts, and Principles

In the previous section we spoke of the need to shorten the course. Now we stress the converse position, namely, the necessity for a more extended treatment of the topics or principles that are taught. Black (**9**) found that a certain few concepts are almost unteachable in the classes he observed. Hurd (**37**) concludes that the mastery of a few intensive teaching units is preferable to attempting to cover the whole subject; Delano (**25**), as though to give testimony to the values of intensive learning in a small area, devotes a whole dissertation to the study of a single concept.

a) Understanding a principle in physics. Of a student who has a thorough functional understanding of a principle in physics, the following statements are probably true:

1. He knows the underlying facts.
2. He can state the relationship in his own words.
3. He knows the units in which measurements involved in the principle are made.
4. He can solve mathematical problems based upon the principle.
5. He can apply the principle to new situations.

6. He has a feeling of pleasurable satisfaction with respect to the understanding
—a feeling deriving in large part from the fact that he "knows he knows."
7. He knows the assumptions on which the principle is based as well as the limits
of its applicability.

Too many times learning stops with a glib repetition of the principle (a
poor substitute for statement No. 2) and with statement No. 4. That
these are not enough has been shown by several investigations. Schindler
(**55**) developed tests of two types. One type (A) tested only verbal recall;
the other (B) required that the student recognize the original A-type
statement when presented in "a different and often unfamiliar form."
By this means Schindler determined the extent to which pupils really
understood the statements on which A-type items were based. He concluded that while 70 per cent memorized, only 17 per cent understood.

Ralya (**49**) found that pupils often could recall the formulas and work
out the answers to problems and still not understand the principle involved.

b) Mathematics in physics. Some ability in the use of mathematics is
evidently necessary if students are to develop understanding of many of
the principles. High-school students often fail to elect physics because
they believe the amount and difficulty of this mathematics to be greater
than it is. Several studies, notably that of Kilzer (**39**), have revealed
that the mathematical skill really needed amounts to no more than competence in arithmetic, reasonable facility in simple algebra, and a smat-
tering of geometry and trigonometry (the latter not absolutely necessary). Kilzer concludes that "the information is usually taught well
enough in existing mathematics classes." Carter (**22**) has shown that
ability to recognize the mathematical concepts is just as closely correlated with success in physics as is mathematical ability, itself.

That the mathematical skills are taught well enough for present needs
does not mean that there are not ways in which the mathematics department can be of further help to the student of physics. In another place
(**13**) seven skills which are of value have been elaborated. Space limitations permit only their listing here.

1. Generalizing from data
2. Translating from a word statement of a principle to the algebraic equivalent
3. The ability to go from statements such as AB and AC to the equivalent
   A = KBC
4. An understanding of significant figures
5. Ability to use the slide rule
6. Ability to manipulate numbers expressed in the exponential system
7. Training in the habit of always labeling answers with appropriate units

Feeling that the use of mathematics may further and enrich the understanding of many physics principles, the physics teacher will not hesitate to make a quantitative development in many cases. In others, even those that have been traditionally quantitative, he may decide that a qualitative presentation will yield better results. Where mathematics is employed, the physics teacher must make sure (1) that students have the necessary mathematical skills and (2) that they can apply them to the physics situation.

Only one further suggestion can be given. In working numerical problems, students may well be asked to substitute units directly in formulas along with the numerical values and to handle these units like algebraic terms (**14**).

c) *Applying principles to new situations.* One of the best measures of a student's mastery of an understanding is the ability to apply the principle to new situations. However, like any other outcome of instruction, if we wish to realize it, we must work toward it quite directly. Brewer (**11**) has shown that this may be done in a college survey course. One of the most significant leads would seem to be that suggested by the P.E.A. Committee on Evaluation (**47**). Having taught the principle or principles involved in a given problem, but not the actual problem situation itself, the teacher will then administer a test based upon that situation. For example, the effect of pressure upon boiling point having been demonstrated, the following test, taken from the bulletin cited (only a part is given here) might be administered:

When an egg is cooked in an open kettle of boiling water on a high mountain the cooking time is:

a) greater than the cooking time at sea level........................ ( )*a*.
(Similarly worded, although incorrect, statements, *b* and *c* are omitted here.)

Check the statements below which give the reason or reasons for your explanation above.

d) Water boils at the same temperature everywhere................... ( ) *d*.
e) Just as automobile radiators boil more frequently and quickly at high
   altitudes, so eggs will cook more quickly on a high mountain......... ( ) *e*.
f) A reduction in the boiling point accompanies a reduction in the pressure
   above the water... ( )*f*.
(Statements *g*, *h*, *i* follow.)

The student should have made a correct prediction by checking *a* and *a* only of the first three and have given the correct reasons for his prediction by checking statements *f*, *g*, and *h* of the last group.

In use, still further learning results from an analysis of the errors that the student has made (he usually makes the analysis himself) by use of a checklist of types of reasoning errors.

d) Induction and deduction. Physics texts and teaching are quite commonly deductive in their presentation. Scientific principles are tested (with or without the history of their discovery) and then applications of the principle to various devices are shown. It would seem better psychology and a procedure more likely to give the student an insight into the method of scientific discovery if data were first dealt with in an attempt to answer the question of, shall we say, "What is the relation between the pressure and the volume of a gas at constant temperature?" From the two columns of measured data, students could then be led to generalize the underlying Boyle's law. Deductive application to new situations would then follow. The student should be made conscious of the steps that have been taken: stating the problem, setting up the experimental procedures, gathering data, generalizing from data (induction), and testing the principle by applying it deductively to new situations. This is one of the best ways of developing the student's ability to think reflectively.

Only one study concerning the relative merits of the inductive and deductive methods comes to hand. In that study (**44**) pure deductive teaching was compared with pure inductive teaching. The author, after what seems an inadequate amount of testing, concludes that the inductive method is definitely superior.

e) Worksheets. Recent years have been marked by the appearance of a number of workbooks in physics. The theory back of these teaching aids is that, by filling out the blanks and doing the other tasks called for, the student may help himself to see relationships, recall facts, and understand principles. In some instances these workbooks combine their study-aid features with instructions and questions pertaining to laboratory experiments. Opinions are rather divided as to the merit of these devices. The author of one of the early books of this sort (**36**) tested groups taught by workbook and nonworkbook methods and reports results that are generally inconclusive. His results were generally substantiated by Browning (**18**), who adds that superior students seem to profit most by the use of worksheets.

Different in format and organization, but still designed to help the student to help himself, were the study outlines developed by Clemensen (**23**). Students using these study outlines which stressed organization and relationships, learned more facts, had more concepts of the "broader, more generalized type," and were more inclined to seek and express "causal explanations of science phenomena," than were students taught by ordinary methods.

f) Analysis of pupil difficulties. With a reduction in the amount of physics material to be covered there comes the opportunity to re-teach those portions which, according to test results, are poorly mastered. In this connection, the work of Bail (**5**) should be noted. His drill exercises on 1,952 concepts revealed "dominant" (recurring) errors in 42 per cent of the exercises.

g) *Teacher training and load.* It goes almost without saying that good instruction in physics can result only when teachers are adequately trained and are not overburdened with classes. Unfortunately, these conditions are all too infrequently realized. In a study of physics teaching in Pennsylvania (**59**) it was shown that 44 per cent of those teaching the subject had one college course or less and that only about one-fourth of the group was prepared for teaching the subject through an undergraduate major or graduate study. The task of these physics teachers is rendered much more difficult by the number of subjects they are expected to teach. Only 6 per cent teach physics alone, only 30 per cent teach as few as two other subjects, and some are actually teaching *seven different* subjects.

Methods for Developing Growth in Habits of Thinking, in Attitudes, and in Appreciations

a) *Special abilities.* The *whole* of the art of scientific thinking or problem-solving, as we shall call it, is admittedly greater than the sum of its special-ability *parts*. Nevertheless, it seems reasonable that, if the student be trained in the various special abilities (see chap. xi), a long step is taken toward an attainment of the ability to do the complex whole.

Space limitations do not permit detailed discussion of each ability. One, the ability to apply principles, has already been considered. One other, the ability to draw valid inferences from data (the "ability to interpret data") has been treated significantly by the Committee on Evaluation (**47**) previously referred to.

The shift from a deductive to an inductive presentation will also help students to develop these special abilities. As we have said, the subject matter should be used to help solve problems. These problems may be of varying degrees of length and difficulty, ranging all the way from such a problem as "How does the earth receive its energy?" to the rather personal, "How fast can I throw a ball?" or "What is the highest note that I can sing?" The first may set the work of the class for several days; the latter may define a problem which a student may attempt to solve by laboratory techniques. In the solution of both types of problem, some or perhaps all of the problem-solving abilities may be brought into play.

b) *Scientific attitudes.* There is no such thing as the scientific attitude. There are scientific attitudes: scientific skepticism, open-mindedness, curiosity, belief in cause and effect, and others. Given time for thought and planning it would not be difficult for a physics teacher to plan situations in which a given attitude may be called into play. Thus, students customarily exhibit both skepticism and curiosity in connection with Arago's disk. Difficulty rises in connection with attempts on the part of the teacher to give weight to all the different scientific attitudes. These attitudes can only be developed as the result of activities which evoke them. Activities, both classroom and laboratory, which seem best suited to this purpose are again of the problem-solving type. In such work the teacher must be sure that attitudes implicit in a given action are made explicit to the student.

In connection with scientific attitudes, a group of master's theses done at Colorado State College of Education (**10; 28; 52**) is of interest.

c) Appreciations. As applied to an understanding, an appreciation is probably identical with the "pleasurable satisfaction" referred to in connection with understandings. Many indeed are the appreciations that are developed in physics. They may be appreciations of how dull and dreary the subject may be. More desirably the students may acquire an appreciation of how physics principles explain the operation of such devices as the electric refrigerator, of how the energy concept relates seemingly disparate phenomena, of the beauty of the scientific method of problem-solving. If desirable appreciations are to be acquired, the emphasis must be upon a rich experiencing of a smaller number of principles, upon functional relations between different portions of the subject, upon the applications of the physics material to day-by-day concerns of the student, and upon the intellectual adventure which physics may be.

Materials, Equipment, and Other Teaching Aids

a) Demonstration and laboratory equipment. The cost of adequately equipping a physics laboratory for the number of individual or small-group experiments that may be done in a given year is larger than that for either of the other major high-school sciences. Add to this fact the results of the investigations concerning laboratory teaching, and the apparently increasing tendency to equip schools for only demonstration teaching in physics is quite understandable. Physics teachers will be quite ostrich-like if they take the position that all experiments must be performed individually. And yet there are, or perhaps we should say, may be, values in individual laboratory work that cannot be realized in other ways, particularly if laboratory work approaches the problem-solving ideal described previously. The solution would seem to be to plan to equip the laboratory to demonstrate the more difficult experiments and those of a historical character. Individual apparatus for use in problem-solving experiments would then need to be provided. This latter should include not only the usual types of laboratory equipment but also raw materials and tools which may be used by both teacher and pupil for the construction of apparatus.

In his study of selected high schools in Missouri, Culp (**24**) found that the schools were poorly equipped to do the work and that, because of financial considerations, there was a trend toward dropping the subject. Of the reported list of experiments performed by classes in the Missouri high schools, about half were listed as of individual performance, a number probably not realized in most schools because of the inadequacy of equipment.

b) A physics museum. One possible partial solution to the problem of expensive equipment might be offered by the construction of a physics museum. In such a museum, located in an unused classroom or in other space, would be placed apparatus set up in working condition. Instructions for operation and observation and questions to be answered concerning each experiment should be provided. The gradual establishment of such a museum might give purpose to laboratory work over a period of several years. Once established the museum becomes a valuable adjunct to the course work. Many commercial pieces of apparatus are well adapted for such museum use. Examples include the trajectory apparatus in which a steel ball shot from a blow-gun hits a falling small tin can and a piece which shows both the expansion of a wire and the principle of the hot-wire ammeter. For this sort of work the popular science magazines and, in particular, the book by Sutton (**58**) are excellent references.

c) Multi-sensory aids. In recent years there have been developed a great many teaching films in the field of physics. Many of these are excellent. Some, particularly those films that, through animation, show electron motion, or molecular action, or other phenomena that can never be seen directly in the classroom, or that take the class vicariously to visit a factory or museum that cannot otherwise be reached are indeed valuable.

Physics is fortunate in that, besides the many excellent films that may be rented or purchased, there are a great many other films, many of them excellent and free from undue commercialism, that may be borrowed rent-free.

Radio-education in the field of physics has been little in evidence, although it has been quite successful in certain other areas. And yet, because their work centers so largely in the field of physics, and because of the national need for physicists, it would seem natural for certain large industrial concerns to experiment in this field.

REFERENCES

1. *The American Biology Teacher; Nature; Natural History*, etc.
2. AMERICAN COUNCIL OF SCIENCE TEACHERS. *Redirecting Science Teaching in the Light of Personal Social Needs.* Washington: National Education Association, 1942.
3. ———. *Science Teaching for Better Living.* Washington: National Education Association, 1942.
4. ATKINS, WESLEY C. *Some Probable Outcomes of Partial Self-direction in Tenth-Grade Biology.* Princeton, New Jersey: Princeton University Press, 1936.
5. BAIL, PHILLIP M. "A Critical Analysis of Pupil Responses to the Concepts of Mechanics," *Science Education*, XVII (October, 1933), 226–32; (December, 1933), 321–29.
6. BAILEY, W. W. "Physical Science for the Eleventh Year," *Science Teacher*, IX (December, 1942), Yearbook Supplement, 17.
7. BEAUCHAMP, WILBUR. *Instruction in Science.* U.S. Office of Education Bulletin, 1932, No. 17, Monograph No. 22. Washington: Government Printing Office, 1933.
8. BINGHAM, N. E. *Teaching Nutrition in Biology Classes.* New York: Bureau of Publications, Teachers College, Columbia University, 1939.
9. BLACK, OSWALD F. *The Development of Certain Concepts of Physics in High-School Students.* Potchefstrom, South Africa: "Die Weste" (publishers), 1930.
10. BOWERS, E. C. *The Construction of an Objective Scale To Measure the Scientific Attitude: Weighing Evidence.* Greeley, Colorado: Colorado State College of Education, 1937.
11. BREWER, A. S. *Factors Affecting Student Achievement and Change in a Physical-Science Survey Course.* Teachers College Contributions to Education, No. 868. New York: Teachers College, Columbia University, 1943.
12. BROWN, H. E. "Water-tight Compartments," *School Science and Mathematics*, XXXIX (December, 1939), 840–45.
13. ———. "Mathematics and Physics," *Science Education*, XXVIII (November, 1943), 88–94.
14. ———. "Mismanaged Mathematics," *School Science and Mathematics*, XL (April, 1940), 368–76.
15. ———. *The Development of a Course in the Physical Sciences for the Lincoln School.* New York: Bureau of Publications, Teachers College, Columbia University, 1939.
16. ———. "An Experiment To Show the Effects of Noise," *Science Education*, XXII (December, 1938), 343–48.
17. BROWNELL, WILLIAM A. "Problem Solving," *The Psychology of Learning*, pp. 419–20. Forty-first Yearbook of the National Society for the Study of Education, Part II. Chicago: Distributed by the University of Chicago Press, 1942.
18. BROWNING, CHARLES A. "A Work-sheet for High-School Physics," *Science Education*, XVIII (February, 1934), 37–41.
19. BUSWELL, GUY T. "Organization and Sequence of the Curriculum," *The Psychology of Learning*, pp. 445–63. Forty-first Yearbook of the National Society for the Study of Education, Part II. Chicago: Distributed by the University of Chicago Press, 1942.
20. CARLETON, ROBERT H. "Physical Science for General Education," *Science Counselor*, VII (March, 1941), 7; (June, 1941), 48; (September, 1941), 81.

21. ———. "The Acceptability of Physical Science as a College Entrance Unit," *Science Education*, XXX (April, 1946), 127–32.
22. CARTER, W. R. "A Study of Certain Mathematics Abilities in High-School Physics," *Mathematics Teacher*, XXV (October, 1932), 313–31; (November, 1932), 338–419; (December, 1932), 451–69.
23. CLEMENSON, JESSIE W. *Study Outlines in Physics: Construction and Experimental Evaluation.* Teachers College Contributions to Education, No. 553. New York: Teachers College, Columbia University, 1933.
24. CULP, W. R. "A Study of Laboratory Apparatus in a Number of First-Class Small-Town High Schools in Northwest Missouri," *Science Education*, XXIV (April, 1940), 213–20.
25. DELANO, R. B. *The Acquisition of the Concept of Friction.* Boston: Boston University.
26. DEWEY, JOHN. *Democracy and Education.* New York: Macmillan Co., 1916.
27. EDUCATIONAL POLICIES COMMISSION. *Education for All American Youth.* Washington: National Education Association, 1944.
28. EDWARDS, LON E. *Measurement of the Scientific Attitude: Sensitive Curiosity.* Greeley, Colorado: Colorado State College of Education, 1937.
29. FORD, L. LEMLER. *Film Utilization Guide for University of Michigan Films.* Bureau of Visual Education Extension Service. Ann Arbor, Michigan: University of Michigan, 1942.
30. HARTMAN, G. W., and STEPHENS, D. T. "The Optimal Teaching Sequence for Elementary Physical Principles Based on a Composite Scale of Pleasure-Value and Difficulty of Insight," *Journal of Educational Psychology*, XXVIII (September, 1937), 414–36.
31. HEISS, E. D.; OBOURN, E. S.; and HOFFMAN, C. W. *Modern Methods and Materials for Teaching Science.* New York: Macmillan Co., 1940.
32. HENDRICKS, B. C.; TYLER, R. W.; and FRUTCHEY, F. P. "Testing Ability To Apply Chemical Principles," *Journal of Chemical Education*, XI (November, 1934), 611–13.
33. HORTON, RALPH E. *Measurable Outcomes of Individual Laboratory Work in High-School Chemistry.* Teachers College Contributions to Education, No. 303. New York: Teachers College, Columbia University, 1928.
34. HOWARD, F. T. *The Measurement of the Scientific Attitude: Belief in Cause and Effect Relations.* Greeley, Colorado: Colorado State College of Education, 1937.
35. HUNTER, G. W., and SPORE, LEROY. "Science Sequence and Enrolments in the Secondary Schools of the United States," *Science Education*, XXVI (February, 1942), 66.
36. HURD, A. W. "Instructional Values of Work-sheets," Digest of two studies as reported in *Third Digest of Investigations in the Teaching of Science*, pp. 143–46. Francis D. Curtis, editor. Philadelphia: Blakiston Co., 1939.
37. ———. *Co-operative Experimentation in Materials and Methods in Secondary-School Physics.* New York: Teachers College, Columbia University, 1933.
38. KILGORE, W. A. *Identification of the Ability To Apply Principles of Physics.* Teachers College Contributions to Education, No. 840. New York: Teachers' College, Columbia University, 1933.
39. KILZER, L. R. "The Mathematics Needed in High-School Physics," *Science Education*, XIV (November, 1929), 335–44.
40. LARK-HOROVITZ, KARL. "Physics in the Secondary Schools," *Review of Scientific Instruments*, XIII (April, 1942), 137–39.

41. MARTIN, W. EDGAR. "A Determination of the Principles of the Biological Sciences of Importance for General Education," *Science Education*, XXIX (March, 1945), 100–105; April–May, 1945), 152–63.

42. MILLER, D. F., and BLAYDES, G. W. *Methods and Materials for Teaching Biological Science*. New York: McGraw-Hill Book Co., Inc., 1938.

43. NATIONAL SCIENCE TEACHERS ASSOCIATION. "The Place of Science in the Education of the Consumer." A statement prepared for the Consumer Education Study of the National Association of Secondary-School Principals. Washington: The Consumer Education Study, 1945.

44. PETERS, CHESTER. "An Evaluation of a Reorganization of the Present Core of Subject Matter in High-School Physics," *School Science and Mathematics*, XXVII (February, 1927), 172–82.

45. PETERSON, SHAILER W. "The Evaluation of a One-Year Course, the Fusion of Physics and Chemistry with Other Physical-Science Courses," *Science Education*, XXIX (December, 1945), 255.

46. *A Program for Teaching Science*. Thirty-first Yearbook of the National Society for the Study of Education, Part I. Chicago: Distributed by the University of Chicago Press, 1932.

47. PROGRESSIVE EDUCATION ASSOCIATION. *Application of Principles*. Evaluation in the Eight-Year Study, Bulletin No. 5, P.E.A. 898. Columbus, Ohio: Ohio State University, 1936 (mimeographed).

48. ———. *Science in General Education*. New York: D. Appleton-Century Co., 1938.

49. RALYA, L. L. "Investigations of Accomplishments in High-School Physics by Means of Diagnostic Tests," *Science Education*, XXII (November, 1938), 314–15.

50. "Report of the Harvard Committee," *General Education in a Free Society*. Cambridge, Massachusetts: Harvard University Press, 1945.

51. "Report of the Committee on Secondary-School Science of the National Association for Research in Science Teaching," *Science Education*, XXII (October, 1938), 223–33.

52. RUTHERFORD, R. F. *The Construction of an Objective Scale To Measure the Scientific Attitude: Habit of Delayed Response*. Greeley, Colorado: Colorado State College of Education, 1937.

53. *Science Education; School Science and Mathematics; Science Teacher*.

54. SCHLESINGER, H. I. "The Contributions of Laboratory Work to General Education," *Journal of Chemical Education*, XII (November, 1935), 524–28 .

55. SCHINDLER, A. W. "The Extent of Rote Learning in Certain Units of High-School Physics." Unpublished Doctor's Dissertation, State University of Iowa, 1934.

56. SKINNER, S. M. "The Two-Year Physical-Science Course in the University of Chicago," *School Science and Mathematics*, XL (October, 1940), 631.

57. STRAUSS, SAM. "Some Results of the Test of Scientific Thinking," *Science Education*, XVI (December, 1931), 89–93.

58. SUTTON, RICHARD M. *Demonstration Experiments in Physics*. New York: McGraw-Hill Book Co., Inc., 1938.

59. TRYTTEN, M. H., and LEACH, A. R. "A Study of Secondary-School Physics in Pennsylvania," *American Journal of Physics*, IX (April, 1941), 96–101.

60. TYLER, RALPH W. "Measuring the Results of College Instruction," *Educational Research Bulletin*, XI (May, 1932), 253–60.

61. ———. "What High-School Pupils Forget," *Educational Research Bulletin*, IX (November 19, 1930), 490–92.

62. URBAN, JOHN. *Behavior Changes Resulting from a Study of Communicable Diseases*. New York: Bureau of Publications, Teachers College, Columbia University, 1943.

63. UNITED STATES ARMED FORCES INSTITUTE. "Examination in Chemistry: High School Level." New York: American Council on Education, 1944.

64. VORDENBURG, K. E. "High-School Physics for General Education," *School Science and Mathematics*, XLI (June, 1941), 548–52.

65. WATSON, D. R. "A Comparison of the Growth of Survey Courses in Physical Science in High Schools and Colleges," *Science Education*, XXIV (January, 1940), 14.

66. WISE, H. E. "A Synthesis of the Results of Twelve Curricular Studies in the Fields of Science Education," *Science Education*, XXVII (February, 1943), 36–4; (September–October, 1943), 67–76.

67. ———. "A Determination of the Relative Importance of Principles of Physical Science for General Education," *Science Education*, XXV (December, 1941) 371–79; XXVI (January, 1942), 8–12.

68. WOODRING, M. N.; OAKES, M. E.; and BROWN, H. E. *Enriched Teaching of Science in the High School*. New York: Bureau of Publications, Teachers College, Columbia University, 1944.

69. WRAY, R. P. *The Relative Importance of Items of Chemical Information for General Education*. Doctor's dissertation, Pennsylvania State College, 1933.

CHAPTER XIV

SPECIAL PROBLEMS OF SCIENCE TEACHING
AT THE SECONDARY LEVEL

SCIENCE TEACHING AT THE JUNIOR-COLLEGE LEVEL[1]

The junior college is an institution usually offering two years of work of collegiate grade and quality beyond the high school. Three types of curriculums exist: (1) "lower division" work following the pattern of the first two years of four-year college curriculums; (2) terminal curriculums primarily of the general-education type; and (3) vocational curriculums in agriculture, trade, technical, home economics, business, and semi-professional fields.

There is a considerable amount of writing and talking about the junior college and the position of science in the several curriculums. In the brief space allotted here to the problems of science teaching in the junior college, only a few of the issues can be considered.

In a recent report on his study of terminal curriculums and courses Koos (18:11–32) provides facts of basic importance for characterizing science courses in the junior-college programs. An increasing number of junior colleges have been developing terminal courses, with emphasis on the occupational aims, although some progress has been made toward terminal general courses. In the colleges and universities no notable development of terminal occupational courses has been manifest in the junior-college years. Instead, the development has been toward courses with general-education aims, and more recently instances of terminal-general courses are increasing. Survey courses in science are increasing and are prominent components of junior-college terminal programs.

A number of studies (33:132–40; 11:97–101; 22:10–16; 10:294–99; 7:1–4) dealing with survey courses in science have been reported. These studies vary in their scope, representativeness, completeness, and accuracy, but they serve to indicate some of the attempts that are being made to develop programs and courses designed to make science offerings available for purposes other than the training of specialists in science and of those preparing for the professions. While diversities of patterns characterize these attempts, a few of the more common characteristics can be briefly summarized.

---

[1] The committee has profited from the collaboration of Palmer O. Johnson, University of Minnesota, in the preparation of this section.

Survey courses originated in the early twenties and have increased rapidly in recent years. The three more common types of survey courses in the natural sciences are: (1) a generalized science course embracing both the physical and biological sciences in one course or a sequence of courses, (2) the physical science survey, and (3) the biological science survey. Their purposes are to contribute toward general rather than specialized education. They represent attempts at rather broad syntheses within the areas of the sciences represented, instead of being planned as only systematic factual surveys. Their emphasis is upon general relationships and values, attempting to give some of the fundamental principles of human biology, for instance, in health and disease, and/or the fundamental physical and chemical processes in the universe. The attempt is also to develop insight into the nature of the scientific enterprise involving the union of logical analysis, critical observation and experiment, and resourceful imagination characteristic of the scientific worker. The endeavor is to go beyond the appreciative stage to provide a practical understanding of the scientific method with an impelling urge to apply it to the problems encountered by the student in his individual and social life.

The importance of these aims is generally accepted. There is little agreement on, and, what is more important, little fundamental knowledge of efficient ways of achieving the purposes. Many different practices are in operation, including lecture-discussions, lecture-recitations, lectures only, lectures plus laboratory, lectures combined with recitations and laboratory, and still others. Most instructors attempt to provide contact with reality and materials of science by using varying amounts of demonstrations of experiments and of specimens, motion pictures, lantern slides, and, apparently in all too few cases, opportunities for the students to engage directly in laboratory work and in field observations.

An exceedingly important problem is to secure qualified instructors for such courses. Practices vary by using the services of specialists to present their respective fields in the survey courses or by using one instructor for the course or at least for one quarter or semester. If individuals of the necessary qualifications are available, which seems to be rarely the case, the preferences seem to be for the latter arrangement, on the assumption that it leads to a more co-ordinated and coherent course.

It should be pointed out that movements toward survey and fused courses are under way in the high schools. The ultimate allocation and nature of such courses, should they become a permanent part of the science-education program, are, therefore, uncertain.

While only limited research on science-teaching problems at the junior-college level has been carried on, the information accruing from such studies is useful in setting up various programs in science instruction.

The major studies with their general implications cannot much more than be mentioned here.

The chances of achieving the objectives of instruction are increased by designing programs for their specific achievements. While the correlations among measured achievements are usually substantial and positive, no one of the objectives, if educationally significant, should be assumed to be automatically achieved (**32**:6–17; **14**:93–103).

It should not be assumed that the high-school courses in science lack preparatory value. The resourceful college instructor could probably enhance learning by building upon the high-school science background of students (**1**; **19**:173–81). Likewise, knowledge of the status of entering Freshmen with respect to beliefs and attitudes may be of special significance in courses designed for general education (**3**:727–34; **27**:314–20).

Many variants of procedures exist. The problems of improvising more efficient procedures can be profitably attacked through experimentation (**2**:121–32; **8**:185–91; **13**; **15**:133–42; **16**:70–75; **17**:31–39; **31**:53–75). Each teacher of science could probably be more convincing in his advocacy of the scientific method and attitudes if he would apply them as a basis for improving his own efficiency as an educator.

The Superior Student in the Science Program

The men and women who will be engaged in scientific work will be the most important single element in the advancement of science and in its increasing services to people. Of course, we believe that instruction by means of science is needful for practically all citizens. But universal instruction in science does not imply that an undue proportion of people should engage in science as life careers. It is unfortunate, however, that during World War II the doors of opportunity were closed to hundreds of thousands of young people who might have served themselves and their country by engaging in scientific work. And, according to published statements (**6**), not less than 150,000 men who had started scientific work were placed in the armed forces. That is, our war-generation of future scientists were removed from science and became less than 2 per cent of the total armed forces. Some of our enemy countries did better than we since, even in the duress of war, they diverted into scientific work many of their superior young people. Those countries sensed the national need for training of persons who might maintain the flow of new knowledge. Our own government achieved great successes by utilizing its best adult scientists but largely omitted the development of new scientific personnel.

Some encouraging progress is being made toward providing superior education for superior young people. Many academies of science, realizing that the future will depend chiefly upon our present young people, have co-operated in developing purposeful youth organizations. Science clubs in high schools have been formed throughout the entire country. These clubs, sponsored as added duties by science teachers, are assisted by members of state and municipal academies of science. Science Service (28), through its Science Clubs of America, now assists nearly 8,000 science clubs and does so in co-operation with state junior and senior academies of science. It is estimated that more than a quarter of a million youths are now enlisted in science-club work. School trustees and other administrative officers have slowly discovered that it is highly important to supply science teachers who not only do good classroom teaching but who have ability and interest in leading young people in the work of science clubs. And those who teach English, history, and some other subjects find the science clubs useful in their own work. It might even occur that a good science club would help teachers and administrators to discover that learning is not divided into separate subjects as schoolroom practice often seems to imply.

Membership in science clubs is usually democratic. It includes persons especially interested in science and others perhaps chiefly interested in those individuals who are interested in science. It includes persons of superior abilities and those of ordinary abilities. It includes creative intellects and conforming minds. The programs give opportunities for superior persons to emerge, and they do emerge. When a district or state program is arranged, the topics and papers presented are usually those locally regarded as best. From a program of "bests" there may be made awards and other recognitions to one or a few especially good presentations. Some senior academies invite young scientists to present their papers and demonstrations before the entire senior academy audience. And when so presented the adult critics are expected to scrutinize the young scientists' discussions in the interests of accuracy and significance. Also, the senior academy selects one boy and one girl whom they recommend for appointment to honorary annual junior memberships in the American Association for the Advancement of Science. Such recognition stimulates further worth-while work by pupils.

A nation-wide movement designated "The Science Talent Search" is operated by Science Clubs of America conducted by Science Service, already referred to. By means of a series of selections based upon widely publicized methods, forty high-school Seniors are selected annually. These are invited to Washington, D.C., for a week's visit for further tests and for participation in conferences among themselves and with outstanding scientists. From these forty, two are selected, one boy and one girl, to whom large college-expense prizes are awarded. Others also receive prizes in descending gradations. These are called the Science Talent Winners. This plan has been in operation for five years, and it has been announced that the plan is to continue. Records are being kept regarding later experiences of the Science Talent Winners and further reports will be of interest.

Undoubtedly there are hundreds of thousands of young people whose best future might be developed through studies in science. Well-rounded foundational education is highly important for all superior students. No one thinks that intellectual superiority indicates that a career in science is necessarily to be desired. But intellectual superiority is a personal investment which carries a commensurate responsibility for the individual and for society, of which he should become an important part. We need educational procedures to provide fully, not only for a very few, but for the hundreds of thousands whose intellectual inheritance makes possible successful careers of productive achievement in science, as in any other worthy field of human endeavor. Recognition of superior capacities and appropriate education are needed for any field of future work. If it is the duty of education to teach and guide all so that their inherited capacities may be fully developed, society can no longer omit this duty for its best young persons. The most gifted need the guidance of far-reaching ideals, the quality of intelligent industriousness, and a sense of effective responsibility. It is true that such persons can readily learn to "get by," and they often become alert and shrewd loafers, but, when that occurs, they have lost their possible futures, and society has failed to develop some of its richest minds. To educate its best youth to their full capacity presents supremely important opportunities and problems to which education has thus far given only meager and sporadic attention.

In addition to such organized efforts to find, stimulate, and make provisions for the superior pupil in the science program, alert teachers will find many opportunities to encourage interest in science and further study of it by unusually capable boys and girls. Some teachers have found that the superior pupil may be used to advantage in such activities as (1) caring for museums, (2) assisting in the laboratory, and (3) helping with and sometimes performing demonstrations. Such opportunities are especially suitable for use in smaller high schools where organized science activities outside the classroom may be less common.

RADIO IN THE TEACHING OF SECONDARY-SCHOOL SCIENCE[2]

General Overview of School-Radio Practices

Since the beginning days of radio in the United States there have been attempts to utilize the medium for school and other educational purposes. At present, twenty-one noncommercial standard-band broadcasting stations are operated by educational institutions. Program policies vary. A few do direct educational broadcasting intended for use in the classroom. Others specialize in information for the farmer, the housewife, or the poultryman. Seven educational organizations have been licensed to operate stations in the frequency-modulation band from 42.1 to 42.9 megacycles. Two of these are university-owned while the other five are maintained by city school systems. Most school-owned stations operate as a part of the regular instruction program.

Science Broadcasts

Public school owned-and-operated stations. Only brief examples of typical science broadcasts over public school broadcasting stations are possible. WBOE (**24**) has broadcast a weekly fifteen-minute junior high school science program and one of similar length for senior high schools for a period of five years. At the junior high school level topics are organized in broad areas of health, such as "epidemic and contagious diseases," "medicines and remedies," "mental hygiene," "pest control," "body functions," and "nutrition." A wide range of community agencies have co-operated in this series of broadcasts. These include the Academy of Medicine, the City Health Department, numerous individual physicians, and frequent programs in co-operation with the Department of Health Service of the school system.

Senior high school programs in Cleveland have included materials in broad areas such as aviation, electricity in daily living, transportation, communication, and chemistry in daily living. In all cases, the scriptwriters have emphasized the relationship between the factual materials presented over the radio and everyday areas of human experience, such as vocational perspective, safety, consumership, and conservation of natural resources.

WREZ (**23**) has broadcast series such as "Excursions in Science," "Stories of Famous Inventions," "The Lives of Famous Scientists," and "The Atomic Age." WNYE (**25**) has worked in areas such as "Science

---

[2] The committee has profited from the collaboration of Nathan A. Neal, Radio Station WBOE, Board of Education, Cleveland, Ohio, in the preparation of this section.

and Democracy," "Educating the Consumer," and "Preview of Tomorrow."

University stations. Almost all university-owned stations have broadcast science programs as a regular part of their schedules. These programs are, more often than not, designed primarily for home listening and secondarily for such supplementary classroom listening as may be possible. A typical series is entitled "Science, Current Problems." The program bulletin (26) states that the program "is planned to help listeners understand the current scene and to stimulate interest in science." Through such programs university-owned stations have attempted to explain to the citizens of their respective states almost every phase of traditional and modern science.

Programs dealing with health, gardening, general farming, soil conservation, and crop practices are common over university-owned stations.

Network programs. The nation-wide radio networks have at one time or another carried on extensive programs in the field of science. In school situations where the necessary facilities are available, transcription and rebroadcast of these programs have been useful in supplementing regular classroom procedures. Examples include series such as "Science Frontiers," "Science at Work," and "March of Science" from the Columbia Broadcasting System's School of the Air; "Doctors Look Ahead" and "Home Is What You Make It" from the National Broadcasting Company; "The Human Adventure" series over the Mutual Broadcasting System; and "The Baby Institute" and "The Doctors Talk It Over" from the American Broadcasting Company. The examples given are but a few of those which might be listed.

Trends in Use of Radio in Secondary-School Science Teaching

Use of experts for brief teaching periods. Perhaps the best use of school-owned radio stations for science-teaching purposes takes place when experts who could not visit 1 per cent of all classrooms personally are able to reach all classrooms by means of radio. In one city school system, research men and other scientists from thirty-four different industries have reached large numbers of high-school pupils through the use of the school radio station. This serves as an illustration of how science teachers may take advantage of the uniqueness of the medium to supplement their own efforts.

Suggestions for preparing scripts. Science scripts prepared by teachers are often hopelessly heavy. Science materials presented over radio networks usually emphasize only one important principle and a few related facts in an entire broadcast. This technique, or modifications of such a technique, may well be adopted in writing successful scripts for school use. A broadcast in the field of science cannot teach a large unit of mate- rial; rather, it is most useful if it brings to bear illuminating details which could not otherwise be made available in some highly restricted aspect of a single topic in science.

Wider use of recordings. Most science broadcasts, like others in educa- tion, are on the air at times when they may not go directly into the school classroom. This has led to a variety of recording services. The U.S. Office of Education circulates a large number of recorded programs in the field of science. By writing the networks which originate science programs it is usually possible to obtain information on where and how recorded copies of desired programs may be obtained. Recordings on disc, wire, or film tape seem to hold great possibility for wider distribution of the best of science on the radio.

SCIENCE CLUBS[3]

It seems inevitable that the organization of school work will leave inadequate time for the cultivation of all the special interests which the curriculum or life itself can generate in the minds of young people. Apparently, science instruction is especially rich in such "outgrowth ac- tivities." Hence, there have developed a group of science-club activities and a set of techniques which, though they can readily be applied in all subjects, have seen their most complete and varied growth in relation- ship to the activities of the science classroom. Clubs that grow out of classwork reflect the human tendency to explore with one's fellows some special interests shared by the group.

During the last three decades, teachers of science have sponsored hundreds of varieties of science clubs. Science clubs have banded to- gether in various regions of the country and on a national basis. They present science exhibits, stage science fairs, organize congresses, and con- duct science workshops. In an age of science that is affecting our daily lives and controlling the destiny of mankind, there is no lack of stimulus to the imagination of young minds. No curriculum, no course of study, no textbook can ever be sufficiently up-to-date. Teachers of science find it increasingly necessary to discover outlets for the great interest pressures with which newspapers, magazines, and the radio are overwhelming the science classroom.

Educators know that the ideal solution to this problem involves an identification between the curriculum and the extra-curriculum. Prac- tically, however, this desideratum can be achieved only partially, if at all.

---

[3] The committee has profited from the collaboration of Morris Meister, Bronx High School of Science, New York, in the preparation of this section.

The science teacher is, therefore, confronted with the need of employing techniques and devices which will utilize extra-curriculum activities for the purpose of strengthening the goals of instruction.

In this brief space it is difficult to do justice to a vast educational literature dealing with science clubs and related activities. Numerous studies have been made and have been reported in professional journals. An early survey and study of the field (21) indicated considerable evidence to support the belief that science clubs and other extra-curriculum activities in science compare most favorably with curriculum work in science in terms of educational outcomes of many kinds. It indicated, too, decided superiority in certain other respects. In many sections of the country, groups of science clubs and their sponsors have combined their efforts so that other desirable objectives are achieved which could not possibly be derived from any one class or school activity in science. Examples of this can be found in the work with clubs and science fairs of the American Institute of the City of New York, the Junior State Academies of Science affiliated with the American Association for the Advancement of Science, and, more recently, the extensive work of the Science Clubs of America in Washington, D.C.

Values of the Science Club

Science clubs have many educational values, but teachers sometimes hesitate to give the extra time required for conducting a club. Nevertheless, every teacher-sponsor of a science club will say that such a club yields worth-while returns. In the first place, the work of the club is reflected in improved work of the class. A science-club member becomes an interested and interesting class member. A science club provides experiences from which the class can develop important concepts and generalizations. Working for the club brings about better co-operation among pupils and between teacher and pupils. It improves demonstrations and stimulates laboratory work. It sometimes helps to solve annoying discipline problems. It gives the teacher a standing and dignity in the community that redounds in dozens of ways to the credit of the school and of the teacher.

Science-Club Procedures

The science club holds meetings, conducts lectures, suggests demonstrations, organizes trips, arranges work periods, plans social functions, presents exhibits, engages in competitive programs, and sponsors workshop courses and meetings with other clubs for general discussion.

Normal boys and girls are interested in a wide range of scientific activities and enjoy many kinds of meetings. An occasional business meeting results in careful planning for the work of the club. Club members or invited speakers may give lectures, always making full use of illustrative materials. Demonstration meetings arouse interest. Club members or invited demonstrators from laboratories, colleges, or practical life may often present demonstrations that pupils never forget. Trips offer opportunities for club members to explore scientific and engineering activities near at hand and to learn about scientific and technical work in their community.

Work periods satisfy the desires of boys and girls to tinker, to construct apparatus, and to perform experiments. Social functions provide means of association with members on a friendly basis. They often add a light touch to the routine of the club and offer opportunities to raise needed funds. Regularly scheduled exhibits serve as goals toward which the club may point its work. They form a dramatic means of telling people what the club is doing. Competitive programs create friendly rivalry between one individual and another. They stimulate each individual to strive for better workmanship and better understanding. Workshop courses help each club member to improve in technique and to become familiar with new ways of presenting ideas. They lead to better understanding of how adult scientists accomplish their tasks.

Meetings with other groups and cordial exchange of ideas stimulate progress. Such interclub activities may take the form of a science congress, a science fair, or a regional meeting. Publishing a magazine or a bulletin increases interest in club work.

Types of Science Clubs

The successful club provides a program of diversified interests and activities. These must be adapted to the needs of the particular group and suited to varied abilities.

Occasionally we find a successful science club which limits all its activities to one branch of science. Experience indicates, however, that such a club has an exceptional reason for existence. Where a sponsor is available who is especially talented along one line or where a single interest brings together a small group of members, it is possible to carry on a camera club, a bird club, a radio club, etc. Clubs of this type are found most often in the senior high school. The great majority of science teachers interested in science clubs seldom have the specialized equipment and technique with which to develop a continuous program in one narrow field of science. To most pupils, the appeal is along general rather than specific lines. This type of club is most often found in the elementary and junior high school and in the small high school.

The Demonstration Program

One of the most popular kinds of program is one in which individual members are given opportunity to present experiments to the club. The difficulty here is to get every member to share in the program. Unless something is done by the sponsor, the club often runs short of activities. To meet this problem many sponsors have developed a "requirement plan" (**21**). Just as the group adopts a constitution, so it adopts a set of requirements or accomplishments in science. Each objective is given a different numerical weight and each member seeks to attain a certain point score by the end of the semester. To be awarded the points which any requirement carries, a member must prove his worth by performing that activity at a meeting. These performances make up the demonstration programs.

Equipment Needed for the Science Club

Expensive equipment is not essential for the success of a science club. Often the members themselves will contribute most of the necessities. Amazing collections have been made by science clubs from rummaging in attics and cellars. Discarded toys, things picked up in secondhand shops, etc., are exactly the kind of material which members find most stimulating.

Every successful club eventually accumulates a stock of equipment that includes materials for simple laboratory work, a simple tool kit, and such common articles as screws, nails, saws, hammers, screw drivers, scissors, glass cutters, files, solder, soldering iron, shears, and glue. Members should have access to a number of science books, project books, magazines, and supply-house catalogues. As club activities expand, members may wish special equipment for special experiments. With the aid of the sponsor, such needs can often be met through fund-raising projects.

Clubs use many means for raising funds: members pay dues; student organizations contribute to science clubs; parent associations make donations; individuals in local industries and local businessmen's clubs give assistance. Science clubs may arrange fairs, bazaars, motion pictures, shows, dramatizations, and similar activities for which there is an admission charge. Most often the members construct additional equipment needed for special experiments.

The Critical Problem

The brief and sketchy treatment given of this area in science teaching is sufficient to indicate the rich emotional returns which the science club can yield. The fact that it does yield such returns in many schools is a tribute to professional devotion and sacrifice on the part of thousands of zealous teachers. Unfortunately, the public is not yet awakened to the need for such service, at least, not to the point where educational budgets will provide for the time and the special training called for by sponsorship of science clubs and related extra-curriculum activities. An analysis of any educational budget will show that the only yardstick of teacher service is in terms of how many times that teacher meets classes every day of the week. This teaching load is usually so exacting that little energy is left for the kind of dramatic life activities which the science classroom stimulates among boys and girls. Every board of education, every superintendent, every principal wants extra-curriculum activities. But no one seems willing to pay for them on the same basis as we do for work in the classroom with large groups. Surely, the modern trend in business and industry is in the direction of limitation of the time factor for services rendered. The professional worker need not sacrifice any aspect of the dignity of his services through adequate budgetary recognition.

Using Community Resources[4]

Early in his school experience, the pupil should be provided with opportunities to expand his classroom experiences with the physical, chemical, and biological phenomena of the environment. By means of his senses he uses acquired learnings continuously to interpret new situations.

Many of the materials of the environment which can aid in the development of this habit of interpretation are permanently fixed and cannot be studied in the science laboratory or brought into the classroom. To do so, even if possible, might interrupt natural existing relationships and reduce the effective use of the materials.

Teachers of science have accepted these assumptions for years and occasionally transferred their pupils from the school laboratory to gardens where seeds germinate and insect pests feed, to machine shops equipped with differential hoists and electric motors, or to wooded areas to observe wild life in a natural setting.

Small groups of pupils may well be excused from the classroom to visit near-by community resources and report back to the class. Such class committees can secure information which is pertinent to the solution of problems formulated and discussed by many pupils who have not observed, firsthand, the evidence available.

The number of such trips and their nature will depend largely on the relationships which the teacher of science can establish while using prob-

---

[4] The committee has profited from the collaboration of Gaylord C. Montgomery, John Burroughs School, Clayton, Missouri, in the preparation of this section.

lem-solving techniques. The school journey may also be used to summarize means of effective control over facts, principles, and concepts. A field trip may precede the formulation of a problem, with little previous class discussion. This setting of the stage for arousing interest and stimulation of curiosity has been illustrated in professional writings (20:41–42).

Both boys and girls should be encouraged by their science teacher to participate in experiences which offer opportunities to develop skills in planning experiments with equipment and to make excursions into their community to observe applications of electricity and mechanics, for example. The housewife in a modern home uses in her daily work a variety of electrical equipment and probably needs a greater knowledge of the proper use of such equipment than does her husband. Hence, sex should not be a factor which determines who makes a trip to a local food-storage plant, water-purification plant, milk station, or dairy.

All available resources of the community should be surveyed by the teacher of science, individually, or by members of the teaching staff undertaking a co-operative study. Rich as the community may be in resources usable in the study of science, the community will seldom, if ever, be used as the science curriculum at any level of growth. However, the science teacher can link the scientific agencies of the community to the laboratory experiences of his pupils through problem-solving activities. He will observe, of course, that the resources of his community are not just the material things but also the experiences, methods, and attitudes of persons in the community who are engaged in scientific vocations or whose avocational interests are centered around scientific pursuits.

The greatest resource of a community may be its rich soil (5:82–87). Forests, river banks, quarries, beaches, and grasslands will yield samples of a wide variety of soils. The securing of these samples may stimulate speculation concerning the causes of their differences and local uses. The science teacher can, if he chooses, direct the discussion toward the effect of the nature of the soil in the determination of health. Or the problem of the destructive force of erosion can be developed just as readily. To study this problem without visiting local areas where methods of combating erosion are in use would be comparable to a study of weather without observing cloud formations and related phenomena.

Other resources available in many communities are forest lands, wild life, and mineral deposits. The suitable use of these materials by the science teacher may depend on whether he is teaching chemistry, biology, general science, or physics. The teacher of chemistry may be anxious to develop an understanding of the properties of metals obtainable from near-by deposits; a teacher of physics may use the same site to study mechanical methods in use in removing the metals from below the surface of the ground.

In a farming community many resources are available to the science teacher, as farming today is a scientific vocation which requires knowledge of selective breeding of plants and animals, of the use and upkeep of tractors and other machines, or of the refrigeration of unprocessed farm products to be transported to markets.

The science teacher can assume responsibility for applying scientific principles to such things as the preparation and preservation of foods grown locally, the efficient and safe use of an automobile, and the measurement of gas and electricity used in the homes of his pupils, and thus aid in the development of a generation of intelligent consumers. Pupils can be led to realize that through the resources of their community and through their own activities they may apply scientific methods to secure improved conditions for living.

THE ROLE OF THE LABORATORY IN TEACHING SCIENCE[5]

Problem-solving activities are an integral part of science teaching and learning, and the science laboratory is a natural place for pupils to engage in these activities. To avoid the "cook-book recipe" type of laboratory work, the following approaches are suggested.

Use laboratory work to give the pupils practice in raising and defining worth-while problems. Each experiment should contribute to the solution of a problem. Pupils should be encouraged to share in the stating of problems and in planning their solutions. A co-operative approach may be used in which the teacher opens up the field of investigation, draws upon the experiences of pupils to suggest where problems exist, and then encourages them to state the problems in their own words.

The teacher should guide the pupils in stating problems clearly and concisely. Each problem should present a single, clearly defined question which the class can reasonably be expected to solve on the basis of the data which they obtain. Throughout the laboratory period the teacher should make every effort to see that the pupils keep the object of the experiment continually in mind.

Conduct laboratory work in such a way that pupils will learn the meaning and use of controls in experimentation. Pupils should understand clearly the necessity of permitting only one variable in an experiment. Frequently by wise questioning and discussion the teacher can get pupils to state the purpose of an experiment, to suggest the experimental factor, and to plan the necessary controls.

---

[5] The committee has profited from the collaboration of Elwood D. Heiss, State Teachers College, New Haven, Connecticut, in the preparation of this section.

Use laboratory work to test hypotheses and interpret data. Skill in interpreting evidence and drawing inferences in the solution of problems depends, in large measure, on the ability to organize, arrange, and analyze data. Pupils need to be given considerable opportunity for practice in analyzing data from problem situations. Too frequently in laboratory work we pass immediately from data to conclusion. More time should be given to proposing and testing hypotheses as these abilities are exceedingly important in modern living.

Maintain a proper balance between student exploration and teacher guidance. Many teachers assign laboratory manuals or workbooks to guide the students in the completion of laboratory work. The opposite extreme of this practice is the "sink-or-swim" method in which the teacher provides the materials but expects the pupil to invent his own methods of investigation. With the large number of pupils most teachers have to teach and with the great variability in interest and intelligence found in science classes, it seems likely that a happy medium between these two extremes can be found.

Independent exploration on the part of the pupil should be encouraged. With a few suggestions, some pupils will be able to devise their own techniques for solving a problem that has been carefully defined. With others the teacher will need to provide the methods to be followed in the experiment. In every case the teacher should raise stimulating questions and make sure that warranted conclusions are drawn from the data obtained from the experiment.

THE ROLE OF THE DEMONSTRATION IN TEACHING SCIENCE[6]

Teaching by the demonstration method is an important part of science instruction. Combined with a well-directed discussion and a clear explanation, it becomes an effective teaching technique. Because it is time-saving and because it is the least expensive method of utilizing laboratory activities, it is being more widely used in science teaching than ever before.

The success of any method in teaching science depends, in a large measure, upon the teacher's skill with that method. All science teachers should be thoroughly familiar with the basic principles (**12**:69–72; **29**:417–20) useful as a guide in doing demonstrations.

Demonstrations should be used mainly in problem-solving situations—problems that demand the finding of certain facts, the discovery of causes and effects, and the induction and application of science principles. Occasionally a demonstration may be performed as an illustration of

---

[6] The committee has profited from the collaboration of Elwood D. Heiss, State Teachers College, New Haven, Connecticut, in the preparation of this section.

something the pupil has read about in his textbook. However, this procedure should be used sparingly. A demonstration should be a challenge to the pupil and it should stimulate him to search for new knowledge. It should make him feel that he is a partner in the search for the solution of a worth-while problem.

Demonstrations may be used to raise and define worth-while problems. If the pupils are to have a genuine interest in the solution of problems, they need the opportunity to share in discovering and stating them. A co-operative approach may be used. The teacher will open a field for investigation and draw upon the pupil's experiences in such a way as to cause the pupils to raise questions and identify problems. For example, let us suppose a study of "Our Ocean of Air" is to be made. The following demonstrations may be done:

1. An attempt is made to pour water into a flask which has been stoppered with a one-hole stopper carrying a funnel. The water will not run into the flask. Why?
2. A large cylinder is filled with water and covered with a piece of filter paper. The cylinder is inverted but the water does not run out. Why?
3. A flask is stoppered with a one-hole stopper carrying a piece of glass tubing. The open end of the glass tubing is held under water and the flask is heated. Air bubbles out. Why? The flask is allowed to cool and water rises in the glass tubing. Why?

At least three problems will be raised by these simple demonstrations.

1. Is air a substance occupying space?
2. Does air exert pressure?
3. How does heating and cooling affect air?

Demonstrations may be used in collecting data and developing skill in the interpretation of data. Suppose the following problem has been raised: Does air exert pressure? In the solution of this problem the following demonstrations and others are possible.

1. A metal can on the demonstration table will be crumpled when it is closed and air is driven out of it. Why?
2. Fill a piece of glass tubing (at least 32 inches long) with mercury. Invert it in a dish of mercury. Why doesn't all the mercury run out of the tube into the dish?

Ask the pupils to analyze the results of the demonstrations. Can they arrive at a conclusion that air exerts pressure?

Demonstrations may be used to test out pupils' hypotheses. In the preceding illustration, if the class arrived at the conclusion that air exerts pressure, this conclusion may be considered as a hypothesis or tentative solution. Then more demonstrations would be performed showing that air exerts pressure.

Demonstrations may be used to illustrate the applications of principles.
For example, it has been discovered by the class that air does exert pressure. The following application of air pressure in everyday life could be
demonstrated:

1. Use of a medicine dropper
2. Filling a fountain pen
3. Barometers
4. Operation of a siphon
5. Operation of a demonstration pump

By use of the problem-solving approach in demonstration work, not
only will the pupils learn facts and principles of science, but they will also
develop an understanding of how a scientist works and thinks.

GENERAL SOURCES OF SENSORY AIDS[7]

To be effective, science teaching should be built around concrete experiences which make abstract ideas meaningful. The proper use of
sensory aids by science teachers will enrich and vitalize their instruction
and help the pupils develop correct initial concepts.

Within the past decade many valuable sensory aids and devices have
been perfected. Inventions in the fields of photography and photoengrav-
ing, projectors, stereoscopes, models, charts, graphs, microscopes, and
telescopes are all contributing toward making science instruction more
interesting and more meaningful to the learner.

The following description of general sources is offered to assist teachers
in locating the wide variety of sensory aids now available for science
teaching.

Public and commercial museums. Museums assist schools in at least
two important ways: (1) classes may visit the museum to view the exhibits and in some cases receive expert instruction from museum instructors; (2) modern museums loan visual aids to schools for teaching
purposes.

Science teachers should contact the nearest large museum and ascertain what sensory aids are available. Various traveling collections of
birds, invertebrates, insects, mammals, rocks, as well as dioramas and
other materials are sometimes available. In addition, museums may have
thousands of slides and motion-picture reels which are loaned to schools.
The Philadelphia Commercial Museum has excellent traveling exhibits
on commercial subjects.

Corporations. Many corporations, as a part of their publicity and advertising campaigns, prepare a variety of materials (**12, 34**) that are use-

---

[7] The committee has profited from the collaboration of Elwood D. Heiss, State
Teachers College, New Haven, Connecticut, in the preparation of this section.

ful to science teachers. These materials of necessity must be critically evaluated by the teacher. Many of these may be obtained free of charge; for some a small charge is made.

Some industrial concerns send out exhibits illustrating the processes of manufacture and the different commodities produced. They also prepare educational pamphlets which frequently contain interesting pictures and graphs that are useful in teaching science. Some of them have prepared excellent motion pictures which they loan to schools.

In writing to commercial firms for their literature or exhibits, the teacher should always state clearly just what is wanted and the purpose for which it will be used. The requests should be written on school stationery if possible.

Home and community. Observing objects and phenomena in their natural setting is an ideal way to gain knowledge. With our present system of mass education this is not always possible or feasible. It becomes exceedingly important then that things be brought from the immediate surroundings into the classroom and laboratory.

There is a wealth of material within the reach of most public schools. The natural tendency of children to collect and to hoard should be utilized.

A great variety of specimens from the environment may be collected and presented. Schools should make provision for storing and exhibiting these. Insects, cocoons, larvae of insects, snakes, frogs, toads, salamanders, birds' nests, leaves, stems, fruits' flowers, bulbs, seeds, mushrooms, and lichens are just a few of the many kinds of plants and animals that may be available. In addition to living things there are inanimate objects, such as specimens of rocks, soils, minerals, and metals, that may be collected.

Children enjoy collecting and preserving specimens. With the aid of the Riker mount, much botanical and zoological material can be made of permanent value. Skeletons of animals may be mounted. Pupils should be encouraged to work out neat labels and be permitted to sign their names as donors to the museum.

Local stores and industries. Objects, specimens, and exhibits usable for science teaching may sometimes be found in local stores or local industries. Sensory aids frequently may be obtained free or at a low cost from these sources. Local butcher shops and slaughter houses are good places for biology teachers to find anatomical specimens.

Scientific supply houses. In addition to student-collected objects and specimens many valuable materials may be purchased from scientific supply houses. Such supply houses as the General Biological Supply House, Chicago, the Denoyer-Geppart Company, Chicago, the Central

Scientific Company, Chicago, and many other firms sell preserved specimens, mounted specimens, and life histories, either in glass or in Riker mounts. The life histories are carefully labelled so that the pupil can clearly understand the life cycle.

These commercial houses also sell models and charts that make valuable visual demonstration material. The model may be a representation in minature, as, for example, a small model of the working parts of an automobile. Or a model may be an enlargement, such as a model of a paramecium or a model of a hydra. Science teachers should write to these firms for free catalogues.

Colleges and universities. Some higher institutions have departments of visual education which act as distribution centers. Generally the geographical areas to which they supply sensory aids is limited. Science teachers should write to near-by colleges and universities to determine whether or not these institutions render such service to the public schools.

Special visual education centers. Various government and private agencies distribute a wide variety of 16-millimeter silent and sound films for school use. These films may be bought, rented, or used free of charge. Generally, when films are loaned free of charge to schools, the recipient is required to pay the transportation charges both ways. The United States Bureau of Mines and the United States Department of Agriculture supply many excellent films to science teachers free of charge. The Y.M.C.A., the National Society for Visual Education, and other private agencies act as film distribution centers.

PLANNING THE SCIENCE ROOM[8]

Ideally a science room should be planned as a place where students may carry on all the science activities that contribute to the objectives of science instruction. This means that a science room should be equipped for general classroom activities, demonstration work, and laboratory work. Such a room will make it possible for teachers and pupils to change quickly from one type of activity to another and thereby provide better co-ordination between all science activities. Such a plan will also eliminate the economic losses that are encountered when science laboratories are separated from the science classrooms.

Size of science rooms. There is at present no scientifically standardized size for a science room. Science rooms will obviously differ considerably in size, depending upon the number of pupils to be accommodated. For an efficient science program, in justice to both pupils and teacher,

---

[8] The committee has profited from the collaboration of Elwood D. Heiss, State Teachers College, New Haven, Connecticut, in the preparation of this section.

the laboratory class should not exceed twenty pupils. Where classroom work other than individual laboratory work by pupils is conducted, a room sufficiently large to accommodate thirty pupils may be used.

It is highly desirable, when a new school building is to be built, that the science staff, the school administrators, and the architect work together in planning the details of the science rooms.

Laboratory furniture. A large, instructor's demonstration table (8 to 12 feet in length) should be centered in the front of the science room. This should be equipped with running water, a sink, and gas and electrical outlets. It should have an acid-resistant top and drawer space for items needed in demonstrations. Properly designed cupboards should be provided for regular storage of materials and equipment.

Several different plans may be used to provide accommodations for laboratory work. One plan is to provide about thirty arm-table chairs in the front of the room facing the demonstration table. Back of the chairs are placed laboratory tables. Movable stools with rubber tips are provided if pupils sit down when doing experiments. Another plan is to equip the room with special-type laboratory tables, such as the Lincoln desk, which permit the pupils either to sit or stand when doing experiments or when they are participating in demonstration-recitation lessons.

Experience has shown that it is more economical to equip a science room with the very best materials. Laboratory furniture bought from reputable manufacturers is usually better than the homemade variety. The plumbing fixtures should be brass or copper, chromium plated, and made for long, hard service. Laboratory sinks should be made of or lined with soapstone. Plenty of drawer space should be available in the laboratory tables.

Cabinets and chart cases. A wide variety of objects, specimens, and models are used in teaching science. Cases and cabinets for display and storage of these materials are necessary in the science room. Storage and display cabinets should be equipped with rolling doors that move freely on steel tracks. Adjustable shelves are also helpful. An exhibition case for displaying completed student projects is an excellent motivating device in a science room. A notebook cabinet in which the pupils may place their records of completed projects and experiments is also useful.

Since both homemade and commercial wall charts are being widely used to give a clearer meaning to the ideas of science, a chart case or a rack with rollers is very desirable.

Provisions for use of visual aids. Motion-picture, slide, opaque, and micro-projectors are used in teaching science. Special care must be taken with the windows so that the science room may be easily and quickly darkened. Boxed-in opaque window shades are generally considered best for this purpose. Proper screens, both "daylight" and reflecting, are required equipment. Electrical outlets must be conveniently placed in the room.

Bulletin board and blackboard. Every science room needs a large permanent bulletin board. Its uses are many. Photographs, diagrams, and clippings may be posted on it. It may be used as a place to exhibit exceptional work done by pupils. It is an excellent place to post assignments and notices.

A bulletin board may be made by tacking a piece of plain green denim over smooth pine or a piece of Celotex. Bulletin boards may also be made from Compo-board. A frame around the board will make it more attractive.

Blackboards should be provided along the front and at least a part of one side of the science room.

Aquariums, terrariums, and receptacles for growing plants. Space should be provided for aquariums and terrariums in a science room that is to be used for teaching general science or biology. Receptacles such as window boxes for growing plants may also be desirable.

Stockroom and darkroom. The stockroom should be large enough to provide adequate space for storage. It should also provide enough room for the preparation of solutions and demonstration setups. Cases or cupboards containing a large number of drawers and shelves that will provide a space for everything are necessary. A sink with running water should also be provided.

A darkroom should be planned as an adjunct to the science classroom. It is important for experiments in optics and photography in physics and chemistry. It may also be used for certain experiments in general science and biology, such as those dealing with plant growth and tropisms.

The Planning and Purchase of Equipment[9]

The planning and purchase of equipment for demonstration and laboratory work is an important function of the science teacher. Since funds are frequently limited, it is important that these funds be spent wisely and in many cases that inexpensive substitutes be provided for more expensive apparatus. The following suggestions are offered as a guide for systematic planning and purchasing of science materials.

Determine the kinds of equipment that are most needed. Preliminary to the proper selection of equipment, it is necessary, first of all, to ascertain in complete detail the outline of the course of study to be followed in a

---

[9] The committee has profited from the collaboration of Elwood D. Heiss, State Teachers College, New Haven, Connecticut, in the preparation of this section.

particular science subject. Once this has been done the types of materials most desirable may be listed under the following heads:

1. Needs for demonstration work
2. Needs for laboratory work
3. General laboratory equipment, such as tools, electrical, water, and gas supply.

Plans for purchasing equipment. The science teacher needs an annual budget. It is a legitimate function of the science teacher to show the school administrator that a certain annual expenditure is necessary for efficient science teaching and learning. Depending upon the present condition of the laboratory-classroom, it may be advisable to plan two budgets: one budget made up of annual supplies, such as breakable glassware, chemicals, dissecting materials, and other needed yearly replacements, and another budget consisting of items, listed in order of preference, based upon a long-term plan for building up the science equipment.

It is not advisable to depend solely upon scientific supply houses for science materials. Mail-order houses, dime stores, junk yards, auto graveyards, and local industries are excellent potential sources of physical-science equipment. To make science teaching more life-like, "real" articles such as a real lift pump, an auto jack, or a discarded automobile engine should be purchased in preference to models. In the biological field much interest may be aroused and firsthand information acquired when students have to collect the insects, earthworms, leaves, flowers, and stems which they are to dissect and study.

It is desirable to have a system for storing equipment and to keep accurate records of all science materials. Science materials should be card-catalogued. A card for each type of equipment should contain the date of purchase, the number of units, the condition of the equipment, and the date when repairs are made. Cases, bins, drawers, and cabinets should be labeled. This system will assist in preventing apparatus and materials from being misplaced or lost.

HOMEMADE EQUIPMENT[10]

Need for homemade equipment. Experience in science need not be lacking because of the absence of commercial supplies and equipment. In fact, for a program where one desires to stress pupil activity with application of science principles to everyday living, the use of improvised equipment and devices from the home, garage, and farm may prove more functional than an abundance of purchased apparatus. Pupil experiences in making the needed apparatus for a demonstration or project, by using

---

[10] The committee has profited from the collaboration of G. P. Cahoon, Ohio State University, Columbus, Ohio, in the preparation of this section.

tin cans, scrap wood, wire, and glass, with the accompanying tools and techniques, may be more meaningful than utilizing "hand-me-down" devices where one has but to pour in the water or press the button properly to operate them. Often the neat case or nicely painted frame or covering of the commercial apparatus hides the real construction and makes more obscure and formidable an already puzzling science principle.

While there obviously are numerous pieces of apparatus and equipment which it is very desirable, if not necessary, to purchase—such as ammeters, microscopes, bunsen burners, vacuum pumps, thermometers, and electric motors—it is surprising how many pieces one can make or improvise or have constructed by pupils. Whether the teacher- or pupil-time could be spent to better advantage is not the question here—much of the useful and needed apparatus for general science, biology, physics, or chemistry can be satisfactorily and inexpensively made, and the making as well as the using of such apparatus can be worth-while pupil experience.

To make such apparatus, whether because of lack of equipment or because the experience in making and using it seems to be particularly desirable, one needs four things not always available in the school science laboratories but not difficult to provide. These are (1) a variety of "raw materials" or supplies; (2) a few simple tools; (3) a suitable working space and arrangements for such "improvising"; and (4) a small working library of practical references.

Variety of "raw materials." When one starts to make provisions for even a small array of teacher- or pupil-constructed devices, he finds need for a relatively wide range and variety of materials. While the usual materials, such as chemicals, glass and rubber tubing, bell wire, flasks, rubber stoppers, and thermometers are needed, numerous other things outside the lists furnished by the laboratory supply companies for the supplies needed to carry out demonstrations and laboratory experiments will be necessary. Aquarium cement, spring brass, Fahnstock clips, asphaltum paint, nichrome wire, ball bearings, DeKhotinsky cement, 6–32 machine bolts, soldering lugs, and copper tubing are only a few which soon are added to the purchase list. When teacher or pupil is making something, particularly during a limited time such as a class period, it is, to say the least, very disconcerting and inefficient to have to lay aside the project for lack of the proper-sized washer or of suitable waterproof cement. The fact that it can be purchased for a few cents at the ten-cent store is not too pertinent when one needs it immediately.

This suggests, of course, that as many as possible of the supplies which may be needed should be anticipated and that a sufficient store be on hand for immediate use.

Often it is possible for the science teacher or pupils to obtain certain supplies from other departments in the school, particularly the fine- and industrial-arts areas. While this may be satisfactory for emergency needs, it obviously is not a good long-time policy. If one needs a little glue, or stain, or angle iron, or show-card ink, he usually wants it immediately and wants to use it where and how it seems most suitable for his particular project. Frequently, overlapping of the needs of teachers from two or three different areas for the same supplies suggests the possibility of pooling orders so that advantage can be taken of lower prices for quantity lots.

A great deal of scrap material can usually be used in constructing and improvising science apparatus. The scrap boxes of the woodworking and metal-working areas of the industrial-arts department often contain small pieces of wood, of copper, brass, and iron sheets or strips, of metal pipes or tubes, of angle iron, and even of wire that are large enough for use in science devices. Bottles, jars, tin cans, and round and rectangular cartons may usually be obtained from the cafeteria or home-economics department. Mailing tubes useful for winding coils or optical devices can be saved by the offices.

Ten-cent stores, hardware stores, auto-supply stores, as well as electrical and radio stores are quite obviously good sources of useful materials at relatively low cost. Junk yards, garages, and gasoline service stations also offer possibilities for picking up old generators, storage batteries, transformers, induction coils, thermostats, cutouts, tubes, ball bearings, and wire. While most of these may not be in a suitable condition "as is," some may be repaired or rebuilt into other devices, or parts and supplies may be salvaged from them, particularly wire. Pupils often show considerable talent and resourcefulness and prove to have "contacts" which the teacher does not have, if encouraged to bring in such types of supplies.

A workable scheme for helping to keep track of such a wide range of supplies is to have each item listed on a single 3 × 5 or 4 × 6 card, arranged in an alphabetical file. On this card can be indicated suitable places where it may be obtained or purchased, the usual unit used in ordering (lb., doz., qt., liter, gross), the unit price, the amount on hand at a certain date, and any other pertinent data. As one continuously adds to his list of supplies, he can write down each item needed on a card, and later file these cards (or make out a new, neater one) in the permanent supply card file. If one has sufficient drawer or cabinet space in which to store such supplies, the location of each item can be added to the other data on the file card, or a separate file or list giving the location may be kept. The latter is particularly useful for pupil use or where other teachers and classes make somewhat irregular or infrequent use of these materials.

A few simple tools. One cannot make very satisfactory progress in constructing equipment or modifying salvage parts into useful science apparatus without the use of at least a few tools. Perhaps it is obvious what most of these are. Handsaws, including crosscut, rip, back saw, coping saw, and hack saw; claw hammer, ball-peen hammer; mallet, brace for bits, hand drill; wood and cold chisels; screw drivers; folding rules, gas pliers; wire-cutting pliers; tin snips; try square; wood and metal files; planes; auger bits; drills; wrenches; and vise are almost minimum essentials. To this should be added such nearly indispensable items as soldering irons, small c-clamps, oil stones, taps and dies for at least 6–32 and 8–32 machine threads, and emery wheel. Certainly most, if not all, of these should be made available in the science laboratory or shop. One should not rely on borrowing them from the industrial-arts room. For the relatively infrequent use of a few special tools or of power tools, one might count on the usual accommodating co-operation of the school shop.

The small expense involved in providing such a suggested minimum list of tools is more than justified by the savings resulting from the construction of science apparatus and by the learning experiences of pupils and teacher.

Suitable working and storage space. Supplies and tools are of little use without a suitable place to use them. This certainly does not need to be large or elaborate. It may be a small closet or room near the science laboratory. The science preparation room might be arranged for this purpose. Storage and working space might be provided in the science laboratory. Or a combination of two or all of these might be the appropriate solution in some situations. One or more tables to which a vise could be attached, with a work table or two along the wall where outlets for electricity, gas, and water could be provided, would pretty well take care of the needed working space.

The problem of storage, because of the large number of small items, seems best solved by the use of a number of small drawers or boxes, or other type of containers, such as glass jars, or a combination of these. If cabinets or shelving rather than a fairly large number of small drawers are available, the use of a series of different-sized drawers may be quite satisfactory.

With whatever arrangement for storage that is provided, labels should be used on each drawer, box, or container. It is much better to letter them with a lettering pen in rather large size than to type them. The provision of an alphabetical index, either on cards as previously suggested or typed or mimeographed, is a device which will save much time and confusion in finding and replacing supplies. This is particularly valuable where different groups of pupils make use of the supplies semester after semester—though even the teacher, who set it up in the first place, may forget whether the sealing wax was placed in the box with the paraffin wax and candles or in the one with glues and cements.

Practical references. Unless one has a very great deal of resourcefulness and previous practical experience with tools and devices, he will find considerable need and use for references which give suggestions on what to make and how to make it. Such references are particularly needed if pupils participate in working on these or related projects. One will need at hand references which will give information about such things as kinds of glue for certain purposes; chemical formulas; size of drills; size, resistance, and current-carrying capacity of wire; circuits for different devices; how to drill a hole in glass; soldering, brazing, polishing. The teacher with a little ingenuity can, of course, make plans for his own improvisations, modifications, and special apparatus. However, over a period of a hundred or more years a vast array of interesting and useful inexpensive demonstrations, laboratory experiments, projects, and special equipment have been devised and described by resourceful teachers. Recent as well as back issues of such a magazine as *School Science and Mathematics* contain a wealth of suggestions on this phase of science teaching. The catalogues of apparatus companies are particularly suggestive. Many trade journals also contain suggestions for making useful apparatus, as do popular science magazines. Of course, there are also a great many books which treat one or more aspects of this practical phase of constructing devices and working out demonstrations.

ADULT EDUCATION IN SCIENCE[11]

Attempts to popularize science go back over one hundred years. The industrial revolution necessitated a growing supply of workers who understand something of the distinctive mode of scientific thinking as well as some of the new technical procedures. Science remained a significant part of adult education in this country and in England until after the first World War. In recent decades science has been declining as a formal school offering to the lay public, just as elementary instruction in reading and writing for illiterate adults has declined. On the other hand, access to scientific information and scientific thinking has been greatly increased through all sorts of publications from newspaper items to special books in various fields. People learn from the radio, from museums, from advertis-

---

[11] The committee has profited from the collaboration of Benjamin C. Gruenberg, New York City, in the preparation of this section.

ing, and from instructions and explanations that accompany all sorts of new devices, foods, drugs, and other materials. Indeed, such instruction in science as is now available to the public outside of school is recognized even by science teachers to be in some respects more effective than that which our schools furnish.

Scientists and educators are disposed to feel that this kind of adult education is generally lacking in such distinctive virtues of science as accuracy, clear analysis of problems, scrupulous regard for the verities, and absolute integrity. Precisely the same methods serve to diffuse "unsound" doctrines, misinterpretations, or distortions of the scientist's understanding or intent. These criticisms imply educational purposes that transcend the effective transmission of "knowledge" or of accurate information.

Within the schools, training of teachers has increasingly emphasized better methods for transmitting what the syllabus calls for. Our specialization has increasingly restricted the concern of the science teacher to the "content of the subject." And teachers of special subjects have become increasingly incompetent to orient students as to the meaning of science in modern society.

The rapid development of the sciences and the increasing load upon the teachers result in three serious conditions:

1. Teachers have no time to keep abreast of the changes taking place even in their own special field. In large numbers they continue to teach chiefly what they themselves learned in college five to thirty years ago.
2. Teachers seldom have time to keep abreast of what is happening in other areas of scientific research. This is particularly striking when we consider that vast numbers of teachers continue to operate on a theory of learning or a concept of human nature which has long been superseded by scientific students of human biology, psychology, and anthropology.
3. Teachers have no time to keep abreast of the cultural and social changes in which science itself has played so dynamic a role. For the most part they either assume that by teaching their "subjects" they will adequately prepare their pupils to take their places in the adult world, or they attempt to integrate the science they teach and the scientific thinking they practice into a conception of the social world which they had themselves acquired from their teachers, who in turn had completed their training several decades earlier.

We have turned out thousands of young men and women who are equipped to continue scientific studies to higher levels of proficiency. We have prepared our students for a variety of professions in which scientific knowledge and scientific methods are put to work. And we have discovered scientific talents in unexpected corners of the population. We have failed, however, to educate through our science the boys and girls who are not going to be scientists. We have not prepared a generation of adults to find their bearings in an age of science.

Even before the first World War educators were seriously concerned with the lag of the teaching personnel behind the advances in knowledge and behind the advances in the sciences and techniques concerned in education. Numerous attempts have been made to bridge this serious gap by putting a premium on continuous study by teachers in service. The bulk of this extension teaching or in-service training continues to stress supplemental information for content and better techniques of instruction. The great need is still for teachers to learn how to use science as a means of education. The special problem of adult education in science is to reorient teachers in service with reference to the civic, cultural, or social and, eventually, the human and international implications of science.

REFERENCES

1. AIKEN, W. M. *The Story of the Eight-Year Study.* Progressive Education Association, Commission on the Relation of School and College, *Adventures in American Education,* Vol. 1. New York: Harper & Bros., 1942.
2. BARNARD, J. D. "The Lecture-Demonstration versus the Problem-solving Method of Teaching a College Science Course," *Science Education,* XXVI (October–November, 1942), 121–32.
3. BARNES, M. W., and MONSER, G. W. "A Comparative Performance of High-School and University Freshmen on a Test of Biological Misconceptions," *School Science and Mathematics,* XLIII (May, 1943), 447–50.
4. BOND, A. DeM. *An Experiment in the Teaching of Genetics.* Teachers College Contributions to Education, No. 797. New York: Teachers College, Columbia University 1940.
5. BURNETT, R. W. "Conservation: Focus or Incident in Science Education?" *Science Education,* XXVIII (March, 1944), 82–87.
6. BUSH, VANNEVAR. *Science: The Endless Frontier.* Washington: Government Printing Office, 1945.
7. CHARTERS, W. W. "General Survey Courses," *Journal of Higher Education,* XIII (January, 1942), 1–4.
8. FEDOR, D. D., and WRIGHT, E. M., "Some Different Effects of Motivation upon Achievement and Insight in College Physics," *Journal of Educational Research,* XXXVI (November, 1942), 185–91.
9. FONSWORTH, E. C. "Principles in the Field of Light Needed To Interpret General Life Situations," *Science Education,* XXV (January, 1941), 16–20.
10. HARD, H. O., and JEAN, F. C. "Natural Science Survey Courses in Colleges," *Science Education,* XXII (November, 1938), 294–99.
11. HAVIGHURST, R. J. "Survey Courses in the Natural Sciences," *American Physics Teacher,* III (September, 1935), 97–101.
12. HEISS, E. D.; OBOURN, E. S.; and HOFFMAN, C. W. *Modern Methods and Materials for Teaching Science,* chap. x. New York: Macmillan Co., 1940.
13. HOYT, CYRIL. "Tests of Certain Linear Hypotheses and Their Application to Educational Problems in Elementary College Physics." Ph.D. Dissertation, University of Minnesota, 1944.

14. JOHNSON, P. O. "The Differential Functions of Examinations," *Journal of Educational Research*, XXX (October, 1936), 93–103.

15. ———. "Concomitant Learning in Human Biology," *Science Education*, XX (February, 1934), 133–42.

16. ———. "The Measurement of the Effectiveness of Laboratory Procedures upon the Achievement of Students in Zoology with Particular Reference to the Use and Value of Detailed Drawings," *Proceedings of the Minnesota Academy of Science*, VIII (1940), 70–75.

17. KALM, PAUL. An Experimental Study To Compare the Laboratory Method of Instruction with Individual Demonstrations in Elementary College Biology," *Science Education*, XXVI (January, 1942), 31–39.

18. Koos, L. V. "An Overview of Terminal Offerings." *Proceedings of the Institute for Administrative Officers of Higher Institutions*, Vol. XIV, pp. 11–32. Chicago: University of Chicago Press, 1942.

19. LAPP, C. J., *Chairman*. "Measuring the Results of Instruction in College Physics; a Summary Report on the National College-Physics Testing Program, 1933–39," *American Journal of Physics*, VIII (June, 1940), 173–81.

20. MANZER, J. G. "A Chemistry Class Begins the Year's Work," *Science Education*, XXVIII (February, 1944), 41–42.

21. MEISTER, MORRIS. "The Educational Value of Certain After-School Activities in Science." Doctor's dissertation, Teachers College, Columbia University, 1921.

22. PRUITT, C. M. "Survey Courses in the Natural Sciences," *Science Education*, XXI (February, 1937), 10–16.

23. Radio Station WBEZ, Board of Education, Chicago, Ill.

24. Radio Station WBOE, Board of Education, Cleveland, Ohio.

25. Radio Station WNYE, Board of Education, New York City.

26. Radio Station WOSU, Ohio State University, Program Bulletins, April, 1946.

27. RALYA, LYNN L., and RALYA, LILLIAN L. "Some Significant Concepts and Beliefs in Astronomy and Geology of Entering College Freshmen and the Relation of These to General Scholastic Aptitude," *School Science and Mathematics*," XL (November, 1940), 727–34.

28. Science Service, 1719 N Street, N.W., Washington, D.C.

29. SELBERG, EDITH M. "A Plan for Developing a Better Technique in Giving Science Demonstrations," *Science Education*, XVI (October, 1932), 417–20.

30. STEVENSON, E. N. "Questionnaire Results on the Value and Extent of the Field Trip in General Biology," *Science Education*, XXIV (December, 1940), 380–82.

31. THELEN, H. A. "A Methodological Study of the Learning of Chemical Concepts and of Certain Abilities To Think Critically in Freshman Chemistry," *Journal of Experimental Education*, XIII (September, 1944), 53–75.

32. TYLER, R. W. "Relations between Recall and Higher Mental Processes," *Education as Cultivation of the Higher Mental Processes*, pp. 6–17. New York: Macmillan Co., 1936.

33. WINOKUR, MORRIS. "A Survey of Generalized Science Courses in Institutions of Higher Learning," *Science Education*, XX (October, 1936), 132–40.

34. WOODRING, M.; OAKES, M. E.; and BROWN, H. E. *Enriched Teaching of Science in the High School*. New York: Bureau of Publications, Teachers College, Columbia University, 1942.

CHAPTER XV

EVALUATION OF OUTCOMES OF INSTRUCTION IN SCIENCE AT THE SECONDARY LEVEL[1]

THE FUNCTION OF EVALUATION

As a classroom activity, evaluation is an integral part of the total instructional process. Any attempt to divorce evaluation from teaching, and to teach without evaluating or to evaluate without regard for the purposes, content, and methods of teaching—any such attempt is artificial, and the consequences are almost certainly misleading. On the other hand, the modern conception of instruction as the direction and guidance of learning at once discloses the essential function of evaluation. It provides data by means of which to determine initial status or readiness for learning, progress and difficulties in learning, final attainment, and extent of retention and transfer.

Evaluation and teaching are thus inextricably associated. Several corollaries follow. (1) Like teaching, evaluation must begin with a consideration of the outcomes to be sought. (2) Evaluation must be comprehensive enough to include *all* outcomes and not merely those outcomes in which learning is most easily assessed (e.g., factual knowledge and mechanical skills). (3) The procedures and devices employed in evaluation must also be comprehensive, for no single procedure is adequate to the task of furnishing to the teacher all the data needed for a complete picture of learning.

LEARNING OUTCOMES IN SCIENCE

The objectives for science instruction have been listed as being:

1. Functional information
2. Functional concepts
3. Functional understanding of principles
4. Instrumental skills
5. Problem-solving skills
6. Attitudes
7. Appreciations
8. Interests

---

[1] In the preparation of this chapter the committee has profited from the collaboration of Professor G. P. Cahoon of Ohio State University.

As they are stated, these objectives represent *types* of expected learning outcomes, and they provide the basis for evaluation. Still, being types, they must, for the purposes both of teaching and of evaluation, be particularized. We do not teach and measure "functional concepts" as a whole; rather, we teach and measure specific concepts, and the concepts vary from grade to grade and from course to course. Hence, in evaluation it is necessary to think concretely: "How can I best determine the degree to which this one concept has been acquired; and this one, and this one?" And similarly with the other types of objectives which are set for science in the secondary school.

In the pages which follow, this process of particularization has been employed, and the suggested devices relate to specific concepts, skills, attitudes, and so on. Moreover, it has been necessary to sample learning outcomes rather widely. Space was not available to show how to measure learning with respect to all learning outcomes.[2]

Evaluation Procedures Available

In science as in other subject-matter fields it has been common to think of evaluation too largely in terms of paper-and-pencil tests. Valuable as they are, written tests have their limitations. For example, they can reveal only how students react to described situations, not how they will react to more natural or "real-life" situations. Recognition of the limitations of written tests has led teachers increasingly to supplement such tests with other procedures in evaluation. And this is as it should be, for by the use of other procedures they are able to extend considerably and profitably the scope of their evaluation.

This is not the place in which to list the special advantages of various evaluation procedures, or to discuss the precautions which need to be served with respect to each. Such theoretical considerations will be found well treated in the standard textbooks on measurement or evaluation. It must suffice here simply to mention the major types of procedures and instruments which are available to teachers of science, many of them illustrated in the remainder of the chapter.

1. Evaluation by paper-and-pencil devices:
   a) Verbal tests, either "objective" or "essay" in form
   b) Diagrams, pictures, charts, etc.
   c) Rating scales and check lists
2. Analysis of work products according to acceptable criteria (apparatus set-ups, notebooks, student collections, committee reports, etc.)
3. Classroom questioning and discussion

---

[2] The reader will find many suggestions in respect to evaluation in chapter viii. Although this chapter is directed to the elementary level, many of the ideas and devices will be found useful at the secondary level as well.

4. Observation of significant behavior, either
   a) Informal, as in day-by-day classroom or laboratory activities, or
   b) Systematic, as in situations specifically planned to elicit known types of behavior
5. Conferences and interviews with individuals or with small groups

The classification above is obviously a rough-and-ready one; it is intended here to serve purely a practical purpose, namely, to provide a means for organizing somewhat differing forms of attacking the problems of evaluation. The categories listed overlap considerably but not undesirably. For example, category 3 really calls attention to one means or opportunity for utilizing the "observation of significant behavior" (category 4); and "rating scales and check lists" (category 1-*c*) are practically essential for success in connection with the "analysis of work products" (category 2) and with "systematic observation" (category 4-*b*).

1. Paper-and-Pencil Devices

As has been implied, the evaluation devices which fall in this category are the ones which are most widely used in the classroom and also the ones which, in the hands of experts, have been studied most thoroughly. For these reasons, and also because the literature[3] contains many illustrations of excellent tests, rating scales, and check lists, a relatively small amount of space is here allocated to paper-and-pencil instruments.

a) Verbal tests

Sample 1. Essay questions.

Demonstration: A little water is placed in the bottom of a can (e.g., a varnish can). A cork fits snugly into the opening of the can. The water is heated until it boils and steam escapes. The cork is then inserted tightly, and the source of heat is immediately removed. The can is allowed to cool, when the sides will be seen to collapse.

Questions (to be answered by pupils):
1. Just what does this demonstration really show? What can you conclude from it?
2. List the important things which you actually observed or saw happen and those things which would need to be mentioned in explaining what happened.
3. Indicate some of the things which you assumed or took for granted, i.e., things which would be necessary in explaining what happened.
4. Show how the points which you actually observed and those which you assumed helped you to arrive at your conclusion (in 1).
5. Why was the source of heat taken away immediately after the cork was put in?
6. What was the purpose of boiling the water?

---

[3] See in particular, "The Measurement of Understanding in Science" in *The Measurement of Understanding,* chap. vi. Forty-fifth Yearbook of the National Society for the Study of Education, Part I. Chicago: University of Chicago Press, 1946.

7. Indicate one or two other ways in which the purpose for which the water was boiled could have been accomplished.

8. Why doesn't the gasoline tank in the rear of an automobile collapse in a way similar to the can in this demonstration when a full tank of gas has been used up?

Sample 2. Essay questions.

Demonstration: A flask is filled with HCl vapor by displacement of air in the usual way. A single-hole stopper is arranged with a glass tube extending into the flask and with a rubber tube attached which extends a short distance outside the flask. The rubber tube should be provided with a pinch clamp (or it may be closed and opened by pinching with the fingers). As soon as the flask is filled with vapor, the stopper with tube is inserted, the flask is inverted, and the closed end of the rubber tube is placed under water in a beaker. When the end of the tube is opened, the water rises into the flask to make a fountain. If a little blue litmus solution is put in the lower beaker, the fountain becomes red.

Questions (to be answered by pupils):

1. If the flask was full of HCl vapor, what caused the water to start to rise in the tube?

2. As the first few drops of water entered the flask, what happened?

3. Why didn't the fountain continue indefinitely as long as there was a supply of water in the beaker?

4. Where should the end of the glass tube be located: near the top of the inverted flask, toward the middle, or down into the neck, or doesn't it make any difference? Why is this?

5. Why should the blue-colored water become red in the fountain?

6. What property of HCl vapor is illustrated in the questions and answers to Nos. 1, 2, and 3?

7. Which of these illustrate physical and which chemical properties?

8. If a piece of dry, red litmus paper had been placed in the flask of HCl vapor before the fountain was started, what change would you predict should have taken place? Why?

9. If the HCl vapor had been compressed into the flask, so that the flask contained, say, twice as much as in the demonstration described, and if the same procedure had been followed, what do you think would have happened? Indicate your prediction and reasons why you think this would have happened, then try it out. If, when you try it, the results are different, can you give the reason for what did happen?

Sample 3. Objective questions.

Demonstration: A storage battery is connected in series with a tap switch by means of flexible wire, with a suitable resistance to permit a flow of from five to ten amperes. The wire is arranged so that it can be placed first just above, then just below, a compass needle, extending parallel to the N-S direction of the compass. When the switch is closed with the wire *above* the compass, the needle turns at right angles to the wire; when closed with the wire *below* the needle, it turns at right angles in the opposite direction. When the switch is *open*, the needle returns to its normal N-S direction.

Questions (to be answered by pupils): A check or cross is to be placed before statements which are justified on the basis of the demonstration.

.... 1. Electricity is magnetism.

.... 2. A stronger current will produce greater magnetism.

.... 3. The wire carrying the current is magnetized.

.... 4. The same magnetic effect is produced anywhere along the wire.

.... 5. A current-carrying wire produces a magnetic effect.

.... 6. An electric current is magnetized.

.... 7. Reversing the poles would reverse the direction in which the needle would turn.

.... 8. In a current-carrying wire a magnetic field is produced which is in concentric circles around the wire.

.... 9. The current *above* the needle is opposite in direction to that *below* the needle.

..........10. This demonstration (or experiment) is known as Oersted's experiment.

..........11. Magnetism always acts at right angles to the electric current producing it.

..........12. Magnetism can produce electricity.

..........13. One end of the wire is an N-pole, and the other an S-pole.

..........14. Magnets can only be made by electricity.

..........15. The electricity was the cause of the magnetism.

..........16. This illustrates the principle of the electric motor.

..........17. Copper wire does not retain its magnetism, as does iron.

..........18. Magnetism cannot be separated from an electric current; i.e., it always is present if a current is flowing.

..........19. The magnetic field around a current-carrying wire is similar in shape to that of an ordinary magnet.

..........20. The magnetic force *above* the wire is in an opposite direction to that *below* the wire.

b) Diagrams, pictures, etc.

Sample 4. Essay question, with no leads.

List the conclusions that may reasonably be drawn from the data given in the graph below.

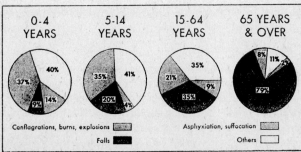

Courtesy of National Safety Council

HOME FATALITIES BY AGE AND TYPE

Sample 5. Identification, completion type.

Directions: In the cut at the left the parts of a dissected flower are shown. Identify each of the four main parts (*A, B, C, D*) by writing the correct name of the part after the proper letter below.

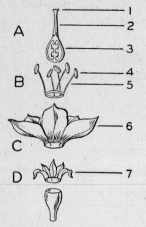

The lettered parts of the flower in the diagram are followed by a number or numbers to indicate sections which may be further identified by name. Write the name for each of these parts in the blank after the proper number.

A. .... { 1. ....
                        { 2. ....
                        { 3. ....

B. .... { 4. ....
                        { 5. ....

C. .... { 6. ....

D. .... { 7. ....

THE PARTS OF A TYPICAL FLOWER

Sample 6. Identification, completion type.

Directions: At the left is shown a diagram of a leaf. At the right is a list of words which name parts of the leaf. After each word write the *letter* for the part of the diagram which illustrates the meaning of that word.

vein   ....
mid-rib   ....
stem   ....
lobe   ....

Sample 7. Objective questions, relatively simple in character.

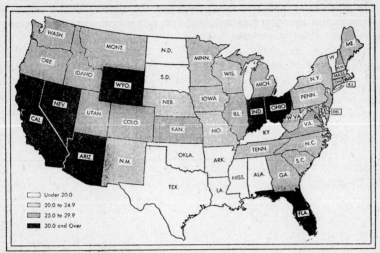

Courtesy of National Safety Council

MOTOR VEHICLE DEATHS PER 100,000 POPULATION BY STATES

From the following list of conclusions, check those that can be supported by the data in the map above.

........1. The darker the shading of a state, the larger the relative number of motor-vehicle deaths.

........2. Kentucky has relatively more vehicle deaths than does Illinois.

........3. The most densely populated states as a rule have the largest relative number of vehicle deaths.

........4. The South has the best automobile drivers.

........5. Probably more people were killed by vehicles in Michigan than in North Dakota.

........6. Motor vehicle accidents are on the increase.

........7. The map does not take into account the actual number of people who live in the different states.

Sample 8. Objective questions, complex relationships.

The graph below appeared in the magazine of the steel industry called *Steel Facts*, for February, 1937. Examine the graph, then do the following exercises.

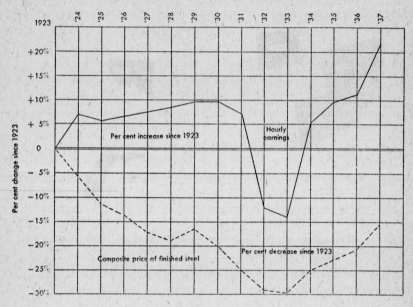

MOVEMENT OF STEEL WAGES AND PRICES SINCE 1923

Assume that the graph portrays actual facts. Then mark statements *a* to *n* as follows:

1, if the evidence from the graph is sufficient to make the statement true;
2, if the evidence from the graph is sufficient to make the statment false;
3, if the evidence from the graph suggests that the statement is probably true;
4, if the evidence from the graph suggests that the statement is probably false;
5, if the evidence from the graph is insufficient to make a decision concerning the statement.

a. Hourly wages of steel employees have increased steadily since 1923. . (   ) *a.*

b. In 1933, hourly wages in the steel industry reached the lowest point since the war . . . . (   ) *b.*

c. The incomes of steel workers have increased more than 30 per cent since 1933. . . . . (   ) *c.*

d. In 1933 the selling price of finished steel was 30 per cent less than it was in 1923. . . . . (   ) *d.*

e. There is a relationship between the price of steel and the wages paid the workers who make it. . . . . (   ) *e.*

f. If the hourly wages paid to employees are increased, the price of steel also increases . . . . (   ) *f.*

g. The steel industry has reduced its profits by paying higher wages while charging lower prices . . . . (   ) *g.*

h. The price of finished steel today is less than it was in 1923. . . . . (   ) *h.*

i. The steel industry has spent more for wages of its workers since 1934 than formerly. . . . . (   ) *i.*

j. Since 1933 the hourly wages of steel workers have increased more than has the price of steel. . . . . (   ) *j.*

k. The wages of steel workers have increased steadily since 1933 . . . . . . (   ) *k.*

l. The income of steel companies was less in 1937 than it was in 1926. . (   ) *l.*

m. Workers in the steel industry are now well paid . . . . (   ) *m.*

n. The finished price of steel began to increase at two points during this period . . . . (   ) *n.*

c) Rating scales and check lists

Sample 9. A self-rating scale on attitudes. The rating scale is given to pupils two or more times a year, with the request that they evaluate their own attitudes. The material so obtained enables the teacher to help children correct attitudes in which their rating is low and provides an excellent basis for individual conferences. The scales are filed, and each pupil is encouraged to compare his own ratings from time to time.

Following is a group of selected scientific attitudes.

Check the square to the left of each one to show the degree to which you have that attitude.

The figure 1 means a high rating (you believe you have the attitude); the figure 2 means that you are quite strong in this attitude, but not strong enough to enter the figure 1. Figures 3 and 4 mean that you have still less of this attitude. The figure 5 means that you do not have it.

Name.. Date...

1	2	3	4	5	
					1. Do not believe in superstitions such as charms of good or bad luck.
					2. Believe that there is no necessary connection between two events because they happen at the same time.
					3. Revise opinions in the light of new evidence.
					4. Listen to, observe, or read evidence which supports ideas contrary to own opinions.
					5. Base opinions on adequate evidence.
					6. Stick to facts; do not exaggerate.
					7. Do not jump to conclusions.
					8. Am tolerant of the ideas and opinions of others.
					9. Am not satisfied with vague explanations.
					10. Am slow to accept as fact anything not supported by evidence.

Sample 10. Check list on the nature of proof.

Two boys from a science class that had been discussing how the sun and moon might be eclipsed suddenly noticed that the light was growing dim. Whereupon one exclaimed, "We must be having an eclipse of the sun!" Was his inference sound?

Directions for Part I. Statements are sometimes made which actually lead away from the conclusion, or which, though true, have nothing to do with it. Read carefully each statement below. Accept each statement as true. Then, decide: Does it lead to the conclusion? Or, does it lead away from the conclusion? Or, does it have nothing to do with the conclusion? Next, check each statement in the appropriate column *at the left.* (Pay no attention now to the columns at the right.)

Leads to	Irrele-vant	Leads away	Statements	Fact	As-sump-tion	Neither
			1. The paper had forecast an eclipse of the sun for this month.			
			2. The moon was full on this day.			
			3. This was the day of May 14, 1929.			
			4. No eclipse of the moon can occur when there is a full moon.			
			5. It was evening, and the sun was setting.			
			6. A cloud had appeared and partially covered the sun.			
			7. It had been a clear day with no clouds in the sky.			
			8. The boys were in an open field.			
			9. As one of the boys looked up, he saw a disc creeping across the face of the sun.			
			10. The boys were playing close to a tall building.			
			11. They both noticed that the light was growing dim.			
			12. The science teacher had told them to expect an eclipse that day.			
			13. The boys' science teacher was a reliable instructor.			

Directions for Part II. Another way to test a proof is to identify the part of the evidence which can be accepted as facts and to determine what part of the evidence must be regarded as assumptions.

This time do not accept the thirteen statements above as true. Instead, critically examine each one in the light of the conclusion and mark in the appropriate column *at the right* whether it is a fact, or an assumption, or whether you are undecided what to call it.

Sample 11. Check list on problem-solving behavior (skills and attitudes). In schools where analytical reports are written on pupils at intervals during the year, the teacher sometimes has no firsthand evidence to which to refer when the reports must be prepared. It is impossible for the teacher to make full notes the instant at which a pupil gives evidence on such items as good interpretation of data or the formulating of a good hypothesis.

The device described below can be used to "catch" significant behavior by a sort of shorthand, which can be elaborated later so as to give a permanent record of a whole event. A sheet of paper is mimeographed with spaces for pupils' names in the left column and with parallel columns for the types of behavior to be noted. (There should not be more than three or four types of behavior for observation at a given time. It is better to concentrate for a time on a few, passing on to another group after a few days.) The sheet is kept on the demonstration desk. As a pupil shows significant behavior, positive (+) or negative (−), the corresponding check mark is inserted in the appropriate cell on the chart.

Suitable categories for use in the chart are: *skills:* (1) sensitivity to problems; (2) defining problems; (3) interpreting data; (4) proposing hypotheses; (5) proposing controlled experiments; (6) testing hypotheses; (7) drawing conclusions; (8) applying principles; *attitudes:* (1) tolerance; (2) tendency to draw conclusions slowly and carefully; (3) open-mindedness; (4) curiosity.

2. Analysis of Pupils' Work Products

There is, of course, nothing new in the suggestion that pupils' work products may reveal much concerning the degree to which they are attaining the objectives of instruction. Science teachers have always had pupils (*a*) hand in written records of their experiences in the laboratory, (*b*) keep notebooks, (*c*) prepare written and oral reports on specially assigned readings, (*d*) make collections of pertinent materials, (*e*) assemble apparatus for individual experiments or demonstrations, (*f*) make illustrative drawings and diagrams, (*g*) construct aquariums, terrariums, and other materials useful in science. All these, and others that might be mentioned, are "pupils' work products" in the sense in which the term is used here; and all afford opportunities for teachers to assess the progress of their pupils.

But note the phrase, "afford opportunities" for evaluation. They do not necessarily and automatically supply evidence of learning. They do so only when teachers plan their pupils' activities with an eye to evaluation, with the intention of utilizing their work products to discover achievement in connection with particular objectives. Judged in terms of their *potentialities* for the purposes of evaluation, pupils' work products are unquestionably employed far less generally and far less acutely than should be the case.

Sample 12. Analysis of specified apparatus setups. Evidence with respect both to the manipulative skills possessed by pupils and to their understanding of the requirements of appropriate experimental apparatus is to be had by examining the way in which they assemble apparatus for prescribed experiments. No elaborate procedure is called for. A simple check list with an appropriate system of symbols suffices. The names of pupils may be listed in a column at the left on a sheet of paper. Parallel columns at the right should be headed by the criteria to be used in evaluating the apparatus. Suggested headings are:

1. Selection of proper items of equipment
2. Assembly in most direct and economical order
3. Neatness of setup
4. Stability of assemblage
5. Promptness in finding needed parts and in assembling the apparatus as a whole

Sample 13. Analysis of original apparatus setups. Beauchamp and Webb (24) have reported a series of laboratory situations by means of which pupils' resourcefulness in the use of apparatus may be tested. (The same situations may be dealt with in the form of paper-and-pencil tests, in which case each situation is described, and the pupil writes out his plan of action.) A few illustrative situations appear below:

1. *Given:* Bunsen burner, fastened down; gas supply; matches; short rubber tubes; glass tubes
   Required: To light the Bunsen burner without moving it
2. *Given:* Two bottles of odd shape, nearly the same in size; pan of water
   Required: To find which bottle holds the more
3. *Given:* A mixture of sugar, sand, and iron filings; also some water; magnet; towel
   Required: To separate each of the three substances in the mixture from the other two
4. *Given:* One pound of sand; paper towels; one balance (no weights)
   Required: To secure accurately 4 oz. of sand

Sample 14. Evaluation of typical reports of experimental work. Not uncommonly pupils are required to prepare written reports of their experiences in the laboratory for no apparent purpose other than to provide "busy work." Under such conditions the opportunities for evaluation which are inherent in these reports are wasted. On the other hand, the grading of pupil reports for the purposes of evaluation can easily become a laborious task, so much so as to discourage teachers from making the attempt at all. What is needed is a simple procedure which will supply pertinent evidence with a minimum of effort on the teacher's part.

The use of a check list is recommended. First, the teacher should give his pupils clear and complete information concerning the content expected in reports and the form in which it should appear (perhaps an outline of topics). Then as the reports are read, entries can be inserted by symbols in a special check list. The names of the pupils appear in a column at the left. Parallel columns are headed by the criteria to be used in evaluation, these criteria having been previously explained to the pupils. Suggested criteria, which can be abbreviated on the check list, are:

1. Is the laboratory problem clearly stated?
2. Is the experimental factor correctly identified and manipulated?
3. Is the experiment adequately controlled?
4. Are the data within the limits of error to be expected in view of the equipment used?
5. Are the data correctly organized and recorded?
6. Is the interpretation of data reasonable?
7. Is the conclusion consistent with the statement of the problem and with the data obtained?

Sample 15. Evaluation of reports simplified for particular purposes. Sharpe (15) describes a unique plan for reporting experiments which enables the teacher (and the pupil) to concentrate upon designated elements of growth. Following is an adapted sample report, with the facts entered in parentheses as they might be supplied by a pupil:

SCIENTIFIC METHOD EXPERIMENT SHEET

Date:........[March 4, 1947]........................ Name:....[Mary Hessington].................
Question:............[Does aspirin keep cut flowers longer?]....

Main Drawing		Control Drawing	

Main Steps	Main Observations	Control Steps	Control Observations
[I mounted some freshly cut flowers in water containing aspirin, as shown above, and observed them four times a day.]	[Flowers faded noticeably on the third day.]	[I mounted some freshly cut flowers in ordinary water, as shown above, and observed them four times a day.]	[Flowers faded noticeably on the third day.]

Answer	
[No; aspirin did not keep these cut flowers fresh longer.]	*Because* [the aspirin-tested flowers faded just as quickly as the untreated flowers.]
	The control shows [that there was nothing to affect the duration of the aspirin flowers that would not also affect the untreated flowers, except the aspirin. There were no other variables.]

3. Classroom Questioning and Discussion

Nowhere else is the intimate relationship between instruction and evaluation more apparent than in the daily give-and-take of classroom discussion. This statement is true even when the teacher uses the period simply to hear his pupils recite the isolated facts of a textbook assignment, since evaluation of one kind of achievement takes place. But when the teacher creates in the classroom an atmosphere of problem-solving he thereby assures himself unlimited occasions for assessing learning toward many worthy goals. The teacher's questions elicit responses, if nothing more than "I don't know," which are as significant for evaluation as they are for teaching. Equally significant for evaluation are the questions raised and the statements volunteered by pupils.

Sample 16. Oral questioning as a substitute for paper-and-pencil tests. Samples 1, 2, and 4, above, contain essay questions, and Samples 3, 5, and 6 objective questions designed for paper-and-pencil tests. Substantially the same questions could be presented orally as a basis for classroom discussion. One advantage of the oral presentation is that pupils can be "pursued" further than in the case of written tests. That is to say, they can be led to reveal the *reasons* for their answers, information which is usually missing on test papers. Another advantage is that in the course of discussion pupils reveal attitudes, appreciations, and interests which have small chance to display themselves on written tests. A third advantage is that remedial instruction can be undertaken at precisely the critical instant. Ignorance of essential facts is disclosed and can be corrected; misconceptions evident in answers can be identified and cleared up at once; faulty thinking is detected in the act and can be redirected; undesirable attitudes, once they are known to the teacher, become amenable to change.

Sample 17. Sensing and defining problems. The instructor makes a hole in a can of tomato juice and pours out the liquid without difficulty. He then makes a single hole of the same size in a can of evaporated milk and tries to decant the fluid, but with little success. Two holes are needed.

This situation, presented to a class, aroused considerable curiosity and elicited many questions, none of which was answered at the time. Instead, the pupils were encouraged to isolate the problem and to state it, with due attention to the critical or key ideas. In the course of the discussion marked differences, significant for evaluation, appeared among the pupils, in such aspects of behavior as keenness of interest, fertility of suggestions, precision in use of terms, clarity in defining the problem, etc. A series of such classroom events enabled the teacher, by means of check lists, to arrive at fairly reliable estimates of his pupils' abilities in several phases of science learning.

Sample 18. Proposing hypotheses. The following situations have been used to advantage in stimulating class discussion, with a view to determining the relative ability of pupils to suggest hypotheses or explanations:

1. Electric light bulbs in the house circuit dim momentarily when a toaster is plugged in or when the electric refrigerator motor starts.

2. When a person wearing glasses comes into a room from out of doors in the winter time, mist forms on the glasses.

3. A car is regularly parked facing the east. On cold days in the winter the windows on the north and west sides are heavily misted or frosted. No moisture collects on the other windows.

4. The water in a Silex coffee-maker rises through the tube into the upper chamber when the water in the lower chamber boils. When the coffee-maker is removed from the flame, the water (coffee) returns to the lower chamber.

5. Some burned-out electric bulbs are black on the inside while others are coated with a white powder.

Sample 19. Determining the facts essential to an explanation. A class in science had experimented with two guinea pigs to find out the effect of sugar in their diet. They were fed the same diet except that Animal A was given thirty grams of sugar a day. The experiment was carefully carried out, and the animals were weighed before the diet was started, at frequent intervals during the experiment, and at the close of the experiment. The data indicated that Animal A had gained seventy-five grams more than Animal B. From these facts the class concluded that sugar causes guinea pigs to increase in weight.

Through classroom discussion this conclusion was called into question. The next step, again through discussion, was to get the pupils to isolate uncontrolled factors and weaknesses in the experiment and to suggest check experiments by means of which to ascertain the validity of the conclusion. Of course, no two pupils reacted in quite the same way, and their differences in behavior (thinking, attitudes) afforded data for the purposes of evaluation.

Sample 20. Applying scientific principles. A general-science class had just completed the study of the principle of inertia. To determine the extent and usefulness of their understanding—and so, really to *evaluate* their learning—several questions involving the principle were presented for discussion, among them:

1. When an elevator starts suddenly, a person momentarily feels heavier if the elevator goes up and lighter if it goes down. Why?
2. Rugs are shaken to remove dust and dirt? Why?
3. The loose head of a hammer or pick is driven onto the handle by striking the end of the handle against a stone. Why?

4. Observation of Significant Behavior

If science instruction is expected to produce desirable changes in pupil behavior, then the best place to look for evidence of success in teaching is within pupil behavior itself. In a way, paper-and-pencil instruments do this; but they may impose certain restrictions on pupil behavior and make it more or less artificial. On the other hand, the natural, voluntary use of scientific concepts, principles, and skills, and the natural, voluntary expression of attitudes, appreciations, and interests in behavior afford unmistakable and indisputable evidence that the objectives of science instruction are being achieved.

Success in observing behavior for the purposes of evaluation is dependent, first, upon accurate knowledge of what the objectives mean in terms of behavior, and, second, upon ability to distinguish in pupil behavior between that which is significantly related to desirable forms of growth and that which is not. This means that the science teacher will be alert at all times to his pupils' statements and actions and be ready to interpret them in the light of accepted objectives.

a) Informal observation

Sample 21. An observed attitude of inflexibility. In a class which had been reading, voluntarily and by assignment, about nuclear fission, one boy announced that he had found an error—that in a certain article the writer had referred to chemical elements numbered 93, 94, and 95. His chemistry text had told him that there are only ninety-two elements, and he therefore refused to accept the statement in the periodical. He held to this position in spite of the fact that several other children were able to cite from their reading apparently valid evidence that three new elements *had* been proposed.

The teacher noted the incident in an anecdotal record and described the boy's behavior. During the year at least three other similar reactions were recorded for the same boy in one class and two more in another area. This accumulated evidence, based upon observation, enabled the teacher to evaluate the boy as one who was unwilling to change his opinions in the light of new and reliable evidence. (Had it not been for other observations which revealed the same tendency, the behavior cited might just as well have been interpreted to signify on the boy's part the desirable attitude of reasonable doubt in the presence of incomplete data.)

Sample 22. An out-of-school use of scientific method. A junior high school girl, after drinking canned orange juice for the first time, wondered about the relative cost and quality of the canned and fresh juices. Instead of asking someone for the answer to her question, she purchased a can of orange juice and as many oranges as she could buy for the same amount of money. She squeezed the orange juice and then compared this amount with that in the can. She next compared them for taste and finally came to the question of their relative values for health. This new problem led her to procure bulletins from reliable agencies.

The mere fact that this observed behavior did not take place in school, but in the home, in no way invalidates the girl's apparent understanding of scientific method, however elementary. As a matter of fact, it could be argued that the out-of-school occurrence of the behavior in question enhanced its value for the purposes of evaluation.

Sample 23. A long-time observation of growth toward science objectives. A girl, one of the better students in a class, became interested in the effects of various amounts of chemical elements in the soil on the growth of plants. The girl's interest was unaffected by her inability to carry out exact experimentation in the school laboratory. Instead, she visited a local plant-research center, talked with the soil chemist there, and with his aid arrived at a definition of her problem. She secured a quantity of sand and devised a method of sterilizing it. She learned how to weigh precisely on chemical balances, for she worked with as little as a milligram of some substances. She selected her plants, devised controls, and started the experiment. After about two weeks nearly all her plants were dead. She located the cause as inability to control the temperature in the growing room, designed a glass box with a top, secured a thermostat, placed light bulbs in the glass box to provide heat, and started out again. The study was carried on for more than six months, and some of the factors were studied over and over. Finally her results were checked with those of a trained research worker and found to be reliable.

Over this period of several weeks the instructor had innumerable opportunities to note significant behavior changes—in skills, concepts, attitudes, etc.—and recorded his observations in permanent form. On the basis of the data so obtained the instructor was able to recommend the girl for an important college scholarship competition. (Incidentally the girl is now preparing for a career in plant research.)

Sample 24. Carry-over to the community. A class had been studying the problem of insects in relation to the transmission of disease. Some pupils observed a little later that there were a great many flies about the school kitchen and lunchroom. A committee from the class went to the principal and volunteered to locate the source of the flies. The committee found the source in a manure pile outside a barn near by. They suggested to the owner that he clean up the place. Upon his failure to do anything, they went to the local health department, and the manure pile was removed. In the meantime other members of the class had voluntarily painted screens with a solution of D.D.T. and remained after school each night during the spring to spray the kitchen.

Needless to say, various parts of the situation as described provided the instructor with many instances of "significant behavior" upon which to base evaluations.

Sample 25. Carry-over within the school. A school was in the throes of an epidemic of colds. The school doctor suggested that the humidity of the classrooms was inadequate for good health. A number of boys in a general-science class overheard his remark and undertook to find the facts. They measured the humidity of all classrooms several times a day and recorded their findings. At the close of a month's study they summarized their data and presented their conclusions to the school doctor. He in turn gave the data to the school authorities, who took steps to improve conditions respecting humidity in all classrooms.

b) Systematic observation

The instances of evaluation described in Samples 21 to 25 involve behavior which arose more or less unpredictably. That is to say, there was no prearrangement with respect either to behavior situation or to objectives to be included in the evaluation. Instead, the instructor in each case took the behavior as it came to him and made the most of it for the purposes of evaluation. Hence, these samples are cited as instances of evaluation by *informal* observation.

But it is, of course, possible to observe behavior *systematically*—regularly, with a plan—to secure data for evaluation. For example, pupils, one at a time, may be exposed to the same prearranged situation, and differences in their behavior noted in a number of respects previously decided upon. Or, a given situation may be presented (as is usually the case) to a group of pupils. In the latter case, evaluation becomes more difficult, and certain precautions must be taken. (1) A check list of some kind is advisable. (2) Only a few children, not more than four or five, should be observed at a time. (3) Likewise, the number of behavior characteristics to be noted must be limited to not more than four or five. If these precautions are not respected, the teacher is likely to become confused and to observe some pupils (and behavior patterns) too often and others not often enough. On the other hand, if these precautions *are* respected, and if the group observations are made frequently enough over a period of weeks, reliable evidence on the attainment of science objectives can be had.

5. The Interview and Conference

The interview and the conference introduce no new procedures in evaluation. Rather, they simply call for the use of procedures already described in this chapter, principally those of questioning and discussion (3) and of the observation of significant behavior (4). Nevertheless, there is reason to list the interview and conference for separate discussion, for they improve immeasurably the conditions of using the customary procedures of evaluation. Every good teacher knows the value of extended conversation with and observation of the same individual, as a means of understanding him and of guiding his learning to better advantage.

Just as oral questioning transcends the more or less stilted written-examination question as a means of getting at the pupil's knowledge and understanding, so the interview, with the chances it affords for continued probing, transcends the ordinary classroom questioning. There is a corresponding progression in the number and the validity of opportunities to detect attitudes as one passes from the written examination to the interview. In the interview, once a wholesome atmosphere has been established, the pupil can be led to talk freely of his likes and dislikes, his hobbies, his interests, his ambitions and plans. Implicit in all that he says and does (and in all that he does not say and do) is an abundance of data on his learning status and progress. These data are most accessible to the teacher in the intimate relationships of the personal conference.

SUMMARY

In this chapter, suggestions and illustrations of many types of evaluative procedures in science instruction have been presented. These range from formal to most informal. They include a variety of written and oral techniques, all of which are practicable. They are capable of adaptation to any classroom or laboratory by the teacher who is interested in measuring growth of his pupils with respect to each of the various objectives of science instruction.

REFERENCES

1. COLVIN, ROBERT B. "Applications Used for Improving Tests and Widening the Scope of General Science," *School Science and Mathematics*, XXXIV (December, 1934), 945–48.

2. CURTIS, F. D. "Testing as a Means of Improving Instruction," *Science Education*, XXVIII (February, 1944), 29–32.

3. DAVIS, IRA C. "The Measurement of Scientific Attitudes," *Science Education*, XIX (October, 1935), 117–23.

4. HANCOCK, CYRIL. "Evaluation of Popular Misconceptions Related to Science," *Science Education*, XXIV (April, 1940), 208–13.

5. HEIL, LOUIS M., *et al.* "The Measurement of Understanding in Science," *The Measurement of Understanding*, chap. vi. Forty-fifth Yearbook of the National Society for the Study of Education, Part I. Chicago: University of Chicago Press, 1946.

6. HEISS, E. D.; OBOURN, E. S.; and HOFFMAN, C. W. *Modern Methods and Materials for Teaching Science*, chap. vii. New York: Macmillan Co., 1940.

7. HOWARD, FREDERICK T., and ROBERTSON, M. L. "Scaling the Intangibles," *Science Education*, XXIV (October, 1940), 241–49.

8. HURD, A. W. "A Commonsense Interpretation of Attitudes in Science Instruction," *Science Education*, XXIV (January, 1940), 7–10.

9. NOLL, VICTOR H. "Measuring the Scientific Attitude," *Journal of Abnormal and Social Psychology*, XXX (July–September, 1935), 145–54.

10. ———. *Teaching of Science in Elementary and Secondary Schools*, pp. 154–96. New York: Longmans, Green & Co., 1939.

11. PETERSON, SHAILER. "The Evaluation of a One-Year Course: The Fusion of Physics and Chemistry with other Physical Sciences," *Science Education*, XXIX (December, 1945), 255–65.

12. PROGRESSIVE EDUCATION ASSOCIATION. *Science in General Education*, pp. 17–106. Prepared by Committee on the Function of Science in General Education of the Commission on Secondary School Curriculum. New York: D. Appleton-Century Co., 1938.

13. RATHS, LOUIS E. "Techniques for Test Construction," *Educational Research Bulletin* (Ohio State University), XVII (April 13, 1938), 85–114.

14. REINER, C. F. "The Correlation between Scientific Attitude and Factual Knowledge in a High-School Chemistry Topic," *Science Education*, XXIII (November, 1939), 327–31.

15. SHARPE, PHILLIP B. "Why Not Use Control Experiments?" *Science Education*, XXII (January, 1938), 19–22.

16. SIMMONS, MAITLAND P. "Evaluating General Science Projects," *Science Education*, XXIII (December, 1939), 379–81.

17. STEWART, A. W. "Measuring Ability To Apply Principles," *School Science and Mathematics*, XXXV (October, 1935), 695, 699.

18. TYLER, RALPH W. "Ability To Use Scientific Method," *Educational Research Bulletin* (Ohio State University), XI (January 6, 1932), 1–9.

19. ———. "Assumptions Involved in Achievement-Test Construction," *Educational Research Bulletin* (Ohio State University), XII (February 8, 1933), 29–36.

20. ———. "Formulating Objectives for Tests," *Educational Research Bulletin* (Ohio State University), XII (October 11, 1933), 197–206.

21. ———. "A Generalized Technique for Constructing Achievement Tests," *Educational Research Bulletin* (Ohio State University), X (April 15, 1931), 199–208.

22. ———. "Measuring the Ability To Infer," *Educational Research Bulletin* (Ohio State University), IX (November 19, 1930), 475–80.

23. ———. "Tests in Biology," *School Science and Mathematics*, XXXIII (June, 1933), 590–95.

24. WEBB, H. A., and BEAUCHAMP, R. O. "Test of Laboratory Resourcefulness," *School Science and Mathematics*, XXII (March, 1922), 259–67; XXVII (May, 1927), 457–65.

25. WEST, JOE YOUNG. "A Technique for Appraising Certain Observable Behavior of Children in Science in Elementary Schools," *Science Education*, XXII (October, 1938), 234–44.

26. ZEIGLER, ROBERT T. "A Study of Fact Retention in General Science," *Science Education*, XXVI (February, 1942), 83–85.

CHAPTER XVI

THE EDUCATION OF SCIENCE TEACHERS
FOR SECONDARY SCHOOLS[1]

THE PROBLEM

In approaching the discussion of the education of science teachers for secondary schools, two important aspects of the problem must be recognized, namely, preservice education and in-service education. Both of these will be treated in this discussion. The general purposes to be achieved both by preservice and by in-service education are in many respects closely similar, although the materials and methods to be used in dealing with prospective teachers in colleges and with teachers of experience who are actually on a job may be different in many particulars.

Teacher education should be thought of as continuous from its inception throughout the life of the teacher. It does not cease as the prospective teacher enters upon his profession. It goes on as he learns to put into practice what he has learned in college and as he gains in practice new insights into the meaning of the professional work he has undertaken.

A most important phase of in-service education is to help teachers to keep abreast of changes in knowledge of subject matter and in educational theory and practice. Procedures in the schools are not static. Policy in education changes continually as leaders in education strive to keep the schools abreast of the changing needs of young people and of society. Inasmuch as the general purposes of preservice and in-service education are closely similar, successful practices in each aspect of teacher education will tend to reduce the gap between the instruction given in college and the things beginning teachers will be called upon to do. Successful teacher education implies co-operation between the professional college and the schools it serves. Schools that are active in in-service education are prepared to receive the student from college, and the student entering upon his new work will recognize his assignment as one for which he is prepared.

THE IN-SERVICE PROGRAM

The responsibility for helping teachers who are already on the job to meet the rapidly changing conditions of our times, to keep up with new

---

[1] The committee has profited from the collaboration of S. R. Powers, Teachers College, Columbia University, in the preparation of this chapter.

professional developments, and constantly to grow in competence as teachers and counselors of young people presents a tremendous challenge. If leadership to meet this challenge is lacking, teachers will tend to go on doing much as they learned to do in the beginning. They are likely to become victims of fixed habits and to lose the flexibility that is so essential to their success.

As policies in education change, the work of the teacher must change. Two illustrations will suffice to make the point clear. (a) In the normal course of events he will surely be asked to undertake new duties and to abandon some in which he may feel he has become proficient. There is, for example, a tendency, developing over many years, toward relating the work of the school more closely to the immediate needs and interests of youth. This requires, among other things, that the teacher shall know more about the local community in which he is employed. (b) Similarly, teachers are expected to assume increasingly larger responsibilities as guidance workers, as counselors for pupil organizations, and as workers competent in educational measurement and evaluation. Many will get their first education in some of these activities after they have entered upon their work as a teacher. In-service education is a co-operative enterprise under leadership carried on to help young teachers establish themselves in the work of the school and to help them as they continue in their work to keep alert and growing and adaptable to such new responsibilities as may be required of them.

How then can these things be accomplished? A comprehensive report dealing with such purposes has been prepared for the Commission on Teacher Education (9). Mainly the report consists of an account of three years of co-operation involving public schools and colleges. The co-operating school systems made special effort to encourage their personnel to increase their competence and effectiveness. Experiences in planning and methods of group work as carried on through the academic year and in summer workshops are reported in some detail. Also, experience gained in helping teachers in certain areas of study, such as child study, community resources, and staff relations, is described. For those interested in exercising leadership in in-service teacher education, this volume is of basic importance.

Another discussion of this problem, particularly related to science teachers, is contained in a report by the National Committee on Science Teaching (2). As in the publication of the Commission on Teacher Education, emphasis is placed in this report on the importance of co-operative planning and local initiative in developing programs of in-service education. In fact, the implication is clear that programs for in-service education should usually be planned by the teachers themselves in co-operation with supervisory and administrative officials. Emphasis is placed on decentralization of authority and on encouragement and stimulation of teachers to initiate, plan, and carry out programs of in-service education.

The report suggests many fine activities for the improvement of teachers, such as the use of consultants, teachers' meetings, participation in courses and workshops, observation of the work of superior teachers, and participation in community activities. Illustrations of these as worked out in specific situations are given. A more detailed review of such activities as employed in the in-service education of teachers will be found in chapter x. Although they are discussed there with particular reference to elementary teachers, they are equally applicable to teachers at the secondary level.

It is suggested that staff members of state departments of education and of colleges for the education of teachers and local supervisory officers may help in providing stimulation and consultative services, in organizing classes and workshops, and in addressing teachers' meetings and conferences. Continuing growth and improvement of teachers will best be realized, however, when these services are made available as a result of requests engendered by local interest. There is a good deal of feeling on the part of teachers that in-service education to be most helpful must recognize and deal with problems as they exist at the local level; and it is observed that each community, yes, even each school and teacher have problems with certain features that set them off from those of other teachers or communities and that these problems must be dealt with on that basis.

The point of view of the yearbook committee on the in-service education of science teachers for secondary schools may be summarized briefly as follows:

1. In-service education should be locally initiated, directed to the needs of the individual teacher, co-operatively planned and carried out.
2. Staff members of colleges and of state departments and local administrative and supervisory officials may exercise leadership and stimulate, encourage, and assist in the local setting.
3. Certification requirements may be defined in such a manner as to encourage teachers to keep alert and to grow professionally through continued study and other professional activities.
4. In-service education should be planned so as to develop competence of teachers in all phases of personal and professional development. It should not be narrow in conception or confine itself to purely local problems, though these need attention and often provide a point of departure for the development of broader concepts and more penetrating insights.
5. All available resources, local, state, and federal, should be utilized to the fullest possible extent in the in-service education of science teachers. Every

effort should be made to develop in science teachers an understanding of their responsibilities as citizens and of the important contribution which they can make to society through the teaching of science.

6. Teachers in service should be encouraged to pursue additional courses, both professional and subject matter, to insure continued growth in competence as classroom teachers.

PRESERVICE EDUCATION
The Science Offerings at the Secondary Level

In order to formulate a plan of education for prospective teachers of science in junior and senior high schools it is advisable first to consider the kinds of positions and responsibilities science teachers generally fill. The most recent data on science offerings in secondary schools (**6, 8**; see also chap. xi) show that at the junior high school level from one to three years of general science are usually taught. When less than three years of instruction in this subject is offered, biology is often given in the ninth grade. In a four-year high school the common sequence is general science, biology, chemistry, and physics, one year of each. If biology is the ninth-grade science, chemistry and physics are nearly always electives in the three upper grades, that is, in the senior high school. Certain other courses such as advanced biology, advanced chemistry, senior science, physical science, and "consumer science" are finding a place in the high-school science program to the extent of about 14 per cent of the total offering (**6**). Older science courses, such as physical geography, botany, zoology, and physiology, have practically disappeared from the science offering of public secondary schools. In most states general science is required, or practically required, for at least one year and sometimes more (**6**:365).

The tendency is away from strictly subject-matter bounded courses toward organization around functional areas in the lives of pupils. This trend is decisive, and it is well recognized in the reports of authoritative policy-making bodies (**5**); and it is important in relation to planning for the education of science teachers. There is also revealed a growing awareness of the importance of science as a subject of instruction.

Teaching Loads and Working Conditions of Science Teachers in Secondary Schools

Many studies have been made of the teaching assignments and load of high-school science teachers. Without specific citation of such investigations it may be said they all show that beginning teachers of science usually are required to teach at least three subjects, one of which may often be mathematics or some other nonscience subject; that except in larger schools and systems most science teachers, including those with considerable experience, teach more than one science; and that state certification requirements and the policies of accrediting agencies like the North Central Association, the New York Regents, and others generally recognize and provide for this situation in requirements for accrediting schools.

Most high schools are small, and recommendations for the education of science teachers must take cognizance of conditions that prevail in small schools as well as in large ones. The recommendations are made with recognition of immediate needs, and among these is the need for competence to work in an institution that, like the society which supports it, is continually changing.

It is also recognized that many colleges in which prospective science teachers are educated fulfil other functions as well. All have responsibility for educating teachers for other areas and departments, and some so-called teachers' colleges educate for types of work and professions other than teaching. The committee feels its function to be that of offering the best possible suggestions for educating prospective science teachers, recognizing that not all institutions offer the same education, even if that were desirable, and that teachers must be able to fill the kinds of jobs which are available to them.

Recommended Programs for the Education of Science Teachers in Secondary Schools

A number of committees and individuals have suggested during the last twenty-five years desirable qualifications and training programs for science teachers. Those which are regarded as most significant will be reviewed here, though rather briefly.

a) The first of these is found in the report of the Science Committee of the Commission on the Reorganization of Secondary Education (3). In a brief appendix to its report this committee gives a general statement of what it considers to be the desirable qualifications of the teacher of science in the secondary school. Among those emphasized are: (1) health, forceful personality, democratic ideals, love of science and belief in its value, industry, and similar desirable personal qualities; (2) extensive as well as thorough knowledge of his subject; (3) some knowledge of basic social sciences, such as history, economics, and sociology; (4) work in psychology and measurement and professional training in methods of teaching and secondary education; (5) membership in professional societies, interest in research and experimentation, and attendance at meetings of organizations for the advancement of education; and (6) interest in the community and willingness to use scientific knowledge for community benefit. Throughout the statement there is stress either directly or by implication on the importance of education for broad aspects of living in a democratic society. The recommendations are presented briefly and in general terms and no special program is suggested. It may be noted that this committee pioneered in offering some suggestions that today have wide acceptance.

b) In the Thirty-first Yearbook of the National Society for the Study of Education (**10**) the programs for the education of science teachers, as offered in state teachers colleges, are reviewed and the committee responsible for that yearbook proposed a program for the education of science teachers who are to teach below the college level. The recommendations are shown in the accompanying tabulation:

Junior High School Teachers of Science

	Hours
1. Orientation	8
2. Introductory courses in three special sciences	24
3. Specialization courses	8
4. Professional courses in Junior high school science	4
5. Electives in science and in mathematics—at least	16

Senior High School Teachers of Science

1. Orientation	8
2. Introductory courses in three special sciences	24
3. Specialization courses	16
4. Professional course in major subject	4
5. Electives	8

The orientation course (1) is described as a general one "built around those generalizations and principles of science that relate most immediately to the needs and interests of liberally educated people." The introductory courses (2) in three special sciences are to be in biology, chemistry, and physics. The specialization courses (3) are second- and third-year courses in the same subjects as the introductory courses. The suggested electives (5) include geology, physiography, astronomy, and bacteriology.

The program proposed was regarded as a minimum. The content of the second- and third-year courses is essentially the same as that of the usual courses offered by accredited colleges and universities in these areas, and it is recommended that state teachers colleges not prepared to offer such specialization "should not attempt to educate teachers for service in secondary schools" until they can meet these requirements.

The recommendations are based upon the assumption of a four-year program and are mainly concerned with the kind of education in science which the committee believed the teacher should have. They do not include consideration of other elements of a desirable program of liberal education for prospective science teachers.

c) Suggested programs for the education of science teachers in secondary schools have appeared in the professional writings of several individuals. Among these are Curtis (**4**), Noll (**7**), and Webb (**11**). All three recommend work in science similar in nature and scope to that recommended in the report just cited. In addition, Curtis and Noll recommend work in social science, Noll and Webb recommend work in mathematics, although Webb permits substitutions in agriculture or home economics for it. Noll alone mentions practice teaching, though it is likely that the others had this in mind in their recommendations for education courses.

In substance, the recommendations of programs reviewed so far are in agreement on these points at least: (1) that for prospective science teachers about one-half of the work for the baccalaureate degree be devoted to science courses; (2) that such courses be selected so as to give training in no less than three fields or subjects and yet provide for a reasonable degree of specialization in one of them.

d) Two other sets of recommendations on this problem will be reviewed. The first of these is a report previously referred to, made by the National Committee on Science Teaching (**2**).

The major portion of this report concerns itself with a discussion of the function of science education in this country today and of the preparation needed by prospective teachers of science in order to discharge that function properly. Great stress is laid on the social role of science and the scientific method. The science teacher is regarded as having, at least potentially, a position of high significance in the school and in the community. Evidence is cited to show that science teachers feel that they are not exerting the influence which they, through science, should be able to exert; that they do not discuss and treat topics of great social significance and vital interest to their pupils when science has much to contribute in understanding and dealing with such questions; and that they do not "keep up" with significant scientific developments. The science teachers explain their failure to meet these challenges as due to (1) disapproval by parents of the teacher's effort to deal with important issues, (2) their own incompetence in knowledge and experience, and especially (3) the belief on their own part that their pupils are so immature that they will not profit from the study of issues. Many illustrations are given of how science teachers are discharging these responsibilities in specific situations and overcoming the handicaps cited.

The report discusses in detail how science teachers may acquire proficiency in developing and using curricular materials in functional areas, such as personal and public health, distribution and consumption of materials, and in scientific method. It also discusses the need of the science teacher to have an understanding of his role in community life and the contribution which he can make, the importance of his having adequate understanding of child growth and development, and other essential preparation for effective work in classroom and laboratory.

In its recommendations for a program the committee report outlines in some detail what it considers to be the minimum of desirable preparation. This cannot be reproduced in its entirety here, but essentially it is as shown in the accompanying tabulation.

First and Second Years

	Semester Hours
Functional social studies	12
Functional arts and humanities	12
Functional science	12
Growth and development of children	9
Total required	45
Electives in philosophy, social studies, science	15

Third and Fourth Years

Special interest field, science	18
Special interest field, other than science	12
Observation and teaching with conferences	6
Professional orientation and philosophy of science teaching	6
Foundations course in education (fourth year)	12
Electives (philosophy, psychology, sociology, etc.)	6

The suggestions above are offered for application within the four-year college and represent the committee's effort to put what it considers to be first things, first. There is less provision in these suggestions for subject-matter specialization than in the earlier reports. On the other hand, there is more provision for general education and for the professional orientation and the specific work of the teacher. The proposed program may be fairly adequate for the education of teachers of general science, but it is doubtful that it provides sufficient opportunity for the advanced courses in science needed by a teacher of biology, chemistry, or physics in a senior high school.

The report is to be commended for striking out in the direction of liberal education in the social sciences, particularly as these are or can be related to scientific progress and developments. The preparation of science teachers for secondary schools undoubtedly has been too narrow. Prospective science teachers, especially in liberal-arts colleges and in universities, have generally been obliged to follow the same curriculums as those preparing for work of a technical nature as chemists, bacteriologists, physicists, medical students, and the like. All too often, such prospective teachers have qualified for a teacher's certificate merely by electing the minimum amount of work in professional courses in psychology and education without much or any planning of a program with teaching as an objective of first importance. This haphazard method of collecting college credit must be radically changed if the quality of science instruction in secondary schools is to be greatly improved.

e) The last report (**1**) to be discussed here relates to the preparation of teachers for the small high school. It states that three-fourths of all high schools in the United States have ten or fewer teachers, and that nearly all beginning teachers start in the small high school. In such a situation, science teachers must be broadly trained and also sufficiently specialized to teach one or more sciences, such as chemistry, physics, or biology. The report recommends:

1. Certification in closely related subjects, three to be chosen in each case from biological science (including both botany and zoology), chemistry, mathematics, physics, and general science
2. That approximately one-half the work for the baccalaureate degree be in the sciences (which in this report includes mathematics)
3. That certification to teach general science in junior high school grades be limited to those having college courses in all the subjects concerned in general science (see "1" above)
4. A five-year program for the preparation of science teachers as a desirable future goal
5. Curriculum improvement in the high school to go with improvement in teacher preparation.

In addition to the foregoing, a set of proficiency examinations measuring both knowledge and abilities essential to success in teaching science and mathematics is recommended. It is implied, though not explicitly stated, that these examinations would be voluntary for the prospective teacher, and that those who took them would be given a record of competence. The report strongly urges co-operative action between the department of education and science departments in institutions educating teachers and it is stated that responsibility for seeking such co-operation should rest with the science departments concerned.

The report is brief and explicit. It does not go into detail as to the kinds of courses which should be taken either in science or in other fields or the combinations of courses which it deems desirable. It does no more than touch on the social implications of science with which the effective science teacher must deal. It recognizes the need for a broad overview of the sciences, especially for those who will teach general science, and for an understanding of the relationships and common areas between different sciences. It does not say how the integration of different sciences is to be attained; it recommends no procedure or courses designed to do this for the prospective teacher. One is left with the feeling that the report favors development of such integration without really having faced the issue of how it can be accomplished. It has been distributed for immediate and widespread application.

Significance for Teacher Education of Objectives
Presented by the Yearbook Committee

Chapter iii presents a statement of objectives for science teaching at elementary and secondary levels. This statement is intended to show the major desirable directions of growth in young people to which science teaching can contribute. It seems self-evident that the education of a prospective science teacher should qualify him to assist to the maximal degree in stimulating, aiding, and bringing about growth in functional understanding of facts, concepts, and principles; in both instrumental and problem-solving skills; and in the attitudes, appreciations, and interests of science. To be able to do this, the science teacher must be competent in the subject matter and skills of science and must himself possess the desired attitudes, appreciations, and interests.

To develop functional understandings of science in the prospective teacher, he must not only take courses in separate sciences but he must also have assistance in integrating them and seeing relationships. It is generally considered essential for him to have work in broad areas such as physical science and biological science so that these important relationships can be brought out and understood. In theory, there are some arguments for having such courses follow other courses in the separate sciences, but all practical considerations, as well as the weight of experience, seem to indicate that these integrating courses should come early.

Also, to assist in developing understandings of science which will be functional in their social ramifications, the prospective science teacher should have a good foundation in social science and its application in the study of issues of today. Here again, a fused or survey course including some basic principles of anthropology, the development of civilization, American history, economics, sociology, and perhaps political science seems most likely to be helpful. It is important that those responsible for the respective survey courses in natural science and in social science have contact with each other, and that every opportunity be utilized to bring out relationships between these courses through experience, directly or vicariously, in such projects as community surveys.

A prospective science teacher must be competent in his own field, otherwise he cannot teach it well or command the respect of his pupils or his associates. This means that he must have enough specialization in at least one science to enable him to feel at ease in dealing with its basic content; also, he must have had enough work in two other sciences to handle them competently at the high-school level. The only possible exception to the requirement of specialization in one field might be the prospective teacher of general science at the junior high school level.

Although the amount of mathematics actually required for understanding and proficiency in high-school sciences is not great, the prospective teacher of science would profit from its study to the extent of at least one year of algebra, one semester of plane geometry, and one semester of trigonometry. Whether this be taken while in high school or in college is probably not very important, but no one should be a teacher of science without this minimum preparation in mathematics. The lack of it would constitute a serious deficiency in solving or trying to teach pupils to solve problems in science or to understand quantitative relationships and many applications of science to daily life.

A Suggested Program for the Education of High-School Science Teachers

In keeping with the stated objectives of science instruction and with the immediately preceding discussion of them, the following suggestions for the education of high-school science teachers are offered. It will be noted that no courses in education and psychology are listed in the outline of courses in the sciences. However, following the proposed program, the areas of instructional techniques in which science teachers should be competent are discussed.

A. For all prospective teachers of science in secondary grades:
  1. Survey or integrated course in biological science (drawing from anatomy, bacteriology, botany, ecology, entomology, health, physiology, and zoology, and possibly others, including lectures, laboratory, field work)

     9 to 12 semester hours
  2. Survey or integrated course in physical science (drawing from astronomy, chemistry, geology, meteorology, and physics, and possibly others, and including lectures, laboratory, and field trips or excursions)

     9 to 12 semester hours
  3. Survey or integrated course in social science (drawing from anthropology, the development of civilization, American history with emphasis on economic, geographic, and sociological factors, and the development of political and social institutions and problems—lectures, laboratory, and field work using the community as a laboratory

     9 to 12 semester hours
  4. Algebra, plane geometry, and trigonometry

     2 high-school units or 9 semester hours

It is advised that those responsible for the respective survey courses work closely with one another at all times. The separation between biological and physical sciences is now generally recognized as a matter of convenience rather than of advantage. In studies relating to such matters as health, conservation, consumer problems, scientific method, to name but a few illustrations, no arbitrary divisions between biological and physical sciences should be maintained. Furthermore, the separate survey courses should be truly integrated; they should not consist of a series of lectures in one subject such as botany, followed by another series in bacteriology, and so on. The sociological and economic aspects of such topics should also be considered when they are being studied in science with the cooperation of those responsible for the work in social science. By cooperation and close contact between instructors in each area much can be done to assist prospective science teachers to learn how they may help their students use science in dealing with the important issues of today. At the same time, the staffs of departments or divisions responsible for the three survey courses will not feel that fields of specialization are being invaded or pre-empted but rather that advice and counsel of specialists are being sought and used constructively. This is important in dealing with college faculties and is fundamental to the success of a co-operative enterprise.

B. In addition to the above, prospective teachers of general science in junior high school grades would take:
  1. Courses in botany, human physiology, and/or zoology
     9 to 12 semester hours
  2. Courses in chemistry and/or physics . . . . 9 to 12 semester hours
  3. Courses in astronomy, geology, meteorology, and/or physical geography
     9 to 12 semester hours

With the survey courses this would amount to 45–60 semester hours in science and would provide a broad, yet reasonably thorough, education in the natural sciences. It would leave at least one-half the work required for a Bachelor's degree available for social sciences, arts, languages, and professional courses for teachers.

C. Prospective teachers of science in senior high school grades would take, in addition to the survey courses 1, 2, and 3, the following:
  1. Additional work in (a) biological sciences (including both botany and zoology), or (b) chemistry, or (c) physics to obtain a total in one area including the corresponding survey course of at least 24 semester hours
  2. Additional work in the two areas not chosen in (1) to obtain with the other science survey an average of 18 semester hours in each or a total of 36 semester hours

This recommendation of a minimum total of 60 semester hours in science, with 24 semester hours in one science and approximately 18 semester hours in each of two other sciences, is in close agreement with the recommendations of the Thirty-first Yearbook (**10**) and with other sources cited in this chapter. It is believed that this constitutes a desirable minimum for teaching biology, chemistry, physics, or other senior high school science and for further study and specialization if desired. It leaves approximately one-half the requirement for a Bachelor's degree available for work in other fields, including professional courses for prospective teachers.

On the side of instructional techniques, the prospective teacher of science needs an understanding of human growth and of the learning processes, some knowledge of acceptable procedures for measurement and evaluation, some command of principles of educational guidance, a good deal of help in methods of organizing and presenting the materials of instruction, and as much preservice experience under competent supervision in actually conducting classroom and laboratory work as can be provided. He needs also a philosophy of science teaching which envisages the teaching of science as contributing to the kinds of objectives presented in chapter iii and which fires him with the desire to make his contribution to growth toward them.

Among the areas listed, understanding of human growth and the learning process is fundamental. A great deal of the early work in educational psychology has been rather remote from classroom and laboratory, and not uncommonly teachers are unable to bridge the gap between theory and practice. It does not follow, however, that we must therefore throw out everything that has before been done in principles of education and educational psychology as a waste of time. Instead, the work in such courses must be related more closely to actual learning situations and prospective teachers given practice in applying theory. The whole area of educational psychology, including growth, learning, individual differences, and evaluation, should be related as directly as possible to observation and work with children.

Another very important phase of professional education is student-teaching with supervision and conference under skilful and understanding teachers. It is commonly offered near the end of the student's preservice work and provides opportunity to bring to a focus much of the education and experience which have gone before. The prospective teacher will gain the necessary confidence in his ability as a teacher through student teaching if it is carried on long enough and if the supervision is what it should be. In too many cases, the time is too short and the supervising teacher has too many student teachers to care for. Frequently, also, student teaching is done entirely in a laboratory school where conditions are different from those which the student teacher will encounter on his first job or perhaps on any job. Although the laboratory school is in many respects a necessary part of the teachers' college, its use as a place for practice teaching has disadvantages. Every prospective public school teacher should have an opportunity to experience conditions in a public school as part of his preparation for his job. It would be desirable, also, for the prospective science teacher to have some opportunity for observation and participation under classroom conditions early in his professional education. This would be followed later by more experience with assumption, eventually, of full responsibility for conducting classroom and laboratory as a student teacher.

All the science courses suggested, including the survey courses, should provide abundant opportunity to use the scientific method in dealing with important issues and problems. Furthermore, science teachers should be made thoroughly conversant with it in its logical and philosophical aspects. In order to insure that they will understand scientific method and know something of the literature dealing with its procedures, it is recommended that the course in philosophy and methods of teaching science be in part the study and development of techniques for illustrating and inculcating scientific methods of problem-solving through science teaching. All too often, college students take numerous courses in science without having their attention in any of them brought to this fundamental procedure as a *method of inquiry*. It is left entirely to them to divine or to sense without help or attention on the part of the instructors in such courses. Those responsible for the professional courses for prospective science teachers should assume responsibility for assisting in this matter, enlisting, if possible, the co-operation of the instructors in science. Experience has shown beyond a doubt that the majority of students in college courses in science do not gain a functional understanding of the scientific method *as a method*, or as an objective of science instruction, unless this is systematically brought to their attention and frequently illustrated and explained in its practical application. It is too important to be left to chance.

The course in methods and philosophy of science teaching should be closely tied in with the other elements in the program of professional courses. This is particularly important in student teaching where the student will have an opportunity to try out some of the methods and points of view suggested by his college instructors and where he may raise questions with those instructors, deepen his understanding, and obtain needed assistance.

Other professional courses, such as a foundation or orientation course in education, courses in guidance, history of education, and others, may be taken as the needs and interests of individual students dictate and as may be required by certification and accrediting agencies.

In making these recommendations for the education of prospective teachers of science the committee recognizes the time limitations of the four-year course in college. As more time is given over to specialization in science, less time is available for the study of such phases of the school as its broad function in education in the United States; for the kind of practical education that helps the science teacher to know that he is a part of the total school organization; and for specialization in the professional aspects of education. Similarly, there is less time for orientation in the arts, languages, and humanities, and for the pursuit of special interests. These considerations emphasize the need of expanding the usual four-year program of teacher education. It is the purpose here to outline a strong program which will lead to the attainment of the desired objective. If more than the usual allotment of time is needed, then additional time must be found. In agreement with this point of view and with other reports reviewed in this chapter the committee indorses a five-year program for the general and professional education of high-school teachers, a practice which is already followed in some colleges and which is required in several states.

Summary

1. The major problem in the improvement of the education of science teachers for secondary schools is viewed here as being both preservice and in-service education. There is, in fact, no sharp division between them; the one merges into the other.

2. The areas in which science teachers may have competence are envisaged as (*a*) functional understanding of subject matter; (*b*) professional understanding and skill as teachers of youth, (*c*) a social philosophy of science teaching

3. The suggestions offered in this chapter are believed to be practical in that they may be immediately and widely applied. Special attention has been given to the needs for better teachers in small schools and in states with low requirements for teacher certification.

4. This committee is in general agreement with the recommendations of the earlier reports reviewed in this chapter. In its review of these reports, it has pointed out specific aspects with which it is partially or wholly in disagreement.

5. The suggested program of courses is presented as a part of the offering of a four-year college. The inadequacies of this program, especially for the education of senior high school teachers, on account of limitations of time, are recognized.

6. These suggestions are offered to be incorporated within the framework of a comprehensive plan for science teaching as defined and developed in the committee's statement of objectives given in chapter iii. It is hoped that these will furnish a guide and a stimulus to substantial improvement of existing practices in institutions engaged in the education of science teachers.

REFERENCES

1. AMERICAN ASSOCIATION FOR THE ADVANCEMENT OF SCIENCE. Co-operative Committee on Science Teaching. "The Preparation of High-School Science and Mathematics Teachers," *School Science and Mathematics*, XLVI (February, 1946), 107–18; also, XLII (October, 1942), 636–50.
2. AMERICAN COUNCIL OF SCIENCE TEACHERS, NATIONAL COMMITTEE ON SCIENCE TEACHING. *The Education of the Science Teacher.* Washington: National Education Association, 1942.
3. COMMISSION ON REORGANIZATION OF SECONDARY EDUCATION. *Report of Subcommittee on the Teaching of Science.* U.S. Bureau of Education Bulletin No. 26. Washington: Government Printing Office, 1920.
4. CURTIS, F. D. "What Constitutes a Desirable Program of Studies in Science Education for Teachers of Science in Secondary Schools?" *Science Education*, XV (November, 1930), 14–22.
5. EDUCATIONAL POLICIES COMMISSION. *Education for All American Youth.* Washington: National Education Association, 1944.
6. HUNTER, G. W., and SPORE, LEROY. "Science Sequence and Enrolments in the Secondary Schools of the United States," *Science Education*, XXV (December, 1941), 359–70 and XXVI (February, 1942), 66–77.
7. NOLL, V. H. "The Science Teachers' Qualifications," *The Teaching of Science in Elementary and Secondary Schools.* New York: Longmans, Green & Co., 1939.
8. *Offerings and Registrations in High-School Subjects, 1933–1934.* U.S. Office of Education Bulletin, 1938, No. 6. Washington: Government Printing Office, 1938.
9. PRALL, CHARLES E., and CUSHMAN, C. LESLIE. *Teacher Education in Service.* Washington: American Council on Education, 1944.
10. *Program for Teaching Science.* Thirty-first Yearbook of the National Society for the Study of Education, Part I. Chicago: Distributed by University of Chicago Press, 1932.
11. WEBB, H. A. "The Training of Science Teachers for Secondary Schools," *Science Education*, XV (November, 1930), 1–8.

CHAPTER XVII

SCIENCE-EDUCATION IMPERATIVE[1]

Preceding chapters of this volume have presented serious thinking directed toward extension and improvement of science education. Descriptions have been presented of different types and levels of school situations, needs, and possibilities. Recommendations are given from many investigations dealing with the educational uses of science. Specific next steps to be taken are outlined as fully as seem to be justified by an understanding of present practices, tendencies, and purposes. The committee believes that the volume is a reasonable record of where we now are and of tendencies toward further progress. It is expected that much further progress will be made and that this volume will later take its place in the series of publications which record the advancing stages in improvement of science education. The preceding chapters have had cooperative criticism from many teachers and scientists. All members of the responsible committee believe that science must find its social justification not only through increasing knowledge, through improved individual and general welfare and happiness, and through wide uses of the methods of science but also through revealing ways of developing enduring security for worthy human living. The present status of security is disturbing. Its foundations seem "wobbly" and we are not confident about the superstructure. Foundational science, inadequately known, is well understood by only a small part of our so-called democratic society, and the dependable methods of science are far from being commonly used. The marvelous achievements of science, which may be considered its superstructure, are usually regarded as benefits rather than as obligations. Society's security requires that people's sensing of the obligations of knowledge and its achievements shall accompany their sensing of the benefits of science.

---

[1] In recognition of Dr. Caldwell's long and distinguished service as scientist and educator, the committee requested him to prepare this closing chapter of the yearbook. As a member of the committee, he has also contributed to the preparation of the preceding chapters.

Science as a way of living, though frequently advocated, is not commonly exemplified. It has often been claimed that one of the greatest contributions to human welfare seems likely to come from a wide and enduring extension of the people's working adherence to facts and truth and to provable interpretations derived from carefully studied experience. Scientists and those who teach science and write about it need to examine and redirect their own services as leaders in the use of science as a way of living. Admonishing others calls for few words from those who really live their best knowledge; and those who do not so live are but slightly influenced by words. This volume constantly urges that scientists, teachers, and others shall use science and its dependable ways of working as means of advancing human welfare.

It is imperative that those being educated shall think safely and accurately about epoch-making scientific discoveries. Vaccination against many diseases is now available to those who would avoid illness from those diseases. Yet many people oppose legal regulations for vaccination. Disease carriers are a public menace, though some persons are "kind-hearted" and "muddleheaded" about restraining the movements of those proved to be distributors of disease. Most types of cancer can be cured if attended to in the early stages. The miracles and beneficence of modern medicine and surgery are often made impossible because of ignorance, misunderstanding, and unfounded fear. Disgraceful venereal diseases and their transmitted effects can be cured, but science should help cure the reprehensible practices which distribute such diseases. Almost no one believes that mental defectives should perpetuate their deficiencies, but legal and social procedures to give support to common belief have found great difficulty in gaining general use.

Of all the many recently developed and highly potent ideas are those relating to new sources of energy. It seems that almost all the possible types of thinking have been indulged in by persons ranging from the wholly ignorant, but most vocal, to those who know most, but talk least. Probably nothing has better illustrated the tragic dangers of possession without an accompanying and anchoring responsibility.

The reader should not accuse us of engaging merely in alarmist talk. Expert, informed, and reliable scientists, when asked to consider certain high-authority questions, have stated that, in countries other than our own, people already know a large part about such things as bacterial warfare, poison gases, and jet transmission—perhaps more of some aspects of them than what we know about energy released from atoms. Possibly some other people may know of things and of forces whose names are unknown to us. We are told that certain other countries could invent and manufacture an abundance of atomic bombs in from three to seven years.

Other countries have already produced devices for distribution of destructiveness which, if used, could almost instantly terminate the life of many millions of people in scores of large centers of human population. Decentralization of population would not help, if there is truth in the claim that certain types of recently discovered destructiveness might almost momentarily extend for hundreds of miles. Our time is short for discovering and learning to use worthy, effective means for protecting humans and their civilization.

Atoms are wherever matter is, but thus far only a few kinds of matter can be used to release atomic energy. The entire earth, its atmosphere, and the sun which heats and energizes the earth are but a small part of all matter. A few persons have discovered ways of releasing atomic energy and of using it to destroy fellow humans who are temporarily their enemies. The discovery of this force and the inventions for destruction are sometimes claimed by those who made the discovery and the instruments. One country's government may claim the right of control of atomic energy, first, because its scientists made the discovery, and, second, because that government wishes to have control over other countries. Such claims are absurd and cannot be substantiated. Man, in his extreme selfishness and in the limitations of his ideals, foolishly claims for himself or for his country a source of power which is universally distributed. Indeed, the whole earth receives only a very small part of total atomic energy. However, man might, it seems, use his knowledge and selfishness in such a way as to dispose of men and their achievements on all of "God's footstool." Knowledge must become power for good, not for ill.

Anthropologists have disclosed indisputable evidence that in several ancient periods men reached what were conspicuous stages of culture, only to end in catastrophe. Relics, fossils, and collateral evidences which are now being discovered piece together the incomplete book of records of intermittent civilizations. Did an extensive ice age terminate the peoples of the civilization of many thousands of years ago in what is now southwestern United States? Did pestilence and war terminate the ancient Java and Chinese man's primitive civilization? Did tribal wars, greed for territory, and advancing implements of war end the Neanderthal civilization in northern Europe?[2] Who were left, if any, to pick up, preserve, and continue efforts to realize human ideals in their ages-old development?

No one knows certainly what is ahead in our civilization. Wholesale guesses and careful analyses of trends of the present have been

[2] Frank C. Hibben, *The Lost Americans.* New York: Thomas Y. Crowell Co., 1946.

made. H. G. Wells' alleged race between education and catastrophe, proclaimed by that highly intelligent pessimist just prior to a score of years of astounding material achievements, now seems to be subscribed to by many thoughtful people. Frequent conferences and symposiums on what is ahead are participated in by many of our ablest and best-trained men. Magazines and books and the public press anxiously discuss what men can or should do to gain security for future peoples and to continue helpful advances in knowledge and human living. Clubs and home groups discuss solemnly whether men can be trusted with their own planning. Pulpits resound man's fears and hopes, and God is sometimes importuned to take over and to prevent man from bringing crushing disaster upon himself. Sometimes the Spirit of a benevolent God is extolled for man to grasp as his sole anchorage if man would have any future. Intelligent, forward-looking and dependable scientists, like all other such people, are forced by current events to broaden the areas of their thinking; to consider men, human ideals, and human character; to consider how men may live helpfully with one another, how knowledge and its unending development may always be active for worthy human advancement.

The development of science will continue so long as there exist men with courage, curiosity, and ability to observe and to experiment to learn new truth. There can be no stopping of scientific research in order that society may catch up. When ancient man became conscious of his material environment and began to study it, he did this in order to learn and to improve his personal status within his environment. When modern society began to support research, it sought more knowledge and hoped that benefits would come to all men, that is, to society. When human civilization, poorly defined though it may be, began to be conscious of the tremendous importance of the growth and organization of knowledge into available forms, the foundations were laid for widespread improvement in human living under the guidance of organized knowledge. That was not enough. What science may *do for men* must become subordinate to what science may *do to men*. Material benefits are secondary. What men are as human beings is of greatest importance. Knowledge must be directed toward common needs of common men as well as toward individual needs and the advancement of knowledge itself.

Educators, scientists, and statesmen must learn to work together. (The word "must" is used in no dictatorial sense but in the sense of the inevitable.) The alternative is disaster for all. Educators have had too limited vision of their opportunities and obligations and have been timid in approaching their goals. Scientists have probed far into the unknown and have released power and made instruments that are beyond men's proved ability to direct or control. Statesmen, so called, have considered votes, personal preferment, priority on important committees, and party balance of control and have ignored the voices of those who point out that there must be general adoption of factual guidance as the means toward a better world. Appeasement on a basis of trading between groups within our country and with other countries seems to have become a common policy. "For what will you settle?" is the frequent inquiry when difficulties arise. To the reply often there has been an offer of compromise not always based upon facts, justice, and human interest but upon payments of uncertain claims, upon concessions, privileges, and gifts of the people's funds. Concessions and gifts have not come from majority votes by an informed public but often by secret agreements made by those who claim to be our leaders—but they are leaders who have no fixed and clarifying star of purpose to guide their acts. Policy seems to mean making the best immediate terms regardless of whether we move toward worthy ultimate goals for society. Thus, there is expedient temporizing by our elected representatives rather than steady and purposeful progress toward objectives which the people have chosen.

The present situation is not caused by the achievements of science but by the absence of science in aspects of life other than those related to discovery, invention, production, and distribution. Those who have discovered, invented, produced, and distributed are few. The people are many. Neither scientists nor other people wish to destroy civilization, but neither scientists nor other people have as yet adequately considered science as a positive means of avoiding destruction. "What men create they can, if they try, bring themselves to understand well enough to manage."[3] But really good understanding, by more than a majority of the people, is essential if valid thinking, dependable judgments, and intelligent co-operation are to be had. How can uninformed people co-operate intelligently? Even if informed, how can there be certainty of the kinds of characters from which mutually useful co-operation may result?

If science is founded on facts, on truth, and on provable interpretations and if humans must develop their characters through discovery of, belief in, and adherence to facts, truth, and correct interpretations, can society find any better way of saving itself than by use of an education which openly and actively undertakes to use science as one major agency for development of character? Not science for more science or for more knowledge—those will surely come. But we need more citizens with enduring and dependable characters. We need more men who readily understand the universality of scientific knowledge and its character benefits for all men.

---

[3] Franklin Bobbitt, "The Educational Policies Commission Banishes Science," *Scientific Monthly*, LXIII (August, 1946), 117–24.

It is due to the nature of science that its uses in education have developed slowly. Furthermore, many of the advocates of general education have continued to emphasize traditional subjects of study and to give inadequate place to science. Science teachers do not claim that there is no value in the traditional subjects, such as the classical languages, nor do they claim that complete success or perfection may be had through science education. It is a question of relative values. Better proportional distribution in an educational program is needed. Secondary-school pupils cannot secure well-rounded education if most of their program consists chiefly of language study. The study of proper expression is needful, but impressions and their meanings are essential. Impressions, objectively considered, are the foundational materials of good expression. They are the loads to be carried by good language. Cutting wood is the objective of a sharp axe, but unending axe sharpening and no woodchopping leaves the house cold and uninviting.

Substantial progress in science education has already been made. The schools, the public press, libraries, homes, radios, industries, and the constant uses of science make science education unavoidable. There are in the United States more than ten thousand clubs of youthful scientists with a total of more than a quarter of a million members. Science magazines are sold in astounding numbers. Errors in common beliefs are slowly yielding to the proved answers to the question, "What is the truth about it?" Universal education is making its mark, but there are many long roads yet to be traveled.

In this volume there are recognized many important advances already achieved or in an encouraging experimental stage of progress. A continuous program of science study is recognized as needful, and some schools are using that plan. There is wider interest in and increased enrolments in science courses, particularly in elementary science, general science, and biology. Science courses are being adjusted to different types of students and to different vocational and individual needs. Content and organization of courses are being more closely related to life experiences and needs. The interests and capacities of pupils are guides in selecting content and in determining methods of work. Improvements are notable in the best schools in physical facilities for study. Teachers are beginning to gain appreciation of the constant need for field and laboratory provisions as well as for libraries in which there are abundant books and magazines about science. The application of scientific method to determination of problems about science courses is gaining ground. Scientific evaluation of results from science instruction is gaining wide recognition. Indeed, it may now be claimed that the objectives of science instruction have become broader, better defined, and more readily attained, as presented in preceding pages of this volume.

Modern children are living amid constant experiences available for use in school. Failure to use such contacts and experiences means failure to make education tie in with the environment in which people live. Preceding chapters give detailed suggestions and illustrations based upon the conviction that one's own contacts and experiences provide basic concepts for his education. Therefore, those chapters describe the best practices in science teaching and the most commonly approved types of courses and subject organization. To the aspects of progress already achieved in practice, other needs are outlined and urged. It is expected that there may be steady and substantial improvement. No subject of science study is regarded as "finished" in its organization, each being a more or less acceptable present stage in that subject's educational uses. Ways for improvement have been found. Their use must continue. "A creative force in the hands of devoted people can be stronger than the forces of destruction."[4] The science teacher is the major factor in gaining improvement in science education. No subjects other than science offer better opportunities for true leadership. The classroom, club, assembly, playground, camp, field, shop, industry, future vocations, professional callings, and all the other elements which compose the real or possible environment of modern students are tied in with an alert teacher's interpretation of the scope of his assignment. His life is largely with his students and, as he is, so may they become. Real teaching produces its enduring benefits to those taught and to those who teach. The appreciations expressed by those who, later, may far surpass their teachers are values which cause a teacher to discover modestly that his services have placed him in the guild of those who teach with intelligence and with devotion to young people. We need to make good teaching so appealing that a greatly increased number of our superior young scientists will find their own best opportunities in science teaching.

Universal education is the agency, the means, and the force through which security may possibly be achieved. If four-fifths of the earth's people are illiterate, how can they co-operate in programs for the advancement of society? Must those countries in which illiteracy is low promptly assume the obligations to help reduce widespread illiteracy? Science, with its products, its methods, and its ways of developing belief in facts, in truth, in dependability, and in things that endure, is a major

---

[4] Allen Dulles, in an unpublished address before the Near-East College Association, New York City, September 12, 1946.

determining element in our civilization. Science education, therefore, seems imperative if society seeks security. Yet science education cannot guarantee security. Security rests not only in men's knowledge but in their characters. The will to do what is right transcends knowledge of how to do what is right. Science may contribute knowledge and understandings. Their ways of working may exhibit the unprofitableness of errors, but educated human character must assume the decisive role in civilization's future.

INDEX

Adult education in science, 247–49

Aeronautics: place of, in science curriculum, 46

American Association for the Advancement of Science, 21, 225

Analysis of courses of study and textbooks in science, 23–24

Analysis of objectives in science instruction, 30–35

Appreciations, as objectives of science instruction, 29, 33–35, 62–63, 148–49, 187–89

Attitudes, as objectives of science instruction, 29, 33–35, 62–63, 147–48, 187–89

Audio-visual department in science, 103–5

Balance in science program in elementary school, 72–73

Belief in fundamental truth: historical development of, 5–7; in contrast to superstition, 6–7

Biology: one-year course in, 43; in senior high school program, 183–90

Carver, George Washington, 14

Chemistry, content and method of, in senior high school, 199–208

Child: imaginative activities of, 65; as an investigator, 63–64; nature of, as related to purposes of science education, 63–69; participation of, in planning activities, 65–66

College-entrance examinations, recognition of, in science instruction, 58

Commission on Reorganization of Secondary Education, 21, 35–36

Committee of Ten, influence of, on science instruction, 152

Community, educational resources of, for science instruction, 87–88

Community resources: as related to science instruction, 47–48; in secondary schools, 233–35; in urban schools, 121–25; use of, in rural schools, 118–21

Concepts, as objectives of science instruction, 29, 30–31, 143

Conservation: in curriculum of rural schools, 119–20; as illustration of relation of science to general education, 36–38; place of, in science curriculum, 46

Consumer education, place of, in science curriculum, 46

Continuity in science program in elementary schools, 71–72

Co-operative planning in in-service education, 130

Core curriculum: relation of, to junior high school science, 165–66; science program in, 47

Courses of study in science, analysis of, 23–24

Criteria for selection of objectives in science instruction, 24–28

Culture, science as a factor in development of, 13–14

Curie, Marie, 14

Curriculum development, trends of, in elementary-school science, 69–71

Curriculum in science: for rural elementary schools, 118–19; for urban elementary schools, 121–25

Deductive teaching in science courses, 49

Demonstration experiment, value of, as compared to pupil performance of experiment, 53–54

Discoveries, as related to public information, 11–13

Drawings, requirement of, for apparatus and specimens used in experiments, 55–56

Education of high-school science teachers, suggested program for, 283–87

Educational Policies Commission, 20, 22, 36

Elementary-school science: basic areas of, 75–78; equipment for, 98–103; physical and biological environments in, 75–76; social needs in, 76–77; teaching procedures in, 93–98; use of radio in, 104–5

Environment: child reactions to, 64; dependence of living organisms on, 89–91

Equipment for science: in elementary school, 98–103; in secondary school, 242–47

INFORMATION CONCERNING THE NATIONAL SOCIETY FOR THE STUDY OF EDUCATION

1. PURPOSE. The purpose of the National Society is to promote the investigation and discussion of educational questions. To this end it holds an annual meeting and publishes a series of yearbooks.

2. ELIGIBILITY TO MEMBERSHIP. Any person who is interested in receiving its publications may become a member by sending to the Secretary-Treasurer information concerning name, title, and address, and a check for $3.50 (see Item 5).

Membership is not transferable; it is limited to individuals, and may not be held by libraries, schools, or other institutions, either directly or indirectly.

3. PERIOD OF MEMBERSHIP. Applicants for membership may not date their entrance back of the current calendar year, and all memberships terminate automatically on December 31, unless the dues for the ensuing year are paid as indicated in Item 6.

4. DUTIES AND PRIVILEGES OF MEMBERS. Members pay dues of $2.50 annually, receive a cloth-bound copy of each publication, are entitled to vote, to participate in discussion, and (under certain conditions) to hold office. The names of members are printed in the yearbooks.

Persons who are sixty years of age or above may become life members on payment of fee based on average life-expectancy of their age group. For information, apply to Secretary-Treasurer.

5. ENTRANCE FEE. New members are required the first year to pay, in addition to the dues, an entrance fee of one dollar.

6. PAYMENT OF DUES. Statements of dues are rendered in October or November for the following calendar year. Any member so notified whose dues remain unpaid on January 1 thereby loses his membership and can be reinstated only by paying a reinstatement fee of fifty cents, levied to cover the actual clerical cost involved.

School warrants and vouchers from institutions must be accompanied by definite information concerning the name and address of the person for whom membership fee is being paid. Statements of dues are rendered on our own form only. The Secretary's office cannot undertake to fill out special invoice forms of any sort or to affix notary's affidavit to statements or receipts.

Cancelled checks serve as receipts. Members desiring an additional receipt must enclose a stamped and addressed envelope therefor.

7. DISTRIBUTION OF YEARBOOKS TO MEMBERS. The yearbooks, ready prior to each February meeting, will be mailed from the office of the distributors, only to members whose dues for that year have been paid. Members who desire yearbooks prior to the current year must purchase them directly from the distributor (see Item 8).

8. COMMERCIAL SALES. The distribution of all yearbooks prior to the current year, and also of those of the current year not regularly mailed to members in exchange for their dues, is in the hands of the distributor, not of the Secretary. For such commercial sales, communicate directly with the University of Chicago Press, Chicago 37, Illinois, which will gladly send a price list covering all the publications of this Society and of its predecessor, the National Herbart Society. This list is also printed in the yearbook.

9. YEARBOOKS. The yearbooks are issued about one month before the February meeting. They comprise from 600 to 800 pages annually. Unusual effort has been made to make them, on the one hand, of immediate practical value, and, on the other hand, representative of sound scholarship and scientific investigation. Many of them are the fruit of co-operative work by committees of the Society.

10. MEETINGS. The annual meeting, at which the yearbooks are discussed, is held in February at the same time and place as the meeting of the American Association of School Administrators.

Applications for membership will be handled promptly at any time on receipt of name and address, together with check for $3.50 (or $3.00 for reinstatement). Generally speaking, applications entitle the new members to the yearbook slated for discussion during the calendar year the application is made, but those received in December are regarded as pertaining to the next calendar year.

NELSON B. HENRY, *Secretary-Treasurer*

5835 Kimbark Ave.
Chicago 37, Illinois

PUBLICATIONS OF THE NATIONAL HERBART SOCIETY

PUBLICATIONS OF THE NATIONAL SOCIETY FOR THE STUDY OF EDUCATION

Forty-fifth Yearbook, 1946, Part I—*The Measurement of Understanding.* Prepared by the
Society's Committee. William A. Brownell, Chairman. Cloth $3.00
    Paper 2.25
Forty-fifth Yearbook, 1946, Part II—*Changing Conceptions in Educational Administration.* Pre-
pared by the Society's Committee. Alonzo G. Grace, Chairman. Cloth 2.50
    Paper 1.75
Forty-sixth Yearbook, 1947, Part I—*Science Education in American Schools.* Prepared by the
Society's Committee. Victor H. Noll, Chairman. Cloth................................ 3.25
    Paper 2.50
Forty-sixth Yearbook, 1947, Part II—*Early Childhood Education.* Prepared by the Society's
Committee. N. Searle Light, Chairman. Cloth 3.50
    Paper 2.75

Distributed by

THE UNIVERSITY OF CHICAGO PRESS, CHICAGO 37, ILLINOIS

1947